For Virginia E. Sherwood
from the "Editor", Daniel Catton Rich
Chicago, Illinois October 23
1933

EXHIBITION OF
PAINTINGS AND SCULPTURE

THE ART INSTITUTE OF CHICAGO

THE OFFICIAL FINE ARTS DEPARTMENT OF "A CENTURY OF PROGRESS EXPOSITION"

CATALOGUE OF A CENTURY OF PROGRESS EXHIBITION OF PAINTINGS AND SCULPTURE

Lent from American Collections

Second Edition

THE ART INSTITUTE OF CHICAGO

JUNE 1 TO NOVEMBER 1, 1933

PRINTED AT THE LAKESIDE PRESS, R. R. DONNELLEY & SONS COMPANY, CHICAGO

Trustees, Officers, and Committees

THE ART INSTITUTE OF CHICAGO, 1933

COMMITTEE ON PAINTING AND SCULPTURE

Charles H. Worcester, *Chairman*
Chauncey McCormick
Arthur T. Aldis
Percy B. Eckhart
John A. Holabird
Frederic C. Bartlett
Max Epstein
Walter S. Brewster

COMMITTEE ON A CENTURY OF PROGRESS FINE ARTS EXHIBITION

Chauncey McCormick, *General Chairman*

The Art Institute Committee

Charles H. Worcester, *Chairman*
Percy B. Eckhart
John A. Holabird

A Century of Progress Committee

William Allen Pusey, *Chairman*
Mrs. Tiffany Blake
Max Epstein

Honorary Members

Rufus Dawes
Potter Palmer

Staff

OF THE ART INSTITUTE OF CHICAGO

Robert B. Harshe, *Director*
Charles Fabens Kelley, *Assistant Director*
Charles H. Burkholder, *Secretary and Business Manager*
Robert B. Harshe, *Curator of Painting and Sculpture*
Daniel Catton Rich, *Associate Curator of Painting*
Charles Fabens Kelley, *Curator of Oriental Art*
Arthur Upham Pope, *Advisory Curator of Muhammadan Art*
Helen C. Gunsaulus, *Assistant Curator of Oriental Art*
Frederick W. Gookin, *Curator of Buckingham Prints*
Bessie Bennett, *Curator of Decorative Arts*
Helen Mackenzie, *Curator of the Children's Museum*
C. Lindsay Ricketts, *Honorary Curator of Manuscripts*
Mildred J. Prentiss, *Acting Curator of Prints and Drawings*
Guy U. Young, *Manager, Membership Dept.*
Walter J. Sherwood, *Manager of Printing and Publications*
G. E. Kaltenbach, *Museum Registrar*
Etheldred Abbot, *Librarian, the Ryerson and Burnham Libraries*
Charles Fabens Kelley, *Dean of the School*
Norman L. Rice, *Associate Dean*
Marguerita M. Steffenson, *Assistant Dean*
Dudley Crafts Watson, *Membership Lecturer*
Helen Parker, *Head of Department of Museum Instruction*
James F. McCabe, *Superintendent of Buildings*
Henri Gutherz, *In Charge of Sales*

ADVISORY COMMITTEE

Mr. Jere Abbott, Director, The Smith College Museum of Art, Northampton, Massachusetts

Mr. A. Everett Austin, Jr., Director, The Wadsworth Atheneum, Hartford, Connecticut

Mr. Jules S. Bache, New York

Dr. Harry Bakwin, New York

Mr. Alfred H. Barr, Jr., Director, The Museum of Modern Art, New York

Mr. Edward C. Blum, President, The Brooklyn Institute of Arts and Sciences

Mr. George Blumenthal, New York

Mrs. Ralph Harman Booth, Detroit

Mr. Richard D. Brixey, New York

Mr. John Nicholas Brown, Providence, Rhode Island

Mr. William Alanson Bryan, Director, The Los Angeles Museum of History, Science and Art

Mr. Bryson Burroughs, Curator of Paintings, The Metropolitan Museum of Art, New York

Mr. Clyde H. Burroughs, Secretary, The Detroit Institute of Arts

Mr. Samuel Harden Church, President of Carnegie Institute, Pittsburgh

Mr. Stephen C. Clark, New York

Mr. Ralph M. Coe, Cleveland

Mr. William Sloane Coffin, President, The Metropolitan Museum of Art, New York

Mr. and Mrs. Chester Dale, New York

Mrs. Murray S. Danforth, President, The Rhode Island School of Design, Providence, Rhode Island

Mr. Bernard Davis, Philadelphia

Mr. Francis H. Dewey, President, The Worcester Art Museum

Dr. Friedrich Dornhoffer, General Director, Bavarian State Museums, Munich, Germany

Miss Katherine S. Dreier, New York

Mr. Theodore T. Ellis, Worcester, Massachusetts

Mr. Edward W. Forbes, Director, The Fogg Art Museum of Harvard University, Cambridge, Massachusetts

Mrs. Juliana R. Force, Director, The Whitney Museum of American Art, New York

Mr. Edsel B. Ford, President, The Detroit Institute of Arts

Mr. William Henry Fox, Director, The Brooklyn Museum

Mr. Henry Sayles Francis, Curator of Paintings and Prints, The Cleveland Museum of Art

Miss Helen C. Frick, Director, The Frick Art Reference Library

Dr. Max J. Friedlaender, Director, Kaiser-Friedrich Museum, Berlin, Germany

Mr. Gilbert E. Fuller, Boston

Mr. Blake-More Godwin, Director, The Toledo Museum of Art

Mr. William Goldman, New York

Mr. A. Conger Goodyear, President, The Museum of Modern Art, New York

Mr. Maitland F. Griggs, New York

Mr. Leonard C. Hanna, Jr., Cleveland

Mr. Carter H. Harrison, Chicago

Mr. William Preston Harrison, Los Angeles

Mr. Horace Havemeyer, New York

Mr. Philip A. Hendy, Curator of Paintings, The Museum of Fine Arts, Boston

Mr. and Mrs. Charles V. Hickox, New York

Dr. F. H. Hirschland, New York

Mr. Edward Jackson Holmes, Director, The Museum of Fine Arts, Boston

Mr. and Mrs. Otto H. Kahn, New York

Mr. Fiske Kimball, Director, The Pennsylvania Museum of Art, Philadelphia

Mr. Louis La Beaume, President, The City Art Museum of St. Louis

Mr. Albert C. Lehman, Pittsburgh

Mr. and Mrs. Samuel A. Lewisohn, New York

Mr. Charles J. Livingood, President, The Cincinnati Art Museum

Mr. J. B. Manson, Director and Keeper, The National Gallery, Millbank, London

Mr. Henri Gabriel Marceau, Curator of Fine Arts, The Pennsylvania Museum of Art, Philadelphia

Mr. Oscar F. Mayer, Chicago

Mrs. Robert Rutherford McCormick, Chicago

Mr. Roland J. McKinney, Director, The Baltimore Museum of Art

Mr. Everett V. Meeks, Dean and Director, School of the Fine Arts, Yale University, New Haven, Connecticut

Mr. O. A. Miller, President, The Columbus Gallery of Fine Arts

Mr. William M. Milliken, Director, The Cleveland Museum of Art

Mr. C. Powell Minnigerode, Director, The Corcoran Gallery of Art, Washington, D. C.

Mr. John Andrew Myers, Secretary, The Pennsylvania Academy of the Fine Arts, Philadelphia

Mr. and Mrs. Francis Neilson, Chicago

Mr. Julius Oppenheimer, New York

Mr. Robert Treat Paine, 2nd, Boston

Mr. Duncan Phillips, Director, The Phillips Memorial Gallery, Washington, D. C.

Mr. Russell A. Plimpton, Director, The Minneapolis Institute of Arts

Mr. Eli Kirk Price, President, The Pennsylvania Museum of Art, Philadelphia

Mr. Blanchard Randall, Chairman of the Board, The Baltimore Museum of Art

Gen. Lawrason Riggs, President of The Baltimore Museum of Art

Mrs. John D. Rockefeller, Jr., New York

Mr. Meyric R. Rogers, Director, The City Art Museum of St. Louis

Mr. L. Earle Rowe, Director, The Museum of Art, The Rhode Island School of Design, Providence, Rhode Island

Mrs. Martin A. Ryerson, Chicago

Mr. Arthur Sachs, New York

Mr. Paul J. Sachs, Associate Director, The Fogg Art Museum of Harvard University, Cambridge, Massachusetts

Mr. Homer Saint-Gaudens, Director, Department of Fine Arts, Carnegie Institute, Pittsburgh

Mr. Charles B. Sears, President, The Buffalo Fine Arts Academy

Mr. Arthur J. Secor, President, The Toledo Museum of Art

Mr. John L. Severance, President, The Cleveland Museum of Art

Mr. and Mrs. Lesley G. Sheafer, New York

Mr. Walter H. Siple, Director, The Cincinnati Art Museum

Mr. Theodore Sizer, Associate Director, The School of the Fine Arts, Yale University, New Haven, Connecticut

Mr. Frank C. Smith, Worcester, Massachusetts

Mr. William S. Stimmel, Pittsburgh

Mrs. Frank D. Stout, Chicago

Mr. Percy S. Straus, New York

Mrs. Cornelius J. Sullivan, New York

Mr. Francis Henry Taylor, Director, The Worcester Art Museum

Mrs. John R. Thompson, Chicago

Mr. and Mrs. William R. Timken, New York

Dr. William R. Valentiner, Art Director, The Detroit Institute of Arts

Mr. John R. Van Derlip, President, The Minneapolis Institute of Arts

Mr. Henri Verne, Director, The Louvre Museum, Paris

Mr. Gordon B. Washburn, Director, The Albright Art Gallery, Buffalo

Mr. Samuel S. White 3rd, Ardmore, Pennsylvania

Mrs. Harry Payne Whitney, New York

Mr. Joseph Widener, Elkins Park, Pennsylvania

Mr. John N. Willys, New York

Mr. Herbert E. Winlock, Director, The Metropolitan Museum of Art, New York

Mr. Joseph Winterbotham, Burlington, Vermont

Lenders to the Exhibition

Mr. and Mrs. Walter Conrad Arensberg, Hollywood, California
The Babcock Gallery, New York
Mr. Jules S. Bache, New York
Mr. Shreve Badger, Chicago
Dr. and Mrs. Harry Bakwin, New York
The A. M. Barnhart Estate, Chicago
Mr. and Mrs. Frederic Clay Bartlett, Chicago
Mr. and Mrs. Frederic Clay Bartlett, Jr., Chicago
Mr. Gifford Beal, New York
The John Becker Gallery, New York
Mr. Edward J. Berwind, New York
Mr. August Bontoux, Chicago
Mrs. Ralph Harman Booth, Detroit
The Bottenwieser Galleries, New York
Mr. and Mrs. Walter S. Brewster, Chicago
Mr. John Nicholas Brown, Providence, Rhode Island
Brummer Gallery, Inc., New York
Mr. Daniel V. Casey, Chicago
Mrs. Emily Crane Chadbourne, Washington, D. C.
Mr. Stephen C. Clark, New York
The Chicago Galleries Association, Chicago
Estate of Mrs. L. L. Coburn, Chicago
Mr. and Mrs. Ralph M. Coe, Cleveland
Mr. and Mrs. Erich Cohn, New York
Mr. M. H. Collins, Cedar Rapids, Iowa
Miss Etta Cone, Baltimore
Mr. Frank Crowninshield, New York
Mr. Ralph Cudney, Chicago
Mr. and Mrs. Chester Dale, New York
Mr. and Mrs. R. E. Danielson, Boston
Demotte, Inc., New York
The Downtown Gallery, New York
Miss Katherine S. Dreier, New York
A. S. Drey, Munich and New York
Durand-Ruel, Inc., New York
Duveen Brothers, Inc., New York
Mr. and Mrs. Jerome O. Eddy, Skull Valley, Arizona
Mr. and Mrs. E. W. Edwards, Cincinnati
Mr. Theodore T. Ellis, Worcester, Massachusetts
Mr. Max Epstein, Chicago
Mrs. H. A. Everett, Pasadena, California
Ferargil, Inc., New York
Findlay Galleries, Inc., Chicago
Mr. and Mrs. William A. Fisher, Detroit
Rev. Henry Wilder Foote, Belmont, Massachusetts
French and Company, Inc., New York
Mr. and Mrs. Gilbert E. Fuller, Boston
Mr. Albert Gallatin, New York
Mr. Albert Eugene Gallatin, New York
Gallery 144 West 13th Street, New York
Mr. R. W. Glasner, Chicago
Mr. William Goldman, New York
Mr. and Mrs. William Owen Goodman, Chicago
Mr. A. Conger Goodyear, New York
The Grand Central Art Galleries, New York
Mr. Maitland F. Griggs, New York
Mr. Leonard C. Hanna, Jr., Cleveland
Mr. George F. Harding, Chicago
Marie Harriman Gallery, New York
Mr. Carter H. Harrison, Chicago
Mr. and Mrs. William Preston Harrison, Los Angeles
Mr. Frederick T. Haskell, Chicago
Mr. Horace Havemeyer, New York
Mrs. Forbes Hawkes, New York
Mr. Arthur Heun, Chicago
Mrs. Patrick C. Hill, Fort Worth, Texas
Dr. F. H. Hirschland, New York
Mr. Willitts J. Hole, Los Angeles
Mrs. John E. Jenkins, Chicago
Mr. Chester H. Johnson, Chicago
The Chester H. Johnson Galleries, Chicago
Mr. Arthur Judson, New York
Mr. Edgar J. Kaufmann, Pittsburgh
M. Knoedler and Company, New York
Mr. John F. Kraushaar, New York
C. W. Kraushaar Art Galleries, New York
Mr. Samuel H. Kress, New York
La France Art Institute, Philadelphia
Mr. Albert C. Lehman, Pittsburgh
Governor Herbert H. Lehman, New York
Mr. Adolph Lewisohn, New York

Mrs. Edward Drummond Libbey, Toledo
Dr. Karl Lilienfeld, New York
Mr. and Mrs. Frank G. Logan, Chicago
William Macbeth, Inc., New York
Pierre Matisse Gallery, New York
Mr. Oscar F. Mayer, Chicago
Mr. and Mrs. Chauncey McCormick, Chicago
Mr. and Mrs. Cyrus H. McCormick, Chicago
Mrs. Robert Rutherford McCormick, Chicago
Hon. Andrew W. Mellon, Washington, D. C.
E. and A. Milch, Inc., New York
The Mogmar Art Foundation, Inc., New York
The Montross Gallery, New York
Mr. and Mrs. John U. Nef, Chicago
Mr. Francis Neilson, Chicago
Mrs. Charles Netcher, Chicago
Mr. J. B. Neumann, New York
Mr. Julius Oppenheimer, New York
Mr. William Church Osborn, New York
Mr. Robert Treat Paine, 2nd, Boston
Mr. Tage Palm, Chicago
Mr. and Mrs. Potter Palmer, Chicago
Mrs. James Parmelee, Washington, D. C.
Mr. Duncan Phillips, Washington, D. C.
Mr. Herbert Lee Pratt, New York
Mr. Frank K. M. Rehn, New York
General Lawrason Riggs, Baltimore
The Increase Robinson Gallery, Chicago
Mr. John D. Rockefeller, New York
The Rosenbach Company, New York
Mrs. Charles Cary Rumsey, New York
Mrs. Martin A. Ryerson, Chicago
Mr. Arthur Sachs, New York
Mr. and Mrs. Howard J. Sachs, New York
Mr. Homer Saint-Gaudens, Pittsburgh
Mrs. Galka Scheyer, Hollywood
Mrs. Flora I. Schofield, Chicago
Mr. Robert W. Schuette, New York
Scott and Fowles, New York
Mr. Arthur J. Secor, Toledo
Arnold Seligmann, Rey and Company, Inc., New York
Jacques Seligmann and Company, Inc., New York
Mr. E. Felix Shaskan, Cedarhurst, Long Island
Mr. and Mrs. Lesley G. Sheafer, New York
Mr. David A. Smart, Chicago
Mr. and Mrs. James T. Soby, West Hartford
Société Anonyme, New York
Mr. LeRoy J. Steffen, Janesville, Wisconsin
Mr. E. J. Stehli, New York
Mr. Josef von Sternberg, Hollywood
The Marie Sterner Gallery, New York
Mr. Chauncey Devereux Stillman, New York
Mr. William S. Stimmel, Pittsburgh
Mr. Josef Stransky, New York
Mr. and Mrs. Percy S. Straus, New York
Mrs. Cornelius J. Sullivan, New York
Mr. P. M. Sweeney, Brooklyn
Mr. Robert H. Tannahill, Detroit
Mrs. John R. Thompson, Chicago
Mr. John R. Thompson, Jr., Chicago
Mrs. William R. Timken, New York
Mr. Chester D. Tripp, Chicago
The Trustees of the Estate of Miss Lizzie P. Bliss, New York
Mr. Carroll Tyson, Philadelphia
Dr. W. R. Valentiner, Detroit
Mr. Edward M. M. Warburg, New York
Mr. and Mrs. J. Watson Webb, New York
Mr. S. W. Weis, Chicago
The Weyhe Gallery, New York
Mr. Samuel S. White, 3rd, Ardmore, Pennsylvania.
Mr. John Hay Whitney, New York
Mrs. Payne Whitney, New York
Mr. Joseph Widener, Elkins Park, Pennsylvania
Wildenstein and Company, Inc., New York
Mr. and Mrs. John N. Willys, New York
Mr. Joseph Winterbotham, Burlington, Vermont
Mr. and Mrs. Charles H. Worcester, Chicago
The Brooklyn Museum, Brooklyn
The Buffalo Fine Arts Academy, Buffalo
The Cincinnati Art Museum
The Cincinnati Institute of Fine Arts and The Taft Museum, Cincinnati
The City Art Museum of St. Louis
The Cleveland Museum of Art
The College Art Association, New York
The Columbus Gallery of Fine Arts
The Corcoran Gallery of Art, Washington, D. C.
The Department of Fine Arts, Carnegie Institute, Pittsburgh

The Detroit Institute of Arts

The Fogg Art Museum of Harvard University, Cambridge, Massachusetts

The Layton Art Gallery, Milwaukee, Wisconsin

The Los Angeles Museum of History, Science and Art

The Louvre Museum, Paris, France

The Metropolitan Museum of Art, New York

The Minneapolis Institute of Arts

The Museum of Art, Rhode Island School of Design, Providence, Rhode Island

The Museum of Fine Arts, Boston

The Museum of Modern Art, New York

The National Gallery of Art, Smithsonian Institution, Washington, D. C.

The Pennsylvania Museum of Art, Philadelphia

The Phillips Memorial Gallery, Washington, D. C.

The John and Mable Ringling Museum of Art, Sarasota, Florida

The Smith College Museum of Art, Northampton, Massachusetts

The Toledo Museum of Art

The Wadsworth Atheneum, Hartford, Connecticut

The Whitney Museum of American Art, New York

The Worcester Art Museum, Worcester, Massachusetts

Yale University, Gallery of Fine Arts, New Haven, Connecticut

Foreword

THE Exhibition of Paintings and Sculpture celebrating "A Century of Progress" has been assembled (with one exception, Whistler's "Portrait of his Mother") entirely from American sources. Private collectors and the guardians of public collections have been so generous, that, with the significant examples already owned by the Institute, it has been possible to arrange a sequence of the masterpieces of painting, beginning with European works of the thirteenth century and coming down to European and American examples of today.

The theme of the 1933 Exposition, "A Century of Progress," has been broadly interpreted to mean, not only art of the last century, but a hundred years' progress in American collecting. In 1833 very few great works were on this side of the Atlantic; today the United States possesses treasures of amazing quality, inspiring not only to our artists but to the rapidly growing public who are coming to feel the need of art in their daily lives. Particularly during the last twenty-five or thirty years many brilliant examples of painting have made their way westward, some going at once into the museums, more finding their way into private hands. One of the chief aims of the present showing is to exhibit works which are rarely if ever seen by the public, emphasizing in this way the resources of the nation.

The exhibition contains paintings, water colors, drawings, and sculpture. The painting division is made up of three main parts. *First:* European painting from the thirteenth through the eighteenth centuries. These works have been hung in historical sequence. *Second:* Nineteenth century painting, mostly French and American (and containing one gallery of Early American examples), arranged in a series of galleries so as to throw into relief the great artistic personalities of the last hundred years. *Third:* Twentieth century painting, American and International, presenting the art of significant contemporaries.

In the section given to water colors, drawings, and pastels, there will be found a similar division. A small group of old-master drawings will start the survey; then, works by nineteenth-century artists, and last, examples by contemporaries. Over a hundred pieces of sculpture (all of the last hundred years) complete this exhibition. At the same time, in the Print Galleries, a survey of masterpieces in prints, closely paralleling the Exhibition of "A Century of Progress," is being held.

Plan of the Second Floor Galleries

English, French, and German Painting. Fourteenth, Fifteenth, and Sixteenth Centuries .... Room 27
Dutch and Flemish Painting, Fifteenth and Sixteenth Centuries..... Room 28
Dutch and Flemish Painting, Seventeenth Century .... Room 30b
Italian Painting, Thirteenth, Fourteenth, Fifteenth, and Sixteenth Centuries .... Rooms 30, 31
Italian Painting, Sixteenth Century .... Room 32
Italian Painting, Seventeenth and Eighteenth Centuries............. Room 35
English Painting, Eighteenth and Early Nineteenth Centuries........ Room 38
French Painting, Seventeenth and Eighteenth Centuries............. Room 39
French Painting, Nineteenth Century .... Room 40
International Painting, Nineteenth and Twentieth Centuries......... Room 41
Paintings by Degas and Monet.. Room 42
Paintings by Cézanne.......... Room 43
Paintings by Manet and Renoir.. Room 45
Paintings by Gauguin, Rousseau and Seurat .... Room 46
Paintings by Toulouse-Lautrec and Van Gogh .... Room 47
Paintings by Matisse and Picasso. Room 48
Spanish Painting, Fifteenth, Sixteenth, Seventeenth, Eighteenth and Early Nineteenth Centuries............ Room 50
Early American Painting....... Room 26
American Painting, Nineteenth and Early Twentieth Centuries..... Rooms 25, 53
Contemporary American Painting .... Rooms 51, 52, 52b, G52–G56
Contemporary French Painting .... Rooms G57, G60
Contemporary International Painting .... Room G58
Contemporary German Painting .... Room G59
International Abstract Painting. Room G61

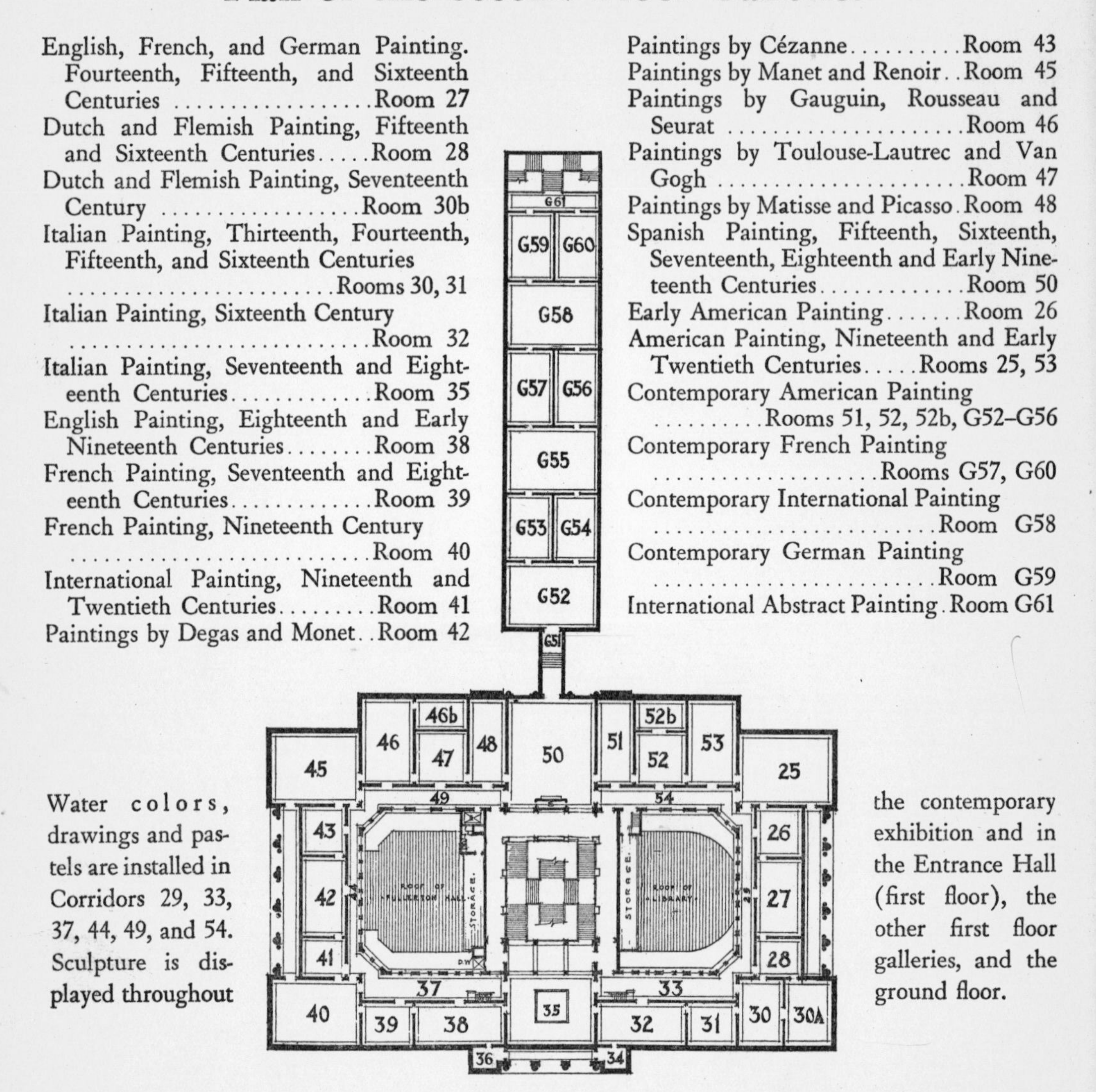

Water colors, drawings and pastels are installed in Corridors 29, 33, 37, 44, 49, and 54. Sculpture is displayed throughout the contemporary exhibition and in the Entrance Hall (first floor), the other first floor galleries, and the ground floor.

The Cafeteria and Soda Fountain (open all day) may be reached by staircases from the Entrance Hall. On the same floor will be found a rest room provided with writing materials.

The Department of Reproductions has for sale post cards, photographs, and color reproductions and framed pictures of many examples in the exhibition. These may be purchased at the Front Door or in Gallery 50.

A companion catalogue for "A Century of Progress" Print Exhibition containing notes on entries and fully illustrated ($.50) is for sale also.

Editorial Note

In the preparation of the catalogue, Mr. Daniel Catton Rich has acted as editor. He has been assisted by Miss Dorothy Stanton who not only helped with many of the entries but wrote the section on Italian painting. Entries for water colors, drawings and pastels were compiled by Mr. G. E. Kaltenbach; the material on sculpture was prepared by Miss Helen F. Mackenzie.

Appreciation is due many members of the Staff. Among these Miss Etheldred Abbot, Librarian of the Ryerson and Burnham Libraries, and the reference staff have given unfailing and systematic help throughout. Mr. G. E. Kaltenbach has very kindly read all entries and the proof and has checked the references for the second edition; Miss Daisy M. Meyer has made the Index. In addition, the assistance of the Library of Congress and the Newberry Library, Chicago, is gratefully acknowledged.

Robert B. Harshe, *Director*

Explanatory Note

In *sizes* height always precedes width.

Under many of the entries in the catalogue will be found the following:

Coll.: (which refers to collections through which the work has passed.)

Exh.: (which refers to exhibitions in which the work has been seen.)

Lit.: (which refers to books and periodicals where the work has been published. In this third category only important references are given; the notes are necessarily incomplete and merely suggest material dealing with further history and description of the work. It has been found impossible to carry through this form with *contemporary* entries.)

In the literary references the following abbreviations have been employed:

B. Berenson, *Cent. Ital.*
Bernhard Berenson, *The Central Italian Painters of the Renaissance*, 1909.

B. Berenson, *Flor.*
Bernhard Berenson, *The Florentine Painters of the Renaissance*, 1909.

B. Berenson, *Ital. Pict.*
Bernhard Berenson, *The Italian Pictures of the Renaissance*, 1932.

B. Berenson, *Venetian*
Bernhard Berenson, *The Venetian Painters of the Renaissance*, 1894.

Bull.
Bulletin of The Art Institute of Chicago, I (1907)—XXVII (1933).

Crowe and Cavalcaselle.

J. A. Crowe and G. B. Cavalcaselle, *History of Painting in Italy,* I–VI. Edited by Langton Douglas, I–IV, T. Borenius, V–VI, 1903–1914.

Crowe and Cavalcaselle, *North Ital.*

J. A. Crowe and G. B. Cavalcaselle, *History of Painting in North Italy,* I–III. Edited by Tancred Borenius.

J. B. de la Faille

L'Oeuvre de Vincent van Gogh, I–IV, 1928

Guide

A Guide to Paintings in the Permanent Collection of The Art Institute of Chicago (2nd edition), 1932

H. de Groot

C. Hofstede de Groot, *Catalogue Raisonné of the Works of the Dutch Painters of the Seventeenth Century* (tr. and ed. by Edwin G. Hawke), I–VIII, 1907–1928

Jamot-Wildenstein-Bataille

P. Jamot, G. Wildenstein, and M. L. Bataille, *Manet,* I and II, 1932

Van Marle

Raimond van Marle, *The Development of the Italian Schools of Painting,* I–XIV, 1923–1933 (in progress).

Reinach, *Répertoire*

S. Reinach, *Répertoire de Peintures du Moyen-Age et de la Renaissance,* I–VI, 1907–1923

J. Smith

John Smith, *Catalogue Raisonné of the Works of Dutch, Flemish, and French Painters,* I–IX, 1829–1842

Tabarant

A. Tabarant, *Manet,* 1931

Thieme-Becker, *Künstlerlexikon*

U. Thieme and F. Becker, *Allgemeines Lexikon der Bildenden Künstler,* I–XXVI, 1901–1932 (in progress).

A. Venturi, *Storia*

Adolfo Venturi, *Storia dell'Arte Italiana,* I–IX, 1901–1933 (in progress).

L. Venturi, *Pitt. Ital.*

Lionello Venturi, *Pitture Italiane in America,* 1931.

The majority of the books referred to in this catalogue are in the Ryerson Library, where they may be consulted.

Paintings

*An * preceding a number indicates that this entry is illustrated.*
Each illustration bears the same number as that
which appears in the catalogue.
Paintings and Sculpture marked † are for sale.
Prices on application at Sales Desk.

ENGLISH, FRENCH AND GERMAN PAINTING

Fourteenth, Fifteenth and Sixteenth Centuries

GALLERY 27

ALBRECHT ALTDORFER, German, 1480–1538

†1. Nativity

Oil on panel, 20¾ x 16½ in.

Lent by A. S. Drey, Munich and New York.

Coll.: Private Coll., Lucca.

Exh.: Cleveland Mus. of Art, 1931; Toronto Art Mus., 1931, No. 55.

Dr. A. L. Mayer attributes it to Altdorfer, calling it an early work; Dr. M. J. Friedländer believes it to have been done in Bavaria round 1520 "and in several characteristics recalling Altdorfer."

CHRISTOPH AMBERGER, German, 1500–1563

2. Portrait of a Man

Oil on panel, 16½ x 13½ in.

Owned by the Art Institute of Chicago.

Coll.: Countess of Dartrey, Monaghan, Ireland; Barbizon Hse., Lond.

Lit.: *Barbizon Hse.,* 1923, No. 38 (repr.); *Guide,* 1932, 31 (repr.).

The attribution is traditional.

AMIENS SCHOOL, French, c. 1480

3a. Madonna and Child
 b. St. John the Baptist
*c. The Last Supper (Pl. V)
*d. The Ascension (Pl. V)
 e. Descent of the Holy Ghost
 f. Saint Honore, Bishop
 g. Saint Hugo, Bishop of Lincoln

Oil on panel, each, 45⅜ x 19⅞ in.

Owned by The Art Institute of Chicago (Mr. and Mrs. Martin A. Ryerson Collection).

Coll.: St. Honoré, Thuison-lès-Abbeville; Church of the Holy Sepulchre, Abbeville, 1795; Kraemer Coll., Paris (Sale, 1913, Nos. 17–23); M. A. Ryerson, Chi. (1913).

Exh.: Exposition of French Primitives, Paris, 1904, No. 353; Kleinberger Gall., N. Y., 1927, Nos. 25–31 (repr. in cat.); the panel of St. Honoré was shown at Detroit Inst. of Arts, 1928, No. 7.

Lit.: For early literature see, E. Délignières, *Réunion des Sociétés des Beaux-Arts des Départements,* 1898, 305–343 (repr.); Reinach, *Répertoire,* V, 1922, 266 (fig. 1); W. Hausenstein (Ed.), *Tafelmalerei der alten Franzosen (Das Bild—Atlanten zur Kunst),* 1923, Pl. 18 (Last Supper) and Pl. 19 (St. Hugo); F. J. Mather, The Arts, XII (1927), 246–7 (repr.); W. Heil, *Pantheon,* III (1929), 76, 78 (for the St. Honoré Panel); A. C. Barnes and V. de Mazia, *The French Primitives and their Forms,* 379–81, 525 (Last Supper, repr. 378).

These seven panels are all that remain of a large altarpiece painted for the high altar of the ancient Carthusian Monastery of St. Honoré at Thuison, a suburb of Abbeville, which, having flourished and grown rich during the fourteenth century, was completely destroyed during the French Revolution. Originally the panels were four, painted on both sides, but they have been sawed apart; one, "The Resurrection of Christ," has disappeared. In the center of the altar was a gilded sculpture of the "Passion of Christ" (since lost). During the Revolution, in 1795, the furniture, altars, retables and paintings were auctioned off; at that time these panels were purchased by the Abbé Cauchy, Curate of the Church of the Holy Sepulchre at Abbeville.

Dr. M. J. Friedländer suggests that they were executed c. 1470.

St. Honoré was born in Port-le-Grand (near Abbeville). He died in 600 a.d., and his remains, after working many miracles, were removed to the cathedral of his episcopal see in the ninth century.

St. Hugo, scion of a noble Burgundian house, took orders at the Grande Chartreuse near Grenoble. Later he was Prior of the Carthusian Monastery of Wittham in England and was made Bishop of Lincoln in 1181. His relics were given to the monks of Thuison-lès-Abbeville.

AVIGNON SCHOOL, French, c. 1400

*4. The Blessed Pierre de Luxembourg Presenting a Donor to the Virgin and Child (Pl. III)

Tempera on panel, 24½ x 16½ in.
Lent by The Worcester Art Museum, Worcester, Massachusetts.

LIT.: R. H-H., *Bull. of the Worcester Art Mus.*, XIV (1923), 22–5 (repr.); *Cat. of Paintings and Drawings: The Worcester Art Mus.*, 1922, 4–5 (repr.); *A Guide to the Collections of the Worcester Art Mus.*, 1932, 54–5 (repr.).

Pierre de Luxembourg, son of Guy de Luxembourg and Matilda del Castiglione, was born at Château de Ligny, July 20, 1369. At the early age of fourteen he was created Bishop of Metz and was made Cardinal Deacon of S. Giorgio in Velabro in 1385, dying four years later. He was beatified in 1527 by Pope Clement VII.
Mr. C. Van Put gives the following inference from the arms: argent a lion rampant crowned gules (Luxembourg), the shield surmounted by a red cardinal's hat, being confirmed by the halo round the head of the figure.

HANS BALDUNG, CALLED GRIEN, GERMAN, c. 1480–1545

†5. PORTRAIT OF A YOUNG MAN
Oil on panel, 12⅛ x 8½ in.
Lent by Wildenstein & Co., Inc., New York.

COLL.: Count Harrach, Vienna, No. 28.

LIT.: K. Feuchtmayr, *Beiträge zur Geschichte der deutschen Kunst,* II (1928), 124–5, 127 (repr.); W. Wescher-Kauert, *Pantheon,* X (1932), 284–5 (repr.).

Formerly called School of Dürer; Dr. M. J. Friedländer calls it an early work of Baldung. Feuchtmayr attributes it to "The Master of the University Altar" (The Monogrammist L. S.); Wescher-Kauert believes it to be painted by "The Master D. S."

BARTEL BRUYN, THE ELDER, COLOGNE SCHOOL, 1493–1555

6. MADONNA AND CHILD WITH ST. ANNE, ST. GEREON AND DONOR
Oil on panel, 30½ x 22½ in.
Owned by The Art Institute of Chicago (Mr. and Mrs. Martin A. Ryerson Collection).

COLL.: Neven (Sale, 1879, No. 2); E. F. Weber, Hamburg (Sale, Berlin, 1912, No. 64, Pl. 29); M. v. Nemes, Budapest (Sale, Paris, 1913, I, No. 23, repr. in cat.); Kleinberger, N. Y.; M. A. Ryerson, Chi. (1913).

EXH.: Düsseldorf, 1904, No. 468.

LIT.: J. J. Merlo, *Die Meister der Altkölnischen Malerschule,* 1852, 159 (new edition, 1895, 136); J. Pflugh-Hartung, *Repertorium für Kunstwissenschaft,* VIII (1885), 3; H. Janitschek, *Gesch. der deutschen Malerei,* III, 1890, 522; E. Firmenich-Richartz, *Bartolomaeus Bruyn und seine Schule,* 1891, 108–9; C. Aldenhoven, *Geschichte der Kölner Malerschule,* 1902, 383; M. Escherich, *Die Schule von Köln,* 1907,131; Firmenich-Richartz, *Thieme-Becker, Künstlerlexikon,* V, 1911, 156.

Painted c. 1525–30. St. Gereon, a favorite saint with painters of this school, was a commander of the Theban Legion in the third century A.D. and was put to death at Cologne with many of his soldiers for refusing to renounce Christianity at the command of the Emperor Maximianus.

BARTEL BRUYN, THE YOUNGER, COLOGNE SCHOOL, 1530–1610

7. WOMAN WITH PRAYERBOOK
Oil on panel, 17¾ x 12¾ in.
Lent by Mr. and Mrs. Charles H. Worcester, Chicago.

COLL.: Sedelmeyer, Paris; C. H. Johnson, Chi.

EXH.: Kleinberger Gall., N. Y., 1928, No. 54 (repr. in cat.); The Art Inst. of Chi., 1930–3.

According to Dr. M. J. Friedländer, painted c. 1560.

JEAN CLOUET, c. working c. 1516–1546

*8. CHARLOTTE OF FRANCE (Pl. VI)
Oil on panel, 12 x 9 in.
Lent by Max Epstein, Chicago.

COLL.: Reinhardt Gall., New York.

EXH.: Kleinberger Gall., N. Y., 1927, No. 46 (repr. in cat.); The Art Inst. of Chi., 1927, 1930; Royal Academy, Lond., 1932, No. 49 (in the cat. this picture is confused with a replica).

Painted c. 1540. Clouet painted a replica with several variations. Formerly in the collection of Mrs. Thomson, Lond., it was exhibited in Paris in 1904. (See L. Dimier, *Hist. de la Peinture de Portrait en France,* I, 1924, Pl. 5.) This replica has recently been acquired by Mr. John R. Van Derlip, Minneapolis.
Charlotte of France, first daughter of François I (1516–1524). She is here portrayed at about the age of seven.

FRANÇOIS CLOUET, before 1522–1572

9. PORTRAIT OF ELISABETH OF AUSTRIA
Oil on panel, 14¼ x 10½ in.
Inscribed: ELISABET. D'AUSTRICHE. DITE. DE. BOHÊME. EPOV. DU ROY CHARLES IX
Lent by Mrs. William R. Timken, New York.

Another portrait of Queen Elisabeth (1554–1592), wife of Charles IX of France, by François Clouet is in the Louvre. The same features appear here with different details of costume. Other portraits of the Queen are in the Louvre and at Versailles, while copies and replicas are known.

FRANÇOIS CLOUET, FRENCH, before 1522–1572

†10. PORTRAIT OF A NOBLE LADY
Oil on panel, 18 x 13 in.
Lent by Arnold Seligmann, Rey and Co., Inc., New York.

COLL.: Cook, Newcastle-on-Tyne.

EXH.: Kansas City Art Mus., 1932.

Dr. W. Bode, Dr. M. J. Friedländer, and Dr. G. Glück attribute it to François Clouet, and date it c. 1560. Bode suggests that it may represent Queen Elisabeth of France (1554–1592).

CORNEILLE DE LYON, FRENCH, c. 1520–1574

11. LOUISE HALLEWYN, DAME DE CYPIERRE

Oil on panel, 8 x 6¾ in.

Owned by The Art Institute of Chicago (Mr. and Mrs. Martin A. Ryerson Collection).

COLL.: M. A. Ryerson, Chi. (1913).

EXH.: Kleinberger Gall., N. Y., 1927, No. 66 (repr. in cat.).

Louise de Hallewyn (Halluin, Hallewin) was married in 1560 to Philibert de Marcilly, Seigneur de Cypierre, Governor of King Charles IX. Another painting of her, almost identical, but somewhat smaller, is in the Museum at Versailles.
According to L. Dimier, painted c. 1555.

CORNEILLE DE LYON, FRENCH, c. 1520–1574

12. PORTRAIT OF A WOMAN

Oil on panel, 8 x 6⅜ in.

Lent anonymously.

COLL.: Wildenstein, N. Y.

EXH.: Kleinberger Gall., N. Y., 1927, No. 70 (repr. in cat.); Royal Academy, Lond., 1932, No. 98.

Painted c. 1560.

LUCAS CRANACH, THE ELDER, GERMAN, 1472–1553

*13. CRUCIFIXION (1538) (Pl. I)

Oil on panel, 47¼ x 32¼ in.

Signed with winged dragon and dated 1538.

Lent by Mr. and Mrs. Charles H. Worcester, Chicago.

COLL.: Sir Fairfax Cartwright, Squire of Aynho; J. Böhler, Munich.

EXH.: Kleinberger Gall., N. Y., 1928, No. 28 (repr. in cat.); Van Diemen Gall., N. Y., 1929; Renaissance Society, University of Chicago, 1930; The Art Inst. of Chi., 1930–3.

LIT.: *Bull.*, XXIII (1929), 6–7 (repr.); *International Studio,* XCI (December, 1928), 65 (repr.), 78; M. J. Friedländer and J. Rosenberg, *Die Gemälde von Lucas Cranach,* 1932, 85, No. and Pl. 302 (where the suggestion is made that the date is probably 1538).

LUCAS CRANACH, THE ELDER, GERMAN, 1472–1553

†14. MADONNA AND CHILD GATHERING STRAWBERRIES

Oil on panel, 29 x 19½ in.

Signed with the winged dragon.

Lent by A. S. Drey, Munich and New York.

EXH.: Toronto Art Mus., 1931, No. 52.

LIT.: M. J. Friedländer and J. Rosenberg, *Die Gemälde von Lucas Cranach,* 1932, 88, No. 315, d.; *Art News,* XXVIII (Mar. 29, 1930), 14 (repr.).

Dr. M. J. Friedländer and J. Rosenberg date it after 1537, comparing it with versions in the Fischer Coll., Lucerne, and the Stumpf Sale, Berlin, 1918.

LUCAS CRANACH, THE ELDER, GERMAN, 1472–1553

16. PORTRAIT OF A PRINCE OF SAXONY

Oil on panel, 17⅛ x 13⅛ in.

Lent by Mrs. Ralph Harman Booth, wife of the late Honorable Ralph Harman Booth, former Minister to Denmark.

COLL.: J. Böhler, Munich; A. Salomon, Dresden.

EXH.: Detroit Inst. of Arts, 1926, No. 17.

LIT.: *International Studio,* XCIV (October, 1929), cover (repr.); M. J. Friedländer and J. Rosenberg, *Die Gemälde von Lucas Cranach,* 1932, 50, No. and Pl. 104.

Painted 1516–18. The companion portrait of the Princess is in the same coll. Friedländer suggests that they are perhaps the children of Duke George the Bearded, Prince Friedrich (b. 1504) and Princess Christine (b. 1505).

ENGLISH (?) SCHOOL, SECOND HALF OF THE FOURTEENTH CENTURY

17. THE MARTYRDOM OF ST. CATHERINE OF ALEXANDRIA

Tempera on panel, 14 x 13 in.

Owned by The Art Institute of Chicago.

COLL.: Arnold Seligmann, Rey and Co., Paris and N. Y.

The date and nationality of this panel are uncertain. According to Mr. Mann, Assistant-Director of the Courtauld Inst., Lond., an authority on armor, the soldier's helmet, gorget and close-fitting tunic would place its execution in the second half of the fourteenth century.
J. A. Herbert, who has made a special study of the painting, suggests that it may have been done in Scandinavia, under English influence, and compares it with A. Lindblom, *La Peinture Gothique en Suède et en Norvège,* 1916, especially Pl. 36. L. Réau calls it "Anglo-Norman School" and dates it in the first quarter of the fourteenth century.
St. Catherine of Alexandria, virgin and martyr, upbraided the Emperor Maxentius for his cruelty and false religion, whereupon she was sentenced to be broken upon a wheel, which, however, was miraculously shattered before the execution could be carried out.

FRENCH SCHOOL, c. 1540

18. PORTRAIT OF A NOBLEMAN

Oil on panel, 15 x 12¾ in.

Lent by Mr. William Goldman, New York.

COLL.: G. de Stroganoff, Rome (1912); Bottenwieser, Berlin, 1926.

Assigned by Dr. M. J. Friedländer to "a preëminent French master of about 1540."

HANS HOLBEIN, THE YOUNGER, German, 1497–1543

*19. Portrait of Catherine Howard, Queen of England (Pl. II)
Oil on panel, 29 x 20 in.
Inscribed: Aetatis Suae 21.
Lent by The Toledo Museum of Art (The Edward Drummond Libbey Collection), Toledo, Ohio.

Coll.: C. Bush, Lond.; J. H. Dunn, Canada; Colnaghi & Co., Lond.; E. D. Libbey.

Exh.: Reinhardt Gall., N. Y., 1928, No. 3 (repr. in cat.).

Lit.: L. Cust, *Burlington Magazine,* XVII (1910), 192 (repr.), 193–9; A. C. Chamberlain, *Hans Holbein the Younger,* 1913, II, 194–6, 348; P. Ganz, *Holbein* (Klassiker der Kunst), 1921, 126 (repr.); *The Arts,* V (1924), 211 (repr.), 223; M. Vaughn, *International Studio,* LXXXVIII (December, 1927), 65 (repr.). 68, 94; A. L. Mayer, *Pantheon,* II (1928), 331 (repr.).

According to Cust, painted between July 1540 and October 1541. Other portraits of the Queen by Holbein are in the collections of the Duke of Buccleuch and the Royal Library, Windsor Castle. A drawing (in reverse) is also at Windsor. The brooch was designed by Holbein who was an accomplished goldsmith. A copy of the picture, probably contemporary, is in the National Portrait Gall., Lond.

Catherine Howard (1520/21–1542), daughter of Lord Edmund Howard and granddaughter of the Duke of Norfolk, became the fifth queen of Henry VIII in July 1540. She was beheaded in February 1542.

HANS HOLBEIN, THE YOUNGER, German, 1497–1543

*20. Portrait of a Member of the Wedigh Family of Cologne (1532) (Pl. II)
Oil on panel, 15¾ x 12¼ in.
Signed: H. H. and inscribed: Her. Wid.; on the projecting sheet of paper is the motto: Veritas odium parit (Truth brings hatred). On the background: Anno 1532 and Aetatis Suae 29.
Lent anonymously.

Coll.: Count von Schönborn-Buchheim, Vienna.

Exh.: The Art Inst. of Chi., 1924.

Lit.: A. Woltmann, *Holbein und seine Zeit,* I, 1874, 262, No. 26; H. Knackfuss, *Holbein* (trans. by C. Dodgson), 1899, 121 (repr.); G. S. Davies, *Hans Holbein the Younger,* 1903, 145; P. Ganz, *Hans Holbein d. J.* (Klassiker der Kunst), 1912, 97 (repr.); A. B. Chamberlain, *Hans Holbein the Younger,* II, 1913, 15–16, 349; F. von Reber and A. Mayersdorfer, *Klassischer Bilderschatz,* VI, n. d., No. 94 (repr.); F. Benoit, *Holbein* (Les Maîtres de l'Art), n. d., 159; M. Vaughn, *International Studio,* LXXXVIII (November, 1927), 24 (repr.).

A portrait of Hermann (?) Wedigh, a member of a patrician family of Cologne, painted in London in 1532. The device on his ring bears the family arms. Another member of the family (a brother?) was painted by Holbein and is today in the Kaiser-Friedrich Mus., Berlin. Both pictures were mentioned as early as 1746 in an inventory.

JOHANN KOERBECKE, Muenster School, fl. 1446–1491

21. Annunciation
Tempera on panel transferred to canvas, 36¼ x 24⅝ in.
Owned by The Art Institute of Chicago (Mr. and Mrs. Martin A. Ryerson Collection).

Coll.: Abbey of Marienfeld, Westphalia, 1457–1803; M. A. Ryerson, Chi. (1923).

Lit.: For complete bibliography on the Marienfeld altar see M. Lippe, *Thieme-Becker,* XXI (1927), 176. There is to be added an important article by W. Hügelshofer, *Der Cicerone,* XXII (1930), 371–6.

Probably to be identified with the Marienfeld altar painted for the Westphalian Abbey of Marienfeld by Koerbecke in 1457. The coat-of-arms, according to various critics, suggests that it was ordered by a Cistercian abbey. Originally the work consisted of sixteen panels, but in 1804 one was known to have been broken. Of the remaining, all but one have come to light. Three are in the Mus. of Münster, four in the Musée Calvet, Avignon, one is in the Cracow Mus., one in the Brocard Coll., Moscow, one is in the Kaiser-Friedrich Mus., Berlin, one in the H. Wagner Coll., N. Y., one in the Castle Rohoncz Coll., one the property of the Hinrichsen and Lindpainter Gall., Berlin, and one appeared in the Doetsch Sale, Lond.

According to Hügelshofer, eight depicted the life of Christ and Mary and eight the Passion of the Lord. He believes the present panel to have occupied an inside position.

ATTRIBUTED TO HANS VON KULMBACH, German, c. 1480–1522

22. St. Matthias and Donor
Oil on panel, 20 x 8 in.
Lent by Mr. and Mrs. Charles H. Worcester, Chicago.

Coll.: Roerich Mus., N. Y. (Sale, 1930).

A wing from a triptych. Companion to No. 23.

ATTRIBUTED TO HANS VON KULMBACH, German, c. 1480–1522

23. St. Peter and Donor
Oil on panel, 20 x 8 in.
Lent by Mr. and Mrs. Charles H. Worcester, Chicago.

See No. 22.

HANS MALER ZU SCHWAZ, South German, fl. 1510–1529

24. Christ Bearing the Cross
Oil on panel, 13¼ x 22½ in.
Lent by Mr. and Mrs. Charles H. Worcester, Chicago.

Exh.: The Art Inst. of Chi., 1930–3.

Attributed by Dr. M. J. Friedländer.

HANS MALER ZU SCHWAZ, South German, fl. 1510–1529

25. Young Man

Oil on panel, 16½ x 13 in.

Lent by Mr. and Mrs. Charles H. Worcester, Chicago.

Coll.: Col. Vombwell, Lond.

Exh.: Kleinberger Gall., N. Y., 1928, No. 42 (repr. in cat.).

Attributed by Dr. W. R. Valentiner.

MASTER ANDRE (?), Viennese, active c. 1410–1425

*26. Christ Carrying the Cross (Pl. I)

Tempera on panel, 9⅛ x 7⅛ in.

Lent by Mr. and Mrs. Charles H. Worcester, Chicago.

Coll.: J. Böhler, Munich.

Exh.: Kleinberger Gall., N. Y., 1928, No. 3; The Art Inst. of Chi., 1930–3.

Dr. W. Hügelshofer connects it with a group of similar works painted in Vienna at the beginning of the fifteenth century.

MASTER OF THE KRAINBURG ALTAR, Austrian, fifteenth century

27. The Funeral of St. Florian

Tempera on panel, 32½ x 33 in.

Lent by Mr. and Mrs. Charles H. Worcester, Chicago.

Coll.: Roerich Mus., N. Y., (Sale, 1930, No. 129, repr. in cat.).

Exh.: The Art Inst. of Chi., 1930–3.

Lit.: O. Benesch, *Wiener Jahrb. für Kunstgeschichte,* VII (1930), 138.

According to Dr. Otto Benesch, this panel is one of a series representing scenes in the life of St. Florian, further examples of which are in the Museum Joanneum at Graz. Another panel, "The Massacre of the Innocents," has since disappeared. Dr. Benesch dates it c. 1499. (See a monograph by Benesch, published by Dr. Benno Filser Verlag, Augsburg, on the altar.)

MASTER OF MOULINS, French, active 1480–1520

*28. The Annunciation (Pl. V)

Oil on panel, 29 x 20 in.

Owned by The Art Institute of Chicago (Mr. and Mrs. Martin A. Ryerson Collection).

Coll.: Private Coll., Paris; Messrs. Dowdeswell & Dowdeswell, Lond. (1906); M. A. Ryerson, Chi. (1914).

Exh.: Grafton Gall., Lond., 1909, No. 76 (repr. in cat.); Kleinberger Gall., N. Y., 1927, No. 35 (repr. in cat.); Detroit Inst. of Arts, 1928, No. 9; Royal Academy, Lond., 1932, No. 63.

Lit.: R. Fry, *Burlington Magazine,* IX (1906), 330–1 (repr.); Reinach, *Répertoire,* IV, 54 (repr.); M. Nicolle, *Revue de l'Art Ancien et Moderne,* XXVII (1910), 55 (repr.); F. Monod, *Gaz. des Beaux-Arts,* Per. 4, III (1910), 243 (repr.), 244–5; Monod, *Revue de l'Art* (1910), 55; J. Guiffrey and P. Marcel, *La Peinture Française: les Primitifs,* 1913, 18, Pls. 53 and 54; M. Conway, *The Van Eycks and their Followers,* 1921, 187; M. Brockwell, *The Connoisseur,* LXII (Apr., 1922), 206; M. J. Friedländer, *Burlington Mag.,* XLVII (1925), 186–188 (repr.); W. Heil, *Pantheon,* III (1929), 76; A. C. Barnes and V. de Mazia, *The French Primitives and their Forms,* 1931, 431–2, 437 (repr.).

According to Friedländer painted c. 1495. He believes this and "The Meeting of Joachim and St. Anne" in the Nat. Gall., Lond., to have belonged to the same altarpiece, the central portion of which is missing.

MASTER OF ST. VERONICA, Cologne School, early fifteenth century

29. Crucifixion with Representatives of the Church and the Synagogue

Tempera on panel, 15¼ x 9¼ in.

Lent by Mr. and Mrs. Charles H. Worcester, Chicago.

Coll.: Lersch, Aix-la-Chapelle; D. Heinemann, Munich, 1927.

Exh.: Kleinberger Gall., N. Y., 1928, No. 4; The Art Inst. of Chi., 1930–3.

Lit.: C. Aldenhoven, *Geschichte der Kölner Malerschule,* 1902, 90.

Formerly attributed to Master Wilhelm. Dr. E. Buchner now connects it with the Master of St. Veronica, and dates it 1420–25.

NORTH FRENCH SCHOOL, c. 1460

30. Pietà

Oil on panel, 16¾ x 11¼ in.

Lent by Mr. Max Epstein, Chicago.

Exh.: The Art Inst. of Chi., 1930.

The attribution and date are Dr. M. J. Friedländer's.

SEBASTIAN SCHEL, School of Innsbruck, c. 1479–1554

32. Altarpiece: Madonna and Child with SS. Agatha, Apollonia, Barbara, Cecelia, Lucia, and Margaret

Tempera on panel, 54½ x 39½ in.

St. Agnes,—St. Ursula.

Tempera on panel, each 54½ x 16¼ in.

Owned by The Art Institute of Chicago (Mr. and Mrs. Martin A. Ryerson Collection).

Coll.: J. Böhler, Munich; M. A. Ryerson, Chi. (1913).

The reverse of the wings is decorated with a scene of Pilate and the populace. On the left wing are Pilate's words: "INNOCENS EGO SUM A SANG: HUIUS" ("I am innocent of the blood of this man."); on the right "CRUCIFIGE! CRUCIFIGE!" ("Crucify! Crucify!").

BERNHARD STRIGEL, German, c. 1460–1528

32a. Portrait of a Man

Oil on panel, 17 x 13½ in.

Lent by Mrs. Ralph Harman Booth, wife of the

late Honorable Ralph Harman Booth, former Minister to Denmark.

EXH.: Detroit Inst. of Arts, 1923.

LIT.: W. R. Valentiner, *Bull. of the Detroit Inst. of Arts,* LV (1923), 51–2, 54 (repr.).

The companion portrait of a woman is in the same collection.

On the original frame is inscribed: GLEICH IN GEMELDTEM IAR AUCH ICH. DO LIESZ ICH CONTERFETEN MICH 1527. UND WARD OCTOBRIS SECHTZEHN TAG. ALT SECHSUNDZWAINTZG IAR WIE ICH SAG ("Just in the year reported I too had myself painted 1527 and it was done on the 16th day of October my age being 26 as I stated.")

SCHOOL OF PARIS (?), c. 1500

*33. ENTOMBMENT (Pl. VII)

Oil (?) on panel, 18¾ x 27⁵⁄₁₆ in.

Owned by The Art Institute of Chicago (Munger Collection).

COLL.: R. Kann., Paris; A. Chiesa (Sale, N. Y., 1926).

EXH.: Kleinberger Gall., N. Y., 1927, No. 9; Detroit Inst. of Arts, 1928, No. 6.

LIT.; R. M. F., *Bull.,* XX (1926), 73 (repr.), 75–6; W. Heil, *Pantheon,* III (1929), 78 (repr.); *Guide,* 1932, 37 (repr.).

Formerly attributed to the School of Avignon. Heil suggests that it was painted by the artist of the Louvre panel representing a Pietà with St. Germain-des-Prés in the background and assigns it to School of Paris, c. 1500.

DUTCH AND FLEMISH PAINTING

Fifteenth and Sixteenth Centuries

GALLERY 28

PIETER BREUGHEL, THE ELDER, FLEMISH, c. 1525–1569

*34. THE WEDDING DANCE (1566) (Pl. VIII)

Oil on panel, 47 x 62 in.

Inscribed: MDLXVI.

Lent by The Detroit Institute of Arts.

COLL.: English art dealer.

LIT.: W. R. Valentiner, *Bull. of The Detroit Inst. of Arts,* XII (1930), 16–18 (repr.); Valentiner, *Apollo,* XII (1930), 395–9 (repr.); *Cat. of Paintings, Detroit Inst. of Arts,* 1930, No. 22 (repr.); Valentiner, *Art in America,* XIX (1931), 117, Fig. 9, 120; G. Glück, *Bruegels Gemälde,* 1932, 69–71, No. 24 (repr.).

Glück notes the following copies: 1. Antwerp Mus. 2. Kaiser-Friedrich Mus., Berlin (seventeenth century). 3. Formerly the property of Gen. Fabritius, Leningrad. 4. A. Kiewicz Sale, Vienna, 1926. A copy of a portion of the picture belongs to M. van Valkenburg, Laaren, Holland.

PETRUS CHRISTUS, FLEMISH, c. 1410–after 1472

*35. ST. JEROME IN HIS STUDY (Pl. X)

Oil on panel, 8¼ x 5½ in.

Lent by The Detroit Institute of Arts.

EXH.: Royal Academy, Lond., 1927, No. 14 (Pl. X of *Memorial Cat.*).

LIT.: W. R. Valentiner, *Bull. of The Detroit Inst. of Arts,* VI (1925), 57 (repr.), 58–9; M. J. Friedländer, *Kunstwanderer,* VI (1925), 297 (repr.); *Apollo,* I (1925), 290–1 (repr.); P. Lambotte, *Apollo,* V (1927), 51, 54 (repr.); R. Fry, *Burlington Magazine,* L (1927), 66 (repr.), 67; L. Baldass, *Belvedere,* II (1927), 82 (repr.); F. Winkler, *Festschrift für Max J. Friedländer,* 1927, 94–8 (repr.); M. Vaughan, *International Studio,* LXXXIX (Feb., 1928), 54 (repr.); *Cat. of the Detroit Inst.,* 1930, No. 33 (repr.).

Baldass advances the theory that it may be an early work by Jan van Eyck, as a *tavoletta* by that master is mentioned in an inventory of Lorenzo dei Medici's art collection from 1492, while another very similar one described by Facio, is said to have been in the possession of Alfonso, King of Naples. Winkler regards it as a copy by Christus of a lost composition by Jan van Eyck. Friedländer and Valentiner connect it with Petrus Christus.

JOOS VAN CLEVE, THE ELDER, FLEMISH, c. 1485–1540/1

36. THE HOLY FAMILY WITH ST. JOSEPH READING

Oil on panel, 19 x 14 in.

Owned by The Art Institute of Chicago (Mr. and Mrs. Martin A. Ryerson Collection).

COLL.: M. v. Nemes, Budapest (Sale, Paris, 1913, No. 18, repr. in cat.), M. A. Ryerson, Chi. (1913).

EXH.: Burlington Fine Arts Club, Lond., 1892; Budapest Mus.; Kleinberger Gall., N. Y., 1929, No. 56 (repr. in cat.).

LIT.: M. J. Friedländer, *Joos van Cleve, Jan Provost, Joachim Patenier* (Die Altniederländische Malerei IX), 1931, 138, No. 66-1.

Painted c. 1520. The composition was often repeated by the master and by members of his school, Friedländer listing seventeen versions.

COLIJN DE COTER, FLEMISH, c. 1467–c. 1509

37. CORONATION OF THE VIRGIN

Oil on panel, 58 x 33½ in.

Owned by The Art Institute of Chicago (Mr. and Mrs. Martin A. Ryerson Collection).

COLL.: P. and D. Colnaghi and Co., Lond.; Knoedler and Co., Paris; M. A. Ryerson, Chi.

LIT.: M. J. Friedländer, *Jahrbuch der Preussischen Kunstsammlungen,* XXIX (1908), 229–231 (repr.); W. Cohen,

Thieme-Becker, Künstlerlexikon, VII, 1912, 553; M. W. Conway, *The Van Eycks and their Followers,* 1921, 264 (Pl. XII, 3); E. Hensler, *Jahrbuch der Preussischen Kunstsammlungen,* XLV (1924), 117–120 (repr. and details); Fierens-Gevaert and P. Fierens, *Histoire de la Peinture Flamande,* III, 1929, 92.

Hensler notes its great similarity to another version of the subject in a private German collection.

JACOB CORNELISZ VAN AMSTERDAM, Dutch, before 1470–1533

*38. Holy Family and St. Anne (Pl. X)
Oil on panel, 36¾ x 33½ in.
Lent anonymously.

Coll.: Schaumburg-Lippe, Castle Bueckeburg, Ahrensburg nr. Hameln; J. Böhler, Munich.

Lit.: Scheibler, *Jahrbuch der Preussischen Kunstsammlungen* III, (1882), 19.

Dr. Friedländer considers it an early work executed c. 1500.

JACOB CORNELISZ VAN AMSTERDAM, Dutch, before 1470–1533

39. The Mourning Virgin and St. John
Oil on panel, 12⅞ x 10⅜ in.
Lent by Mrs. Martin A. Ryerson, Chicago.

According to Dr. W. R. Valentiner, a fragment from a "Pietà." The top of the panel was originally arched.

GERAERD DAVID, Flemish, 1450 or 60–1523

*40. Lamentation at the Foot of the Cross (Pl. VIII)
Oil on panel, 21½ x 24½ in.
Owned by The Art Institute of Chicago (Mr. and Mrs. Martin A. Ryerson Collection).

Coll.: Cardinal Despuig, Palma, Majorca; Countess René de Béarn, Paris; W. Gay, Paris; Marczell de Nemes, Budapest (Sale, Paris, 1913, No. 17, repr. in cat.); M. A. Ryerson, Chi. (1913).

Exh.: Düsseldorf Mus., 1912, No. 22; Kleinberger Gall., N. Y., 1929, No. 31 (repr. in cat.).

Lit.: K. Justi, *Zeitschrift für Bildende Kunst,* XXI (1886), 137; C. Benoit, *Chronique des Arts,* 1903, 105; E. von Bodenhausen, *Geraerd David und seine Schule,* 1905, 168, no. 31; Bodenhausen and W. Valentiner, *Zeitschrift für Bildende Kunst,* XXII (1911), 184; F. Winkler, *Thieme-Becker, Künstlerlexikon,* VIII (1913), 454; *L'Art et les Artistes,* XVII (1913), supplt.; M. J. Friedländer, *Von Eyck bis Bruegel,* 1921, 191; M. Conway, *The Van Eycks and their Followers,* 1921, 286; F. Winkler, *Die Altniederländische Kunst,* 1924; Friedländer, *Memling und Gerhard David,* (Die Altniederländische Malerei VI), 1928, 150–1, No. 195.

It has been suggested that this panel belonged originally to the large St. Anne altar, seen by Justi in Majorca (1886). The center panel and two wings are now the property of Joseph Widener, Elkins Park, Penn., while the six predella panels belong to Lady Wantage, Lockinge Hse. This panel may have been placed under the center. According to Friedländer painted c. 1508–12. He records a weak replica in the de Jado Coll., Bilbao.

ADRIAEN ISENBRANT, Flemish, working 1510–1551

41. Madonna and Child
Oil on panel, 15¼ x 12 in.
Owned by The Art Institute of Chicago (Mr. and Mrs. Martin A. Ryerson Collection).

Coll.: M. A. Ryerson, Chi. (1911).

Exh.: Kleinberger Gall., N. Y., 1929, No. 66 (repr. in cat.).

Dr. W. R. Valentiner notes that Isenbrant has utilized a composition by Geraerd David, "Repose on the Flight," in the Jules S. Bache Coll., N. Y., for the motif of his design.

ADRIAEN ISENBRANT, Flemish, working 1510–1551

42. Madonna and Child
Oil on panel, 17¾ x 11⅞ in.
Owned by The Art Institute of Chicago (Munger Collection).

Coll.: Dowdeswell and Co., Lond., 1903; J. Cramer, Dortmund (Sale, Berlin, 1929).

Lit.: M. J. Friedländer, *Jahrbuch der Preussischen Kunstsammlungen,* XXVII (1906), 144, No. 9, 145 (repr.); A. Scharf, *Der Cicerone,* XXI (1929), 259 (repr.).

Friedländer points out that the motif is from a painting by Rogier van der Weyden, known in a number of replicas and popular in the work of Isenbrant and his followers.

LUCAS VAN LEYDEN, Dutch, 1494–1533

*43. Adoration of the Magi (Pl. VII)
Oil on panel, 11 x 13⅜ in.
Owned by The Art Institute of Chicago (Mr. and Mrs. Martin A. Ryerson Collection).

Coll.: Spanish Gall., Lond.; M. A. Ryerson, Chi.

Lit.: M. J. Friedländer, *Von Eyck bis Bruegel,* 1921, 200, Pl. 28; M. Conway, *The Van Eycks and their Followers,* 1921, 471, Pl. XXIV, 1; L. Baldass, *Die Gemälde des Lucas van Leyden,* 1923, 18, 19, Pl. III; F. Winkler, *Die Altniederländische Kunst,* 1924, 264; P. Wescher, *Thieme-Becker, Künstlerlexikon,* XXIII, 1929, 168, 9; Friedländer, *Der Cicerone,* XXII (1930), 495 (repr.), 498; Friedländer, *Lucas van Leyden, Jan Mostaert, C. Engelbrechtsz* (Die Altniederländische Malerei X), 1932, 89–90, 135, No. 120, Pl. LXXIII.

According to Dr. W. R. Valentiner, a copy, executed by the Bruges miniaturist, Simeon Bening (1483–c. 1560), was formerly in the Somzée Coll., Brussels. Friedländer dates it c. 1510.

MABUSE (JAN GOSSAERT), Flemish, 1478–1535 (?)

44. Portrait of Anne de Berghes, Wife of Adolphe of Burgundy
Oil on panel, 21½ x 16⅛ in.
Lent by Governor Herbert H. Lehman, New York.

Coll.: Sir A. Hume (1834); Lord Alford; Earl of Brownlow, Belton Hse., near Grantham (Sale, Lond., 1923, No. 77); Mrs. S. Scott, Lond.

Exh.: New Gall., Lond., 1899–1900; Royal Academy, 1927, No. 188 (*Memorial Cat.*, Pl. LXXVII).

Lit.: M. Conway, *The Van Eycks and their Followers*, 1921, 374; F. Winkler, *Thieme-Becker, Künstlerlexikon*, XIV, 1921, 41; A. Segard, *Jean Gossart, dit Mabuse*, 1923, No. 23; M. J. Friedländer, *Jan Gossart und Bernard van Orley* (Die Altniederländische Malerei VIII), 1930, 61, 163, No. 76, Pl. LIV; P. Hendy, *Cat. of the Gardner Coll.*, 1931, 213.

Painted c. 1530. A replica is in the Isabella Stewart Gardner Coll., Boston (Marquise de Veere). (Hendy suggests the Boston version may be by Jan Scorel.) Anne de Berghes (1489?–1541) was the daughter of Jean, Seigneur de Berghes and married Adolphe, Seigneur de Beveren et de Veere. Her husband was the son of Antoine of Burgundy, the Grand Bastard, son of Philippe le Bon. She is identified from a drawing, No. 106 in the *Recueil d'Arras* (Ms. 266) in the Library of St. Vaast at Arras.

QUENTIN MASSYS, Flemish, 1465/6–1530

*45. Man with a Pink (Pl. IX)
Oil on panel, 17¼ x 11½ in.
Owned by The Art Institute of Chicago.

Coll.: de Beurnonville; Sciarra Gall., Paris (1881); M. E. May, Paris (1890), No. 106 (as Holbein), repr. in cat.; Prince P. Demidoff, Pratolino, Italy.

Exh.: Kleinberger Gall., N. Y., 1929 (repr. in cat.); Belgian Centenary, Antwerp, 1930, No. 197.

Lit.: M. J. Friedländer, *Von Eyck bis Bruegel*, 1921, 95, Pl. 13; M. Conway, *The Van Eycks and their Followers*, 1921, 319, 327; Friedländer, *Quentin Massys* (Die Altniederländische Malerei VII), 1929, 65, 122, No. 47, Pl. XLIV; *Guide*, 1932, 13 (repr.).

THE MASTER OF ALKMAAR, Dutch, c. 1500

46. The Taking of Christ
Oil on panel, 23½ x 9¼ in.
Lent by Mr. William Goldman, New York.

Coll.: Weinberger, Vienna; Goudstikker Gall., Amsterdam (Sales cat., 1930, No. 39, repr.).

Lit.: M. J. Friedländer, *Lucas van Leyden, Jan Mostaert, C. Engelbrechtsz* (Die Altniederländische Malerei X), 1932, 125, No. 51.

According to Friedländer, one of a pair of altar-wings, the companion to which was formerly in the Hoschek Coll., Prague.

THE MASTER OF FRANKFORT, Flemish, working 1495–1520

47a. St. James of Compostela, a Donor and Son

b. St. Elizabeth of Hungary, a Donor and Daughter

Oil on panel, each, 28 x 16¼ in.
Owned by The Art Institute of Chicago (Mr. and Mrs. Martin A. Ryerson Collection).

Coll.: A. S. Drey, Munich; Ehrich Gall., N. Y.; M. A. Ryerson, Chi. (1913).

Lit.: M. J. Friedländer, *Jahrbuch der Preussischen Kunstsammlungen*, XXXVIII (1917), 149, No. 40; Friedländer, *Quentin Massys* (Die Altniederländische Malerei VII), 1929, 139, No. 135.

Wings of an altarpiece. According to Dr. W. R. Valentiner, the coat-of-arms on the left panel is probably that of the Dutch family, Vosmaer; that of the right, of the Van Zeller d'Oosthove family.

MASTER OF THE LEGEND OF ST. URSULA, Flemish, late fifteenth century

48a. St. John the Evangelist and Donor
b. St. John the Baptist
Oil on panel, each, 20⅝ x 5⅝ in.
Owned by The Art Institute of Chicago (Mr. and Mrs. Martin A. Ryerson Collection).

Coll.: E. Noel, Paris; Fievey, Brussels; M. A. Ryerson, Chi. (1923).

Exh.: Kleinberger Gall., N. Y., 1929, No. 38 (repr. in cat.).

Wings of a triptych.

THE MASTER OF THE VIRGO INTER VIRGINES, Dutch, working 1470–1495

49. Ecce Homo
Oil on panel, 20¾ x 9¼ in.
Owned by The Art Institute of Chicago (Mr. and Mrs. Martin A. Ryerson Collection).

Coll.: Convent of San Luca, Rome; Count Contini, Rome, 1923; Roerich Mus., N. Y. (Sale, 1930, No. 64, repr. in cat.); M. A. Ryerson, Chi. (1930).

Lit.: M. J. Friedländer, *Geertgen und Bosch* (Die Altniederländische Malerei V), 1927, 73–4, 140, No. 53, Pl. XXXV; D. C. Rich, *Bull.*, XXV (1931), 33–36 (repr.).

According to Friedländer an early work, painted c. 1480. A replica (weaker and with lettering) is in the F. Burrell Coll. (At one time lent to the Tate Gall., Lond.).

HANS MEMLING, Flemish, c. 1431–1494

*50. Madonna and Child (Pl. IX)
Oil on panel, 14 x 10½ in.
Owned by The Art Institute of Chicago (Mr. and Mrs. Martin A. Ryerson Collection).

Coll.: Unknown Spanish coll.; Paris dealer; M. A. Ryerson, Chi. (1915).

Lit.: M. J. Friedländer, *Von Eyck bis Bruegel*, 1921, 188; Friedländer, *Art in America*, VIII (1920), 111 (repr.), 115; Friedländer, *Memling und Geraerd David* (Die Altniederländische Malerei VI), 1928, 126, No. 50, Pl. XXXI; H. V., *Thieme-Becker, Künstlerlexikon*, XXIV, 1930, 376; A. F. Frankfurter, *The Fine Arts*, XVIII (Mar. 1932), 22.

According to Friedländer painted c. 1485.

HANS MEMLING, Flemish, c. 1430–1494

51. Portrait of a Young Man
Oil on panel, 12¾ x 9 in.
Lent by Mr. John N. Willys, New York.

Coll.: J. E. Taylor, Lond.

Exh.: Toledo Mus. of Art; Reinhardt Gall., N. Y., 1929; Kleinberger Gall., N. Y., 1929, No. 20 (repr. in cat.).

Lit.: M. J. Friedländer, *Memling und Geraerd David* (Die Altniederländische Malerei VI), 1928, 131, No. 80; A. M. Frankfurter, *The Fine Arts,* XVIII (March, 1932), 21 (repr.), 22.

ANTONIO MORO, Dutch, 1519–1577

52. Head of a Woman

Oil on panel, 14⅜ x 10⅞ in.

Lent by Mr. Samuel S. White, 3rd, Philadelphia, Pennsylvania.

Coll.: Lord Annaly, Holmby Hse.; F. T. Sabin Gall., Lond.

Exh.: Penn. Mus., Phil.

Lit.: L. Cust, *Burlington Magazine,* XXI (1912), 52–3 (repr.).

Traditionally known as a portrait of Mary, Queen of Scots. Cust suggests it may be a slightly earlier picturing of Lady Gresham than in the portrait recently acquired by the Rijks Mus., Amsterdam.

ANTONIO MORO, Dutch, 1519–1577

*53. Portrait of a Nobleman (Pl. XXXIV)

Oil on panel, 44½ x 33 in.

Owned by The Art Institute of Chicago.

Coll.: K. von der Heydt, Berlin; Kleinberger, N. Y.

Exh.: Renaissance Exh., Berlin, 1898 (cat., 1899); Düsseldorf, 1904, No. 208.

Lit.: H. Hymans, *Antonio Moro,* 1910, 164; D. C. Rich, *Bull.,* XXVI (1932), 13–15 (repr.).

Hymans considers it doubtful. Friedländer attributes it to Moro. Possibly executed in Spain on Moro's visit of 1558.

JOACHIM PATINIR, Flemish, c. 1480–1524

54. The Holy Family Resting on the Flight

Oil on panel, 13½ x 9¼ in.

Lent by The Minneapolis Institute of Arts, Minneapolis, Minnesota.

Coll.: S. Bourgeois, N. Y.

Lit.: *Bull. Minneapolis Inst. of Arts,* III (1914), 130–2 (repr.) as "The Miraculous Field of Wheat"; *Handbook, Minneapolis Inst. of Arts,* 1917, 46 (repr.); (edition of 1926), 6 (repr.); M. J. Friedländer, *Joos van Cleve, Jan Provost, Joachim Patenier* (Die Altniederländische Malerei IX), 1931, 157, No. 228.

According to Friedländer the landscape closely follows another panel (an altar-wing) formerly in the R. von Kaufmann Coll., Berlin. The Madonna he attributes to another hand.

ROGIER VAN DER WEYDEN, Flemish, 1399/1400–1464

*55. Jan de Gros (Pl. VI)

Oil on panel, 15 x 11 in.

Owned by The Art Institute of Chicago (Mr. and Mrs. Martin A. Ryerson Collection).

Coll.: Dr. de Meyer, Bruges; R. Kann, Paris (Sale, 1907, II, No. 110); Duveen Bros., N. Y.; M. A. Ryerson, Chi. (1913).

Lit.: M. J. Friedländer, *Katalog der Renaissans Ausstellung,* 1899; E. Michel, *Gaz. des Beaux-Arts,* Per. 3, XXV (1901), 498; W. Bode, *La Galerie de Tableaux de M. Rodolphe Kann à Paris,* n.d., Pl. 84; A. Marguillier, *Les Arts,* II (1903), No. 13, 3 (repr.); F. Laban, *Zeitschr. für Bildende Kunst,* XIX (1907), 60 (repr.); S. de Ricci, *Gaz. des Beaux-Arts,* Per. 3, XXXVIII (1907), 185–7 (repr.); F. Winkler, *Der Meister von Flémalle und Rogier van der Weyden,* 1913, 174; M. J. Friedländer, *Von Eyck bis Bruegel,* 1921, 185; Friedländer, *Art in America,* IX (1921), 62, 63 (repr.), 65; M. Conway, *The Van Eycks and their Followers,* 1921, 148; G. Hulin de Loo, *Burlington Magazine,* XLIII (1923), 54; M. J. Friedländer, *Rogier van der Weyden und der Meister von Flémalle* (Die Altniederländische Malerei II), 1924, 37, 40–1, 101, No. 28, Pl. XXV; Hulin de Loo, *Burlington Magazine,* XLIV (1924), 184–9 (repr.); W. Stein, *Jahrbuch der Preuss. Kunstsammlungen,* XLVII (1926), 31–2; Fierens-Gevaert, *Histoire de la Peinture Flamande,* 1928, II, 60, 64, Pl. L, Fig. 84; J. Destrée, *Roger de la Pasture van der Weyden,* 1930, I, 117; II, Pl. 38; D. C. Rich, *Bull.,* XXVII (1933), 11, 13 (repr.).

Hulin de Loo has shown that this is one panel from a diptych, the other wing of which, a Madonna, is in the collection of E. Renders, Bruges. On the back of the Chicago panel is a whitish scroll bearing the words, "Grâces à Dieu" with a windlass in the center from which is suspended the coat-of-arms of the Gros family. On either side of the shield are the initials J. G. The same device is found on the back of the Bruges panel. Painted not earlier than 1454. Jan (Jean, Jehan) de Gros, first secretary to Charles the Bold (b. 1434?). He became *contrôleur* of the King's finances and was also *trésorier* of the Golden Fleece. He built a handsome house at Bruges and gave liberally toward the decoration and rebuilding of the Church of St. Jacques.

ROGIER VAN DER WEYDEN, Flemish, 1399/1400–1464

56. Madonna and Child

Oil on panel, 14½ x 10¾ in.

Owned by The Art Institute of Chicago (Mr. and Mrs. Martin A. Ryerson Collection).

Coll.: V. Steyaert, Bruges, 1867; Mathys, Brussels (Sale, Paris, 1911); Steinmeyer, Paris; M. A. Ryerson, Chi. (1913).

Exh.: Bruges, 1902, No. 28 (repr. in cat., Pl. XIII).

Lit.: H. Hymans, *Gazette des Beaux-Arts,* Per. 3, XXVIII (1902), 194 (repr.); M. J. Friedländer, *Meisterwerke der Niederländischen Malerei,* 1903, 3, 13 (repr.); K. Voll, *Die Altniederländische Malerei von Jan Van Eyck bis Memling,* 1906, 292; Fierens-Gevaert, *Les Primitifs Flamands,* 1908, I, 50; P. Lafond, *Roger van der Weyden,* 1912, 86; F. Winkler, *Der Meister von Flémalle und Rogier van der Weyden,* 1913, 75; M. J. Friedländer, *Von Eyck bis Bruegel,* 1921, 185; M. Conway, *The Van Eycks and their Followers,* 1921, 150; Friedländer, *Rogier van der Weyden und der Meister von Flémalle* (Die Altniederländische Malerei II), 1924, 34, 101, No. 27; Fierens-Gevaert, *Histoire de la Peinture Flamande,* 1928, II, 60, Pl. XLVI, Fig. 76; J. Destrée, *Roger de la Pasture van der Weyden,* 1930, I, 119, II, Pl. 45.

The composition goes back to an original by Rogier (best known through a picture in the Munich Pinakothek) of "St. Luke Painting the Madonna." Two versions by Rogier, himself, are in the E. Renders Coll., Bruges, and the Kaiser-Friedrich Mus., Berlin. For school adaptations of the motif and versions by Gerard David, Isenbrant, etc. see Fierens-Gevaert, *Histoire de la Peinture Flamande,* 1928, II, 63.

DUTCH AND FLEMISH PAINTING

Seventeenth Century

GALLERY 30B

ADRIAEN BROUWER, Dutch, 1605–1638

*57. The Smokers (Adriaen Brouwer and his Friends) (Pl. XXXVI)

Oil on panel, 18 x 14⅜ in.

Signed: BRAUWER

Lent by The Metropolitan Museum of Art, New York.

Coll.: L. van Oukerke, Haarlem (Sale, 1818, No. 6); J. de Vos, Amsterdam (Sale, 1833, No. 2); Steengracht, The Hague (Sale, Paris, 1913, No. 9, repr. in cat.); M. Friedsam, N. Y.

Exh.: Royal Academy, Lond., 1927, No. 291 (repr. in *Memorial Cat.,* Pl. XCVII).

Lit.: W. Burger (Thoré), *L'Artiste,* N. S., VI (1884), 37; P. Mantz, *Gazette des Beaux-Arts,* Per. 2, XXXI (1880), 30–31; W. Bode, *Adriaen Brouwer,* 1884, 37; Ch. Ephrussi, *Gazette des Beaux-Arts,* Per. 2, XXI (1885), 174; A. von Wurzbach, *Niederländisches Künstlerlexikon* (1906–10), I, 197; M. F. Schmidt-Degener, *A. Brouwer et son Evolution artistique,* 1908, 22–3; H. de Groot, III, 1910, No. 113; Schmidt-Degener, *Thieme-Becker, Künstlerlexikon,* V, 1911, 74; Bode, *Brouwer,* 1924, 172, Pl. 117; H. Schneider, *Zeitschrift für Bildende Kunst* (Feb. 1927), 270–2 (repr.); E. J. Reynolds, *Some Brouwer Problems,* 1931, 51–3, Fig. 26; *Bull. of the Metro. Mus. of Art,* XXVII (1932), Sect. II, 44, No. 77 (repr.).

Engraved by W. Steelink; lithographed by F. H. Weissenbruch.
The Louvre "Smoker" is a sketch for this. Schneider shows that Brouwer has represented himself (in the center) and across from him the flower painter, Jan Davidsz. de Heem, and in the figure looking up, the Antwerp artist, Jan Cossiers. Painted c. 1636–7.

AELBERT CUYP, Dutch, 1620–1691

*58. Landscape with Riders (Pl. XXXVII)

Oil on canvas, 41 x 57 in.

Signed: A. CUYP.

Lent anonymously.

Coll.: Duke of Leinster, Carton, Ireland; Lewis and Simmons, N. Y.

Exh.: The Art Inst. of Chi., 1927.

Lit.: H. de Groot, II, 1909, No. 484.

Painted c. 1660.

ANTHONY VAN DYCK, Flemish, 1599–1641

59. Marquesa Polixena Spinola-Guzman de Legañez

Oil on canvas, 44 x 38 in.

Lent by Mr. Samuel H. Kress, New York.

Coll.: Ambrogio Doria Palace, Genoa; Count Contini, Rome.

Lit.: Inventory of the Casa Doria, Genoa, 1680; M. Menotti, *Archivio Storico dell'Arte,* Ser. II, An. III (1897), 375 (repr.), 444–6; L. Cust, *Van Dyck,* 1900, 242; E. Schaeffer, *Van Dyck* (Klassiker der Kunst), 1909, 192; G. Glück, *Van Dyck* (Klassiker der Kunst), 1931, 348, 557 (cf. 177); A. Burroughs, *Burlington Mag.,* LXII (1933), 175, 176, 177 (Pl. II-A).

According to Glück painted in the Netherlands c. 1630–2. She was the wife of Don Diego Filippo Guzman, Marchese di Legañez, Ambassador from Philip IV of Spain to the Genoese Republic. The Marchese later served in the Netherlands. Another portrait of the same lady by Van Dyck was formerly the property of Kleinberger Gall., N. Y. Van Dyck painted her husband in the portrait owned by Lady Lucas.

ARENT DE GELDER, Dutch, 1645–1727

*60. Portrait of a Girl (Pl. XXXIX)

Oil on canvas, 26 x 21 in.

Owned by The Art Institute of Chicago.

Coll.: H. Ker-Colville, Jr., Bellport Towers, England; D. A. Hoogendijk and Co., Amsterdam.

Exh.: Royal Academy, Lond., 1929, No. 289.

Lit.: D. C. Rich, *Bull.,* XXVII (1933), 33–6 (repr.); *The Art Digest,* VII (Feb. 15, 1933), 27 (repr.).

According to Dr. K. Lilienfeld executed c. 1690.

FRANS HALS, Dutch, 1580–1666

61a. Girl Singing from a Book
b. Singing Boy with Violin

Oil on panel, each, 10½ in. sq.

Signed: FH.

Lent from The Angell-Norris Collection (The Art Institute of Chicago).

Coll.: D. Lawrie Gall., Lond.; C. T. Yerkes, N. Y., Nos. 37 and 38; J. N. Gates, Chi.

Lit.: E. N. Moes, *Frans Hals,* 1909, 110, Nos. 237, 238; H. de Groot, III, 1910, Nos. 118 and 87; W. Bode, *Frans Hals,* 1914, I, 18A and 18B (repr.), Nos. 45 and 46; W. R. Valentiner, *Frans Hals* (Klassiker der Kunst), 1921, 66 (repr.), W. A. P., *Bull.,* XVII (1923), 51–2 [63–4], (repr.).

According to Valentiner painted 1627–30.

FRANS HALS, Dutch, 1580–1666

*62. The Merry Lute Player (Pl. XXXV)

Oil on panel, 36 x 30 in.

Signed: FH.

Lent by Mrs. John R. Thompson and Mr. John R. Thompson, Jr., Chicago.

Coll.: Capello, Amsterdam (Sale, 1767, No. 28); Count Bonde, Stockholm; Colnaghi, Lond.; J. Porgès; Baron F. de Rothschild, Waddeston Manor, England; Ch. Sedelmeyer, Paris; A. Veil-Picard, Paris; Duveen Bros., N. Y.

Exh.: Royal Academy, Lond., 1891, No. 72; Jeu de Paume, Paris, 1911, No. 55; Detroit Inst. of Arts, 1925;

Royal Academy, Lond., 1929, No. 373 (repr. in *Souvenir*).

LIT.: Ch. Sedelmeyer, *Cat. of 100 Paintings,* 1896, No. 19 (repr.); H. de Groot, III, 1910, No. 82, IV, 1912, VI (history confused with another painting); W. Bode, *F. Hals,* 1914, I, No. 58, (Pl. 25), 32; W. R. Valentiner, *Frans Hals* (Klassiker der Kunst), 1921, 55 (repr.); A. M. Frankfurter, *The Antiquarian,* XIII (Sept. 1929), 33 (repr.), 84; E. Singleton, *Old World Masters in New World Collections,* 1929, 223–4 (repr.).

Painted c. 1627.

FRANS HALS, DUTCH, 1580–1666

63. PORTRAIT OF AN ARTIST (1644)

Oil on canvas, 32½ x 25½ in.

Signed: FH and inscribed: AETA. 32, 1644.

Owned by The Art Institute of Chicago.

COLL.: Prince A. Demidoff, San Donato, Italy (Sale, 1880, No. 1105, repr. in cat.); Prince P. Demidoff, Pratolino, Italy; C. L. Hutchinson, Chi.

LIT.: E. N. Moes, *Frans Hals,* 1909, opp. 82 (repr.), No. 39; H. de Groot, III, 1910, No. 185; W. Bode, *Frans Hals,* 1914, II, 241, Pl. 152B; W. R. Valentiner, *Frans Hals* (Klassiker der Kunst), 1921, 204 (repr.); A. M. Frankfurter, *The Antiquarian,* XIII (1929), 34 (repr.), 90; *Guide,* 1932, 15 (repr.).

Traditionally known as a portrait of Harmen Hals, second of the artist's seven painter sons. Valentiner suggests that it may possibly represent the Haarlem painter, Leendert van der Cooghen, as it is known Hals painted him and his age agrees with the inscription.

FRANS HALS, DUTCH, 1580–1666

*64. PORTRAIT OF JUDITH LEYSTER (Pl. XXXV)

Oil on canvas, 29¼ x 25¾ in.

Lent anonymously through the Ehrich Galleries, New York.

COLL.: E. M. Grainger, Hastings, Sussex; Ehrich Gall., N. Y.

LIT.: W. R. Valentiner, *Art in America,* XVI (1928), 239, Fig. 2; F. Dülberg, *Frans Hals,* 1930, 41 (repr.); G. D. Gratama, *Oud-Holland,* XLVII (1930), 71–5 (repr.).

According to Valentiner painted 1620–5. The canvas on the easel reproduces one figure from a work by Judith Leyster preserved today in a private collection.

Judith Leyster (c. 1600–1660), pupil of Frans Hals, was the most famous woman painter of seventeenth century Holland. She was the wife of the artist Jan Molenaer.

Dr. Bredius is strongly inclined to consider it as an excellent self-portrait.

FRANS HALS, DUTCH, c. 1580–1666

65. WILLEM VAN HEYTHUYZEN (?)

Oil on panel, 9½ x 7¾ in.

Signed: FH 163 . . .

Owned by The Art Institute of Chicago.

COLL.: H. Hecht, Paris; C. L. Hutchinson, Chi.

EXH.: Hudson-Fulton Exh., Met. Mus. of Art, N. Y., 1909.

LIT.: E. N. Moes, *Frans Hals,* 1909, 102 (No. 47); W. Bode, *Frans Hals,* 1914, II, 226, Pl. 144A; H. de Groot, III, 1910, No. 189; W. R. Valentiner, *Frans Hals* (Klassiker der Kunst), 1921, 152 (repr.); *Bull.,* XIX (1925), 101 (repr.), 103; A. M. Frankfurter, *The Antiquarian,* XIII (1929), 34 (repr.), 88.

The identification is traditional; painted c. 1637.

MEINDERT HOBBEMA, DUTCH, 1638–1709

*66. THE WATER-MILL WITH THE GREAT RED ROOF (Pl. XXXVIII)

Oil on canvas, 31¾ x 43⅛ in.

Signed: MEINDERT HOBBEMA.

Owned by The Art Institute of Chicago.

COLL.: J. Ellis, 1755; Lord Mount Temple, 1870-90 (?); Prince A. Demidoff, San Donato, Italy; Prince P. Demidoff, Pratolino, Italy; F. G. Logan, Chi., 1903.

LIT.: J. Smith, VI, 1835, No. 105 (described as in reverse from a drawing); J. H. Vanderpoel, *Brush and Pencil,* II (1898), 49 (repr.), 53; H. de Groot, IV, 1912, No. 71; W. Bode, *Die Meister der Holländischen und Vlämischen Malerschulen,* 1919, 191; H. de Groot, *Thieme-Becker, Künstlerlexikon,* XVII (1924), 161; *Guide,* 1932, 25 (repr.).

PIETER DE HOOCH, DUTCH, 1629–1683

67. SKITTLE PLAYERS

Oil on canvas, 26¾ x 29 in.

Signed: with monogram P.H.

Lent by The City Art Museum, St. Louis, Missouri.

COLL.: T. Emmerson, Lond. (Sale, 1829, No. 61); P. Perrier (Sale, Paris, 1843, No. 19); Marquis de Colbert, 1866; Countess de l'Aigle; Duchess de Doudeauville; Wildenstein, N. Y.

EXH.: Palais des Champs Elysées, Paris, 1866, No. 262.

LIT.: J. Smith, IV, 1833, No. 58; C. Brière-Misme, *Gaz. des Beaux-Arts,* Per. 5, XVI (1927), 76–9 (repr.); W. R. Valentiner, *Pieter de Hooch* (Klassiker der Kunst), n. d., 82 (repr.), 277; *Bull. of the City Art Museum, St. Louis,* XIV (1929), 32–5 (repr.); W. R. Valentiner, *Pantheon,* I (1928), opp. 1 (repr.), 10.

According to Valentiner painted 1665–8. Two other versions exist, the earlier in the coll. of Miss Mary Hanna, Cincinnati, the later in the possession of Sir James de Rothschild, Lond.

CASPAR NETSCHER, DUTCH, 1639–1684

68. LADY BEFORE A MIRROR

Oil on panel, 14⅛ x 14½ in.

Owned by The Art Institute of Chicago.

COLL.: Charles L. Hutchinson, Chi. (1915).

JACOBUS OCHTERVELT, DUTCH, 1634/5–1708/10

*69. THE ELEGANT COMPANY (Pl. XXXVII)

Oil on canvas, 18½ x 18½ in.

Owned by The Art Institute of Chicago.

COLL.: Bottenwieser Gall., N. Y.

LIT.: W. A. P., *Bull.,* XVII (1923), 25–8 (repr.); H. Gerson, *Thieme-Becker, Künstlerlexikon,* XXV, 1931, 556; *Guide,* 1932, 24 (repr.).

JACOBUS OCHTERVELT, DUTCH, 1634/5–1708/10

70. THE MUSICIANS

Oil on panel, 31 x 25³⁄₁₆ in.

Signed: JAC. OCHTERVELT F.

Owned by The Art Institute of Chicago (Mr. and Mrs. Martin A. Ryerson Collection).

COLL.: M. A. Ryerson, Chi. (1911).

Exh.: Toledo Mus., 1912, No. 197; Detroit Inst. of Arts, 1929, No. 46 (repr. in cat.).
Lit.: W. R. Valentiner, *Art in America,* XII (1924), 269, 270, 274, 277 (Fig. 5); F. E. W. Freund, *Cicerone,* XXI, Pt. 2 (1929), 705 (repr.), 707; W. Heil, *Pantheon,* V (1930), 35 (repr.), 36; H. Gerson, *Thieme-Becker, Künstlerlexikon,* XXV, 1931, 556.

ADRIAEN VAN OSTADE, Dutch, 1610–1685

71. The Golden Wedding (1674)

Oil on panel, 18⅛ x 16 in.
Signed: a v ostade, 1674.
Owned by The Art Institute of Chicago.

Coll.: De Calonne; E. Coxe, Lond., 1807; J. Dent, Lond., 1827; C. J. Nieuwenhuys; R. Foster, Clewer Manor, 1829–1876; Prince A. Demidoff, San Donato, Italy (Sale, 1880, No. 1109, repr. in cat.); Prince P. Demidoff, Pratolino, Italy; Durand-Ruel, Paris.
Exh.: British Institution, 1815.
Lit.: J. Smith, I, 1829, No. 138; Dr. Waagen, *Treasures of Art in Great Britain,* II, 1854, 451; *Brush and Pencil,* II (1898), 49, 52 (repr.); H. de Groot, III, 1910, No. 542; *Guide,* 1932, 20 (repr.).

KAREL VAN DER PLUYM, Dutch, c. 1620–1672

72. The Old Geographer

Oil on canvas, 28 x 20 in.
Signed: karel van d . . .
Lent by Mr. Chester D. Tripp, Chicago.

Coll.: Dr. J. E. Stillwell, N. Y. (Sale, 1927, No. 210, repr. in cat.).
Exh.: The Art Inst. of Chi., 1931.
Lit.: A. Bredius, *Oud-Holland,* XLVIII (1931), 246–7, 255, Pls. 4 and 6.
Bredius mentions a replica or good copy known to Hofstede de Groot.

REMBRANDT VAN RIJN, Dutch, 1606–1669

*73. Aristotle with the Bust of Homer (1653) (Pl. XXXIII)

Oil on canvas, 54½ x 52½ in.
Signed: rembrandt f. 1653.
Lent by Duveen Brothers, Inc., New York.

Coll.: Marquis Antonio Ruffo, Messina (1653); Sir A. Hume, Ashridge Pk., Hertfordshire (1836); Earl Brownlow, Ashridge Pk.; R. Kann, Paris (1907), cat. No. 65; Mrs. C. P. Huntington, N. Y.; A. W. Erickson, N. Y.
Exh.: British Institution, 1815, No. 39; Royal Academy, Lond., 1893, No. 125; Hudson-Fulton celebration, Metro. Mus. of Art, N. Y., 1909, No. 97 (repr. in cat.); Detroit Inst. of Arts, 1931.
Lit.: J. Smith, VII, 1836, No. 302; C. Vosmaer, *Rembrandt,* 1877, 551; W. Bode, *Rembrandt's Künstlerischer Entwickelungsgang,* 1883, B. 578, No. 139; E. Dutuit, *Tableaux et Dessins de Rembrandt,* Supplt., 1885, 43, No. 314; Wurzbach, *Rembrandt Galerie,* 1886, No. 159; E. Michel, *Rembrandt,* 1893, 555 (English edition, 1894, II, 235); J. Six, *Oud-Holland,* XV (1897), 4–5, Fig. 7; W. Bode, *The Complete Works of Rembrandt,* V, 1901, 31, No. 385 (repr.); A. Rosenberg, *Rembrandt* (Klassiker der Kunst), 1906, 282 (repr.), 402; W. R. Valentiner, *Rembrandt* (Klassiker der Kunst), 1909, 426 (repr.); H. de Groot, VI, 1916, No. 413; G. J. Hoogewerff, *Oud-Holland,* XXXV (1917), 129–148 (repr.); J. J. F. Backer, *Gazette des Beaux-Arts,* Per. 5, II (1925), 53–4 (repr.); F. E. W. Freund, *Cicerone,* XXI (1929), 463–5 (repr.); Valentiner, *Burlington Magazine,* LVII (1930), 271; Valentiner, *Rembrandt Paintings in America,* 1931, Pl. 115, also Chronol. List, 115.
Hoogewerff has shown that the painting was ordered by Don Antonio Ruffo of Messina, a famous art patron of the day. Rembrandt doubtless painted for him the "Alexander" (1655), in Glasgow and the "Homer" (1663), in The Hague. Valentiner finds other works employing the same model, and notes that the bust of Homer is mentioned in an inventory of Rembrandt's art collections.

REMBRANDT VAN RIJN, Dutch, 1606–1669

74. Harmen Gerritsz. van Rijn (Rembrandt's father)

Oil on canvas, 33 x30 in.
Signed: rd.
Owned by The Art Institute of Chicago (W. W. Kimball Collection).

Coll.: M. P. W. Boulton, Tew Park, England (Sale, 1911, No. 14); P. and D. Colnaghi and Obach, Lond.; J. Böhler, Munich; M. de Nemes, Budapest (Sale, Paris, 1913, No. 60, repr. in cat.); J. Böhler, Munich; Reinhardt, N. Y.; Mrs. W. W. Kimball, Chi.
Exh.: Düsseldorf, 1912, No. 43; Detroit Inst. of Arts, 1930, No. 9 (repr. in cat.).
Lit.: W. Bode, *Zeitschrift für Bildende Kunst,* XXIII (1912), 210 (repr); H. de Groot, VI, 1916, No. 675; J. C. Van Dyke, *Rembrandt and his School,* 1923, 111; Valentiner, *Rembrandt, Wiedergefundene Gemälde* (Klassiker der Kunst II), 1921, XVI (No. 19), 17 (repr.); Valentiner, *Rembrandt Paintings in America,* 1931, 5 (Pl. 5); *Guide,* 1932, 17 (repr.), 18.
Valentiner dates it 1629. See H. de Groot (*supra*) for notice of copies. A replica, by a weaker hand, was at one time in the collection of S. Neumann of Lond.
Harmen Gerritsz. van Rijn, born in Leiden, 1568, buried there, April 27, 1630.

REMBRANDT VAN RIJN, Dutch, 1606–1669

*75. Young Girl at an Open Half-Door (Hendrickje Stoffels?) (1645) (Pl. XXXIV)

Oil on canvas, 40⅝ x 34⅛ in.
Signed: rembrandt f. 1645.
Owned by The Art Institute of Chicago.

Coll.: De Gueffier, Paris, 1791; Robit (Sale, Paris, 1801); G. Hibbert (Sale, Lond., 1829); Christie, Lond. (1829); N. Hibbert, Lond., 1857; Prince A. Demidoff, San Donato, Italy (Sale, 1880, No. 1114, repr. in cat.); Prince P. Demidoff, Pratolino, Italy (1890); M. A. Ryerson, Chi. (1894).
Exh., British Institution, Lond., 1818, No. 100; 1844, No. 23; 1857, No. 87; Hudson-Fulton celebration, Met. Mus. of Art, N. Y., 1909, 91 (repr. in cat.); Detroit Inst. of Arts, 1930, No. 42 (repr. in cat.).
Lit.: J. Smith, VII, 1836, No. 532; W. Bode, *Rembrandt's Künstlerischer Entwickelungsgang,* 1883, B, No. 373; E. Dutuit, *Tableaux et Dessins de Rembrandt,* 1885, 21; Wurzbach, *Rembrandt Galerie,* 1886, 358; E. Michel, *Rembrandt,* 1893, 303, 561–2 (English edition, 1894, I, 303, II, 248); W. Bode, *The Complete Work of Rembrandt,* IV, 1900, 194–5, No. 301 (repr.); A Rosenberg, *Rembrandt,* 1906, Pl. 225, 400, 413; W. R. Valentiner, *Rembrandt* (Klass. der Kunst), 1909, 313 (repr.); H. de Groot, VI, 1916, No. 324; J. C. Van Dyke, *Rembrandt Rembrandt,* 1906, Pl. 225, 400, 413; W. R. Valentiner, *Rembrandt Paintings in America,* 1931, Pl. 90, Chronol. List, 90; *Guide,* 1932, 19 (repr.).

Engraved by F. C. G. Geyser.

Valentiner believes that it represents Hendrickje Stoffels (b. 1623 or 1626) who probably came into Rembrandt's household at this time. The motif of the girl at the open half-door was a favorite with members of the Rembrandt school.

PETER PAUL RUBENS, Flemish, 1577–1640

76. Head of a Man

Oil on panel, 20 x 15¼ in.

Lent anonymously.

Coll.: Ducal Gallery, Oldenburg, Germany, No. 123.

Lit.: *Die Grossherzogliche Gemälde-Galerie im Augusteum zu Oldenburg,* II, Pl. 62; M. Rooses, *Rubens,* 1904, 383–4, 645, No. 1110.

The same model served for the figure of one of the kings in the "Adoration" in the Antwerp Mus. Rooses dates it c. 1624.

PETER PAUL RUBENS, Flemish, 1577–1640

*77. Samson and Delilah (Sketch) (Pl. XXXVIII)

Oil on panel, 19¾ x 25¾ in.

Owned by The Art Institute of Chicago.

Coll.: F. T. Sabin, Lond.

Exh.: Detroit Inst. of Arts, 1929, No. 10 (repr. in cat.).

Lit.: R. M. F., *Bull.,* XVIII (1924), 35–7 (repr.): E. Tietze-Conrat, *Burlington Magazine,* LXI (1932), 245–6 (repr.).

Attributed to Van Dyck by Dr. W. R. Valentiner. He calls it the first of four versions. The other three are in Dulwich College, R. von Hirsch Coll., Frankfort, and the Vienna Mus. He dates this example c. 1620.
E. Tietze-Conrat connects it with Rubens, showing its likeness to another sketch and to the finished picture in the Munich Pinakothek.

GERARD TER BORCH, Dutch, 1617–1681

*79. The Music Lesson (Pl. XXXVI)

Oil on canvas, 25 x 19¼ in.

Signed: B (?).

Owned by The Art Institute of Chicago.

Coll.: Chevalier Verhulst (Sale, Brussels, 1779, No. 84); Prince Galitzin, Paris, 1825; J. Fairlie, Lond., 1830; Prince A. Demidoff, San Donato, Italy; Prince P. Demidoff, Pratolino; C. T. Yerkes, Chi. (1891).

Exh., Detroit Inst. of Arts, 1929, No. 74 (repr. in cat.).

Lit.: J. Smith, IV, 1833, No. 20; F. Hellens, *Gérard Terborch,* 1911, 127; H. de Groot,, V. 1913, 130; *The Antiquarian,* III (Sept., 1924), 27 (repr.); P. Hendy, *Cat. of the Isabella Stewart Gardner Mus., Boston,* 1931, 355; *Guide,* 1932, 22 (repr.).

Etched by Mordaunt.
Another version is in the Isabella Stewart Gardner Museum, Boston. (The master beats time with his hand.) Another belonged to Sedelmeyer, Paris, in 1898.

From the later period of the artist.

JAN VERMEER, Dutch, 1632–1675

*80. A Woman Weighing Gold (Pl. XXXIX)

Oil on canvas, 16½ x 14 in.

Signed with monogram.

Lent by Mr. Joseph Widener, Elkins Park, Philadelphia, Pennsylvania.

Coll.: Sales in Amsterdam, 1696, 1701, 1777, and Munich, 1826; Lapeyrière Coll.; C. Périer, Lond. (Sale, 1848, sold to M. Casimir Périer, Jr.); Ségur-Périer Coll., Paris; P. & D. Colnaghi, Lond.

Exh.: Detroit Inst. of Arts, 1925, No. 33.

Lit.: W. Burger, *Gazette des Beaux-Arts,* Per. 1, XXI (1866), 554–6, Nos. 26 and 27; H. Havard, *Jan Vermeer,* 1883, Nos. 29 and 30; H. de Groot, I, 1907, No. 10; H. de Groot, *Burlington Magazine,* XVIII (1910), 133–4; W. Bode, *Jahrbuch der Preussischen Kunstsammlungen,* XXXII (1911), 1–2 (repr. Pl. II); T. Frimmel, *Burlington Mag.,* XXII (1912), 48–9; W. R. Valentiner, *Paintings in the P. A. B. Widener Coll.,* 1913, No. 47; *Ibid, Paintings in the Joseph Widener Coll.,* 1923 (repr.); Valentiner, *Pantheon,* X (1932), 322–3.

On the wall hangs a painting of "The Last Judgment."

ITALIAN PAINTING

Thirteenth, Fourteenth and Fifteenth Centuries

GALLERY 30

FRA ANGELICO, Florentine, 1387–1455

81. Temptation of St. Anthony Abbott

Tempera on panel, 7⅜ x 11⅛ in.

Lent by Mr. and Mrs. Percy S. Straus, New York.

Coll.: Count Ingenheim; K. W. Bachstitz, The Hague.

Exh.: Amsterdam, 1929.

Lit.: *Bull. of the Bachstitz Gall.,* IX, 1925, 97–98 (repr.); *Ibid.,* N. S., I, 16–7 (repr.); *Parnassus,* I (Nov., 1929), 19, 16 (repr.); Berenson, *Ital. Pict.,* 1932, 22.

F. Schottmueller dates it c. 1437, relating it stylistically to the predella pieces of the Madonna Altar of San Domenico, Perugia, now in the Vatican and Perugia Gall.

Once St. Anthony went into the desert and seeing a heap of gold in his path, fled from it as a snare of the devil.

BUTINONE (BERNARDINO JACOBI), North Italian, 1436–1507

82. Flight into Egypt

Tempera on panel, 9⅞ x 8¼ in.

Owned by The Art Institute of Chicago (Mr. and Mrs. Martin A. Ryerson Collection).

Coll.: Count de Malherbe; F. Kleinberger Galleries; M. A. Ryerson, Chi. (1927).

Lit.: D. C. R., *Bull.,* XXI (1927), 86–88 (repr.); E. S. Siple, *Burlington Mag.,* LI (1927), 240, 241 (repr.);

M. Salmi, *Dedalo,* X (1929), 351, 347 (repr.); L. Venturi, *Pitt. Ital.,* 1931, Pl. CCCXXV; B. Berenson, *Ital. Picts.,* 1932, 121.
Salmi dates it c. 1480–1485, pointing out its being earlier but close in style to the Treviglio predelle of 1485.
This and the following panel were first attributed to Butinone by Berenson.
Both this and the next panel are to be compared with a triptych by Butinone in the Museo Municipale, Milan. L. Venturi says they formed part of a polyptych which contained also (1) "Nativity," Nat. Gall., Lond. (No. 3336); (2) "Circumcision," Accademia Carrara, Bergamo (No. 283); (3) "Supper at Bethany," Coll. Suida, Baden; (4) "Incredulity of St. Thomas," Malaspina Gall., Pavia; and probably (5) "Lamentation," (6) "Resurrection," both in Coll. Crespi Morbio, Milan; (7) "Adoration of the Magi," formerly in Paris; (8) "Wedding at Cana," Coll. Borromeo, Milan (No. 39), (cf. *Dedalo,* X [1929], 342, 344–50, repr.).

BUTINONE (BERNARDINO JACOBI), NORTH ITALIAN, 1436–1507

83. DESCENT FROM THE CROSS

Tempera on panel, 9⅞ x 7¾ in.
Owned by The Art Institute of Chicago (Mr. and Mrs. Martin A. Ryerson Collection).

COLL.: Count de Malherbe, Kleinberger Galleries; M. A. Ryerson (1927).

LIT.: D. C. R., *Bull.,* XXI (1927), 86–88 (repr.); E. S. Siple, *Burlington Mag.,* LI (1927), 240, 241 (repr.); L. Venturi, *Pitt. Ital.,* 1931, Pl. CCCXXVI; B. Berenson, *Ital. Picts.,* 1932, 121.

This composition is closely related to that of a woodcut by Mantegna in the British Museum.
(Notes, see above.)

BERNARDO DADDI, FLORENTINE, c. 1290–after 1355

84. VISION OF ST. DOMINIC

Tempera on panel, 15 x 13⅝ in.
Lent by Yale University, Gallery of Fine Arts, New Haven, Conn.

COLL.: J. J. Jarves (1871).

EXH.: Derby Gall., N. Y., 1860, No. 24; New York Historical Society, 1863; Yale Art School, 1867–1871 (bought by Yale); Royal Academy, Lond., 1930, No. 13 (repr. in *Commemorative Cat.,* Pl. LXXIX).

LIT.: R. Sturgis, *Manual of the Jarves Coll.,* 1868, 34, No. 20; W. Rankin, *American Jl. of Archaeol.,* (S. I.), X (1895), 141 as "Gaddi"; O. Sirèn, *Burlington Mag.,* XIV (1908), 183 (repr.), 188; *Ibid., Cat. of the Jarves Coll.,* 1916, 22–23 (repr.); *Ibid., Giotto and Some of His Followers,* 1917, I, 180, 271, II, 161 (repr.); A. K. Porter, *Art and Archaeology,* VII (1918), 109 (repr.), 117; Van Marle, III, 1923, 370–375 (repr.); R. Offner, *Italian Primitives at Yale,* 1927, 3–4, 16, Fig. 6; H. Comstock, *Internatl. Stu.,* LXXXIX (Mar., 1928), 72–3 (repr.), 89; T. Borenius, *Apollo,* XI (1930), 154 (repr.); L. Venturi, *Pitt. Ital.,* 1931, Pl. XXXVI; Berenson, *Ital. Pict.,* 1932, 167.

One of a series of panels of which others are in the Raczynski Coll., Posen, the Musée des Arts Décoratifs, Paris, and the Kaiser-Friedrich Museum, Berlin. Sirèn suggests that they formed part of a predella for an altarpiece representing three Dominican Saints which Daddi painted in 1338 for a chapel in S. Maria Novella, Florence.
S.S. Peter and Paul appeared to St. Dominic in a vision. The one gave him a staff and the other a Book of the Gospel, bidding him "Go, preach the Word of God, for He hath chosen thee for that ministry."

GIOVANNI DI PAOLO, SIENESE, 1403?–1482

85. SCENES FROM THE LIFE OF JOHN THE BAPTIST

*a. ST. JOHN IN THE DESERT (Pl. XII)
b. ST. JOHN ON THE BANKS OF THE JORDAN
c. ST. JOHN IN PRISON
d. SALOME BEFORE HEROD
e. THE BEHEADING OF ST. JOHN
f. SALOME PRESENTS THE HEAD OF ST. JOHN

Tempera on panel, each, 27 x 15 in.
Owned by The Art Institute of Chicago (Mr. and Mrs. Martin A. Ryerson Collection).

COLL.: E. Aynard, Lyons (Sale, Paris, 1913, No. 51, repr. in cat.); M. A. Ryerson, Chi. (1913).

EXH.: Kleinberger Gall., N. Y., 1917, Nos. 54–59 (repr. in cat.); Met. Mus., N. Y., 1923, Nos. 12–17 (No. 17 repr. in cat.); Royal Academy, Lond., 1930, Nos. 927–932.

LIT.: Crowe and Cavalcaselle (ed. by Borenius), V, 1914, 178; Reinach, *Répertoire,* I, 1905, 516 (2), 523 (2); F. M. Perkins, *Rassegna d'Arte Senese,* III (1907), 82–3 (repr.); Berenson, *Cent. Ital.,* 1909, 177; P. Schubring, *Rassegna d'Arte,* XIV (1914), 163–8; Schubring, *Cassoni,* 1915, 324–5, Pls. CIV–CVI; G. de Nicola, *Burlington Magazine,* XXXIII (1918), 45–54 (repr.); F. J. Mather, *Hist. of Ital. Ptg.,* 1923, 94–5 (repr. of 85a); R. van Marle, IX, 1927, 427–30 (repr.); R. Offner, *Ital. Prim. at Yale,* 1927, 40; L. Venturi, *Pitt. Ital.,* 1931, Pls. CXXXVI–CXLI; G. H. Edgell, *A History of Sienese Painting,* 1932, 218–20, Figs. 307 (polyptych), 309 (a), 310 (c), 311 (f.); Berenson, *Ital. Pict.,* 1932, 245.

Executed c. 1450–60. These six panels very likely formed part of an altarpiece dedicated to St. John the Baptist, of which two scenes are missing, or as Schubring (*supra*) assumes were parts of an octagonal tabernacle, painted for a baptismal chapel. Two panels of a similar series are in the Provincial Mus. at Münster, and a third is in the Philip Lehman Coll., N. Y. (See De Nicola [*supra*] for further suggestions as to their original arrangement.) Four predella panels with similar scenes, formerly in the Chas. Butler coll., are now the property of J. P. Morgan, N. Y.

JACOBELLO DI BONOMO (?), VENETIAN, c. 1384

86. MADONNA OF HUMILITY

Tempera on panel, 38¾ x 23½ in.
Lent by Mr. and Mrs. Charles H. Worcester, Chicago.

LIT.: D. C. Rich, *Bull.,* XXIV (1930), 85 (repr.), 88–9; L. Venturi, *Pitt. Ital.,* 1931, Pl. CIV.

G. Gronau attributes it to Jacobello di Bonomo, comparing it with the central panel of the Torre di Palme altar, which Van Marle (IV, 90) thinks to be not by Jacobello. L. Venturi considers the present Madonna a work of Jacobello del Fiore (active 1401–39), and suggests affinities with the Coronation of Teramo and the Madonna of 1436 in the Accademia, Venice.

SCHOOL OF LORENZO VENEZIANO, VENETIAN, fl. 1357–1379

87. ST. JOHN THE BAPTIST AND ST. CATHERINE OF ALEXANDRIA

Tempera on panel, 30 x 19¼ in.

Lent by Mr. and Mrs. Charles H. Worcester.

COLL.: Grimaldi, Venice; Roerich Mus., N. Y. (Sale N. Y., 1930, Nos. 150–51, repr. in cat.).

LIT.: *Bull.,* XXIV, 1930, 86–89 (repr.); E. Vavalà, *Burlington Magazine,* LVII, 1930, 171, 177, No. 8.

Vavalà identifies the Master of the Pirano Altarpiece, to whom this and the next panel are more related than to Lorenzo Veneziano, with Master Paolo Veneziano, fl. 1333–1358, and attributes them to Paolo and his sons.

SCHOOL OF LORENZO VENEZIANO, VENETIAN, fl. 1357–1379

88. ST. AUGUSTINE AND ST. PETER

Tempera on panel, 30 x19¼ in.

Lent anonymously.

Pendant to No. 87.

MASOLINO DA PANICALE, FLORENTINE, 1383–1447 (?)

*89. CRUCIFIXION (Pl. XI)

Tempera on panel, 24½ x 19 in.

Lent by Mr. Maitland F. Griggs, New York.

COLL.: Count G. de Stroganoff, Rome (until 1924).

EXH.: Century Association, N. Y., 1930, No. 21.

LIT.: A Muñoz, *Cat. of the Stroganoff Coll.,* 1911, 15, Pl. VIII; L. Venturi, *L'Arte,* N. S., I (1930), 165–6, 167 (repr.); Venturi, *Pitt. Ital.,* 1931, Pl. CLV; Berenson, *Ital. Pict.,* 1932, 494.

L. Venturi considers it an early work of Masolino, while still under the influence of Lorenzo Monaco. Berenson attributes it to Rossello di Jacopo Franchi (1376–1457). Muñoz published it as Giottino.

MASTER OF THE BAMBINO VISPO, TUSCAN, c. 1423

90. THE DEATH OF THE VIRGIN

Tempera on panel, 16⅜ x 25⅞ in.

Owned by The Art Institute of Chicago (Mr. and Mrs. Martin A. Ryerson Collection).

COLL.: Sellar, Lond. (Sale, Paris, June 6, 1889, No. 18); J. Dollfus (Sale, Paris, 1912, III, No. 51, repr. in cat.); M. Nicolle; M. A. Ryerson (1923).

LIT.: Reinach, Répertoire, V (1922), 442; B. Berenson, *Ital. Pict.,* 1932, 339.

A larger variant is in the Johnson Coll., Philadelphia, No. 13, (see Berenson, *Cat.,* I, 1913, 10).

ALLEGRETTO NUZI, UMBRIAN, (active c. 1345–1374)

91. A BISHOP ENTHRONED

Tempera on panel, 34 x 26 in.

Owned by The Art Institute of Chicago (Mr. and Mrs. Martin A. Ryerson Collection).

COLL.: H. Morison, Boston; M. A. Ryerson, Chi. (1916).

EXH.: Fogg Art Mus., Cambridge, Mass., 1914.

LIT.: Crowe and Cavalcaselle (Douglas), III, 1908, 181, note 1; C. R. Post, *Art in America,* III (1915), 222, 219 (repr.); Post, *Detroit Mus. of Art Bull.,* X (Oct., 1915), 5 (repr.), 8; *Art and Archaeol.,* II (1915), 17 (repr.), 20; Van Marle, V, 1925, 160, 163 (repr.).

Post calls it a mature work illustrating Nuzi's definitive style.

ALLEGRETTO NUZI, UMBRIAN, (active c. 1345–1374)

92. CRUCIFIXION WITH ST. JOHN EVANGELIST AND ST. FRANCIS

Tempera on arched panel, 29 x 19¾ in.

Lent by Mrs. Martin A. Ryerson, Chicago.

EXH.: Kleinberger Gall., 1917, No. 71 (repr. in cat.).

LIT.: B. Berenson, *Ital. Pict.,* 1932, 399.

According to O. Sirèn executed c. 1365–70, showing close stylistic affinities with altarpieces by Nuzi at Fabriano and Macerata.
Berenson calls it a studio work.

SANO DI PIETRO, SIENESE, 1406–1481

93. THE MADONNA WITH SAINTS JEROME AND BERNARDINE OF SIENA AND ANGELS

Tempera on panel, 20¼-26 x 17 in.

Owned by The Art Institute of Chicago (Mr. and Mrs. Martin A. Ryerson Collection).

COLL.: M. . . ., Lond. (Sale, 1882, No. 72); J. Dollfus (Sale, in Paris, 1912, No. 76, repr. in cat.); F. Hermann, N. Y., No. 46; Kleinberger Gall., N. Y.; M. A. Ryerson, Chi.

EXH.: Kleinberger Gall., N. Y., 1917, No. 62 (repr. in cat.).

LIT.: B. Berenson, *Cent. Ital.,* 239; E. Gaillard, *L'Antiquario* (June, 1913), 80; Reinach, *Répertoire,* V, 1922, 383 (repr.); E. Gaillard, *Sano di Pietro,* 1915, 204 (repr. frontispiece); *Bull.,* XVII (1923), 1 (repr.), 5; J. Trübner, *Sano di Pietro,* 1925; R. van Marle, IX (1927), 494 (cf. fig. 314); B. Berenson, *Ital. Pict.,* 1932, 498.

Van Marle dates it prior to 1450, while Sano was still strongly under the influence of Sassetta.

SASSETTA, SIENESE, 1392–1450

*94. JOURNEY OF THE MAGI (Pl. XIII)

Tempera on panel, 9 x 12 in.

Lent by Mr. Maitland F. Griggs, New York.

COLL.: S. Rogers (Sale, 1856, No. 639); Bromley-Davenport (Sale, 1863); Monckton Milnes (Lord Houghton); Marchioness of Crewe (1912); L. Douglas, Lond.

EXH.: Royal Academy, London, 1930, No. 64; Wadsworth Atheneum, Hartford, Conn., 1931, No. 2 (repr. in cat.); Detroit Inst. of Arts, 1933, No. 49a (repr. in cat.).

LIT.: R. Fry, *Burlington Mag.,* XXII (1912), 130 (repr.), 131; R. van Marle, IX, 1927, 340, 341 (repr.); H. Comstock, *Internatl. Stu.,* LXXXVIII (Oct., 1927), 37 (repr.), 39, 41; E. Cecchi, *Trecentisti Senesi,* 1928, 117–8, 146, Pl. CCXLVI; T. Borenius, *Apollo,* XI (1930), 155 (repr.); W. Valentiner, *Das Unbekannte Meisterwerk,* I,

1930, Pl. IV (repr.); L. Venturi, *Pitt. Ital.*, 1931, Pl. CXIV; Berenson, *Ital. Pict.*, 1932, 513.

Berenson considers it one of Sassetta's earliest works, dating it c. 1430. It is part of the predella of a polyptych, the main panel of which, with the "Birth of Mary," is in the Collegiata of Asciano.
The arch is the Porta Romana.

SEGNA DI BONAVENTURA, Sienese, fl. 1298–1326

*95. Madonna Enthroned with Saints and Donor (Pl. XII)
Tempera on panel, 17¼ x 11¾ in.
Lent by Mrs. Martin A. Ryerson, Chicago.

Coll.: H. Goldschmidt, Paris (Sale, 1898); M. A. Ryerson, Chi.

Lit.: J. Breck, *Art in America*, I (1913), 112–115 (repr.), as "School of Duccio."

Attributed by Dr. W. R. Valentiner; Breck gives it to an unknown follower of Duccio and dates it "prob. 1311." Once attributed to Segna by Berenson. Van Marle tentatively suggests Barna da Siena († 1380).

SPINELLO ARETINO, Florentine, c. 1346–1410

96. St. Francis and his Companions before Pope Honorius III
Tempera on panel, 33⅜ x 24 in.
Owned by The Art Institute of Chicago (Mr. and Mrs. Martin A. Ryerson Collection).

Coll.: Picture Dealer in Città di Castello; H. Morison, Boston; M. A. Ryerson, Chi. (1916).

Lit.: F. Mason Perkins, *Rassegna d'Arte*, XVIII (1918), 5 (repr.), 6; R. van Marle, III, 1924, 606 (note 1); Berenson, *Ital. Pict.*, 1932, 548.

Van Marle calls it a late work. Berenson says it is in great part by Spinello.
A drawing in the J. P. Morgan Coll., N. Y., attr. to Spinello Aretino, repeats the composition but in reverse. According to Vasari the artist executed the same subject in fresco in San Francesco at Arezzo, in the chapel of the Marsuppini.
Pope Honorius III died in 1227.

GHERARDO STARNINA, Florentine, 1354–1408

97. Crucifixion with St. David and Angels
Tempera on cross-shaped panel, 20 x 9¼ and 5¼ in.
Owned by The Art Institute of Chicago (Mr. and Mrs. Martin A. Ryerson Collection).

Coll.: Achillito Chiesa (Sale, N. Y., 1927, No. 110, repr. in cat. [IV] as Pietro Lorenzetti); M. A. Ryerson, Chi. (1927).

Exh.: Hackley Gall., Muskegon, 1932, No. 1.

Lit.: D. C. Rich, *Bull.*, XXII (1928), 74–5 (repr.); B. Berenson, *Ital. Pict.*, 1932, 165.

Rich and Berenson attribute it to Bernardo Daddi, while Van Marle gives it to Starnina.

TADDEO DI BARTOLO, Sienese, 1362–1422

98. The Crucifixion
Tempera on panel, 12⅞ x 26⅝ in.
Owned by The Art Institute of Chicago (Mr. and Mrs. Martin A. Ryerson Collection).

Coll.: Lord Northwick; Rev. Canon A. F. Sutton, Brant-Broughton, Lincs.; M. A. Ryerson, Chi. (1924).

Exh.: Manchester, 1857.

Lit.: Berenson, *Cent. Ital.*, 1909, 256; F., *Bull.*, XX (1926), 18–9 (repr.); Berenson, *Ital. Pict.*, 1932, 551. Engr. by Giuseppe Grafonara.

Dr. Valentiner suggests that this is a predella panel. It is known that Taddeo painted a predella of the Crucifixion, since lost, for the chapel of the Palazzo Pubblico c. 1401.

TUSCAN SCHOOL, Second Half of Thirteenth Century

*99. Madonna and Child Enthroned (Pl. XI)
Tempera on keyhole shaped panel, 32 x 18¾ in.
Owned by The Art Institute of Chicago (Mr. and Mrs. Martin A. Ryerson Collection).

Coll.: Achille de Clemente.

Lit.: R. M. F., *Bull.*, XX (1926), 77; L. Venturi, *Pitt. Ital.*, 1931, Pl. III (middle XIII C).

Oswald Sirèn places the panel closest to the Tuscan painter whom he calls the Master of Mary Magdalene. R. van Marle finds it nearest to the Madonna formerly in the Cathedral at Fiesole, now Museo Bandini, Fiesole (see *Ital. Schools*, V, 434, repr.).

TUSCAN SCHOOL, Second Half XIII C.

100. Diptych
Left Wing: Madonna and Child, Angels, Gabriel and Raphael
Right Wing: Crucifixion, with Virgin and S. John

Tempera on panel, each 11½ x 8¾ in.
Owned by The Art Institute of Chicago (Mr. and Mrs. Martin A. Ryerson Collection).

Coll.: Albin Chalandon, Paris (1850); Henri Chalandon, La Grange Blanche, Parcieux; Capt. L. Douglas, Lond.; M. A. Ryerson, Chi. (1924).

Lit.: *Bull.*, XX (1926), 78–79 (repr.); E. S. Vavalà in *International Studio*, XCV (April, 1930), 32–36 (repr.), 88.

Vavalà says it is by a Bolognese painter under Umbrian influence. Dr. Valentiner calls it Central-Italian, one generation before Cimabue and Duccio.

MARCO ZOPPO, Bolognese, 1433–1498

101. Pieta
Tempera (?) on panel, 27 13/16 x 21½ in.
Owned by The Art Institute of Chicago (Mr. and Mrs. Martin A. Ryerson Collection).

Coll.: Delaroff (1914); M. A. Ryerson, Chi. (1923).

Lit.: R. M. F., *Bull.*, XX (1926), 55–6 (repr.).

This painting, though differing somewhat in detail, follows the composition of a "Pietà" by Cosimo Tura in the Museo Correr, Venice. Valentiner thinks it a contemporary replica by a Ferrarese Master, possibly done in Tura's workshop c. 1500.

ITALIAN PAINTING

Fifteenth and Sixteenth Centuries

GALLERY 31

BARTOLOMMEO VENETO, Lombardo-Venetian, active 1502–after 1530

102. Portrait of a Youth

Oil on canvas, 16½ x 12⅛ in.

Lent by Mrs. James Parmelee, Washington, D. C. and The Cleveland Museum of Art.

Exh.: Duveen Gall., N. Y., 1924, No. 45 (repr. in cat.).

Lit.: B. Berenson, *Venetian Painting in America,* 1916, opp. 259 (repr.); A. L. Mayer, *Pantheon,* II (1928), 574, 575 (repr.); L. Venturi, *Pitt. Ital.,* 1931, Pl. CCCLXIV; Berenson, *Ital. Pict.,* 1932, 52.

Painted c. 1515. The sitter may possibly be a member of the household of Maximilian Sforza. The medallion in the cap shows an allegorical device. It is after a medal by Andrea Briosco called Riccio (1470–1532), representing "Fortune and Virtue."

GENTILE BELLINI, Venetian, 1429–1507

103. Two Orientals

Tempera on canvas, 27½ x 25 in.

Lent by Mr. and Mrs. Charles H. Worcester, Chicago.

Coll.: Formerly Count Giovio, Padua; in a collection at Treviso; Carlo Foresti, Milan.

Attributed by G. Fiocco, A. Morassi, W. Suida, Van Marle, comparing it with the "Portrait of Mohammed II," the Nat. Gall., Lond. (Layard Coll.). According to Van Marle painted after 1479 and part of a larger work.

GIOVANNI BELLINI, Venetian, c. 1428/30–1516

*105. Madonna and Child (Pl. XVI)

Oil on panel, 28 x 22 in.

Signed: ioannes bellinus.

Owned by The Art Institute of Chicago (Mr. and Mrs. C. H. Worcester Collection).

Coll.: Ferrari, Turin; Carlo Foresti, Milan; C. H. Worcester (1930).

Bode, Fiocco and Van Marle attribute this panel to Giovanni Bellini, calling it earlier than its replica in the John N. Willys collection, New York. Gronau mentions 3 replicas. Fiocco, Van Marle date the Institute picture c. 1480 under influence of Antonello.

GIOVANNI ANTONIO BOLTRAFFIO, Milanese, 1467–1516

106. Portrait of a Boy

Oil on panel, 18¼ x 13¾ in.

Lent by Mrs. Ralph Harman Booth, wife of the late Honorable Ralph Harman Booth, former Minister to Denmark.

Coll.: Baron G. de Rothschild; Sir Philip Sassoon; Duveen Brothers, Inc.

Exh.: Royal Academy, Lond., 1930, No. 314.

Lit.: C. J. Holmes, *Burlington Magazine,* XXXIX (1921), 102 (repr.), 108; W. Suida, *Leonardo und sein Kreis,* 1929, 191 (repr.), 208, 287; T. Borenius, *Apollo,* XI (1930), opp. 160 (repr.), 162; L. Venturi, *Pitt. Ital.,* 1931, Pl. CCCLIV; Berenson, *Ital. Pict.,* 1932, 91.

SANDRO BOTTICELLI, Florentine, 1444–1510

107. Adoration with Angels

Tempera on panel, tondo, diameter 13½ in.

Lent by Mr. Max Epstein, Chicago.

Exh.: The Art Inst. of Chi., 1928; 1930.

Dating from the later period of the artist, c. 1498.

SANDRO BOTTICELLI, Florentine, 1444–1510

*108. Madonna and Child (Pl. XVI)

Tempera on panel, 35¼ x 23¼ in.

Lent by Mr. Max Epstein, Chicago.

Coll.: Féral, Paris, 1917; sold to a Scandinavian collector in 1919; Van Buuren (Sale, Amsterdam, 1925).

Exh.: The Art Inst. of Chi., 1928; 1930.

Lit.: A. Venturi, *Gazette des Beaux-Arts,* Per. 3, XXXVIII (1907), 6–11 (repr.); Y. Yashiro, *Botticelli,* I, 1925, 227; W. von Bode, *Botticelli,* 1926, 4 (repr.); A. Venturi, *Botticelli,* 1927, 116, Pl. CLXXXV; R. Valland, *La Renaissance,* XI (1928), 354 (repr.); E. Singleton, *Old World Masters in New World Collections,* 1929, 64–66 (repr.); R. van Marle, XII, 1931, 46, 48 (repr.).

Bode dates it c. 1468–1469; Yashiro, c. 1472. The picture is closely related to the Chigi Madonna (c. 1470) in the Isabella Stewart Gardner Collection, Boston.
A studio replica, with variations, was formerly in the collection of Mrs. Austin, Horsmonden, Kent, and is now the property of Duveen Brothers, New York.

SANDRO BOTTICELLI, Florentine, 1444–1510

†109. Nativity

Tempera on panel, 22½ x 23⅛ in.

Lent by Wildenstein and Co., Inc., New York.

Coll.: Paravey, Paris, 1878; Mme. Raynaud.

Exh.: Detroit Inst. of Arts, 1933, No. 24 (repr. in cat.).

Lit.: A. L. Mayer, *Pantheon,* VI (1930), 393–394 (repr. opp. 393).

Mayer dates it c. 1490.

SANDRO BOTTICELLI, Florentine, 1444–1510

†110. Portrait of a Youth

Tempera on panel, 22 x 15 in.

Lent by E. and A. Milch, Inc., New York.

Coll.: Crawley-Bovey, Flaxley Abbey.

Attributed to Botticelli by Van Marle, who dates it 1480–85 due to stylistic connections with the Madonna della Melagrana and the Altarpiece of S. Barnaba.

SCHOOL OF BOTTICELLI, (Florentine c. 1480)

111. Madonna and Child with Two Angels
Tempera on panel, 30¾ x 21¾ in.
Lent by Mrs. Martin A. Ryerson, Chicago.

Coll.: Alexander Barker, Lond. (1874); G. P. Boyce, Chelsea (1897); E. F. Weber, Hamburg (Sale, 1912, No. 23).

Exh.: The British Institution, Lond., 1860, No. 108; Leeds, 1868, No. 9; Royal Academy, 1877, No. 142 (in each case as Antonio Pollaiuolo); The Art Society, Berlin, 1907; Kleinberger Gall., N. Y., 1917, No. 27 (repr. in cat.) as Piero Pollaiuolo.

Lit.: *Athenaeum,* Jan. 27, 1877, 123, No. 142; C. Sedelmeyer, *The Fourth Hundred,* 1897 (A. Pollaiuolo), 67 (repr.); Nöhring, *Sammlung Weber,* 1898; B. Berenson, *Ital. Pict.,* 1932, 101.

Berenson calls it an early copy of a Botticelli, while Oswald Sirèn attributes it to Piero Pollaiuolo.

FRANCESCO BOTTICINI, Florentine, 1446–1497

112. Adoration of the Magi
Tempera on panel, tondo, diam. 31 in.
Lent by Mrs. Martin A. Ryerson, Chicago.

Coll.: Emile Gavet, Paris.

Lit.: E. Kühnel, *Botticini,* 1906, 16–17, No. 23, 37, Pl. XI, 3; Berenson, *Flor.,* 1909, 119; Berenson, *Ital. Pict.,* 1932, 107.

Formerly given to Filippino Lippi. Van Marle suggests that it may belong to the early period of Signorelli. Berenson considers it a late work of Botticini.

VITTORE CARPACCIO, Venetian, c. 1455–1526

*113. St. Eustace (Pl. XVII)
Oil on canvas, 84¼ x 59 in.
Lent by Mogmar Art Foundation, Inc., New York.

Coll.: Vernon Wentworth, Wentworth Castle, near Barnsley, Yorks.; Mr. Sulley.

Exh.: Metro. Mus., N. Y., 1923, No. 40 (repr. in cat.).

Lit.: A. Martin, *Burlington Mag.,* XLIV (1924), frontispiece, 58–9; W. Hausenstein, *Das Werk des Vittore Carpaccio,* 1925, Pl. 58, 84, 137; W. M'Cormick, *International Studio,* LXXX (1925), 282, 283 (repr.); L. Venturi, *L'Arte,* N. S., I. (1930), 387 (repr.), 393–94; L. Venturi, *Pitt. Ital.,* 1931, Pl. CCCIV; Berenson, *Ital Pict.,* 1932, 134.

Martin dates it 1490–1500; Hausenstein, 1500 (?); L. Venturi places it in the period of the S. Vitale altar (1514); while a note in the Metro. Mus. Cat. of 1923 states that parts of the armor are as late as 1520.
St. Eustace is said to have suffered martyrdom under Hadrian A.D. 118 (a stag is always shown near by).

LORENZO DI CREDI, Florentine, 1456–1537

114. Self-Portrait (1488)
Oil on canvas, 18 x 12⅜ in.
Lent by Mr. Joseph Widener, Elkins Park, Philadelphia, Pennsylvania.

Coll.: W. Beattie, Glasgow.

Exh.: Lowrie and Co., Lond., 1901.

Lit.: W. Armstrong, *Art Journal,* LIII (1901), 47–8 (repr.); Ch. Loeser, *L'Arte,* IV (1901), 135–7 (repr.); Berenson, *Flor. Paint.,* 1909, 132; G. Gronau, *Thieme-Becker, Künstlerlexikon,* VIII, 1913, 73–4; W. R. Valentiner, *Paintings in the Coll. of Joseph Widener,* 1923 (repr.); L. Venturi, *Pitt. Ital.,* 1931, Pl. CCXIII; B. Degenhart, *Pantheon,* VIII (1931), 360 (repr.), 364; Berenson, *Ital. Pict.,* 1932, 297.

On the reverse is written: LORENZO DI CREDI PITTORE ECC . . . TE, 1488, AETATIS SUAE 32, VIII. ("Lorenzo di Credi, excellent painter, 1488. Aged 32 years and 8 months.") Venturi quotes Vasari who wrote: "Lorenzo made many portraits and when he was young he made one of himself." Berenson considers it Credi's masterpiece.

Lorenzo di Credi (1456–1537), pupil of Verrocchio, influenced by Leonardo.

CARLO CRIVELLI, Venetian, 1430/5– c. 1493

115. Crucifixion
Tempera on panel, 30$^{15}/_{16}$ x 22¾ in.
Owned by The Art Institute of Chicago (W. D. Walker Collection).

Coll.: Alexander Barker, Lond. (1874); Baron de Beurnonville (Sale, Paris, 1881, No. 632); J. Spiridon (Sale, Paris, 1929, No. 15, Pl. XXIII of cat.).

Lit.: F. Drey, *Carlo Crivelli,* 1927, 89f, 147, Pl. LXXIV; D. C. Rich, *Bull.,* XXIII (1929), 141 (repr.), 145–147; *Guide,* 1932, 3 (repr.); B. Berenson, *Ital. Pict.,* 1932, 161.

Drey dates it c. 1490, the period of the Odoni Altar.

RIDOLFO GHIRLANDAJO, (RIDOLFO DI DOMENICO BIGORDI), Florentine, 1483–1561

*116. A Gentleman of Florence (Pl. XV)
Oil on panel, 25 x 19 in.
Owned by The Art Institute of Chicago (Mr. and Mrs. Martin A. Ryerson Collection).

Coll.: Prince Brancacci, Rome; Wm. Beattie, Glasgow; M. A. Ryerson, Chi. (1901).

Lit.: W. Armstrong, *Art Journal,* LIII (1901), 46–7 (repr.); Berenson, *Flor.,* 1909, 139; C. Gamba, *Dedalo,* IX (1929), 465–67 (repr.); L. Venturi, *Pitt. Ital.,* 1931, Pl. CCCXXXVIII; Berenson, *Ital. Pict.,* 1932, 226.

Gamba assigns it to the early period of the artist.
Bode was first to attribute it to R. Ghirlandajo. A drawing from the same model is said to be in the coll. of the Duke of Devonshire, Chatsworth.

LEONARDO DA VINCI (attributed to), Florentine, 1452–1519

117. Madonna of the Yarn Winder
Oil on panel, 24 x 18½ in.
Lent by Mr. and Mrs. E. W. Edwards, Cincinnati, Ohio.

Coll.: Prince Byelozérski, Krestovski Palace, Leningrad.

Exh.: Cincinnati Art Mus., 1930.

Stylistically very close to Bernardino Luini (c. 1475–1531/2).

After an original by Leonardo painted c. 1501 for Florimond Robertet (d. 1522), an official of the French Court, and described in a letter, dated April 9, 1501, written by Fra Pietro da Nuvolaria to Isabella d'Este. Numerous replicas exist. E. Möller considers the one in the possession of the Duke of Buccleuch the original.

LEONARDO DA VINCI, Florentine, 1452–1519

118. San Donato of Arezzo and the Tax Collector

Oil on panel, 5½ x 13¼ in.

Lent by Mr. Theodore T. Ellis, Worcester, Massachusetts.

Coll.: Private Coll., France.

R. Langton Douglas believes it to be part of the same predella as the "Annunciation" in the Louvre, and to have belonged, with it, to the "Madonna di Piazza" of Pistoia commissioned from Verrocchio c. 1475, designed by him, and executed in his studio. At this period Leonardo was his chief assistant and painted the predella.

San Donato of Arezzo (martyred 362 A.D.) was the patron saint of Bishop Donato de' Medici who died in 1474 and in whose memory the altarpiece was ordered. San Donato's legend is related by Surius and other hagiographers. (See Mrs. Jameson, *Sacred and Legendary Art,* II, 1885, 319–21.)

Not previously exhibited.

LO SPAGNA, (GIOVANNI DI PIETRO), Umbrian, fl. 1503–1530

119. St. Catherine of Siena

Oil on panel, 41¼ x 19 in.

Lent by Mrs. Martin A. Ryerson, Chicago.

Coll.: Lord Brownlow, Ashridge (Sale, 1923, No. 50, repr. in cat.); M. A. Ryerson, Chi. (1924).

Lit.: B. Berenson, *Cent. Ital.,* 1909, 253; Berenson, *Ital. Pict.,* 1932, 544.

Berenson dates it in the early period of the artist.

ANDREA MANTEGNA, Venetian, 1431–1506

*120. Tarquin and the Cumaean Sibyl (Pl. XIV)

Oil on canvas, 22⅛ x 19⅛ in.

Lent by The Cincinnati Art Museum (Mary M. Emery Collection), Cincinnati, Ohio.

Coll.: Duke of Buccleuch, Montagu Hse., Lond.; Duveen Bros., N. Y.; Mrs. M. Emery, Cinn.

Exh.: Royal Academy, Lond., 1872, No. 242; Duveen Bros., N. Y., 1924 (No. 39, repr. in cat.).

Lit.: P. Kristeller, *Andrea Mantegna,* 1901, 369 (repr.), 373, 444; C. Yriarte, *Mantegna,* 1901, 212–14; Berenson, *North. Ital.,* 1907, 254; F. Knapp, *Mantegna,* 1910, 118 (repr.); A. Venturi, *Storia,* VII, 3, 1914, 262, footnote; A. Frankfurter, *The Antiquarian,* XIII (1929), 35 (repr.), 96; L. Venturi, *Pitt. Ital.,* 1931, Pl. CCLIX; Berenson, *Ital. Pict.,* 1932, 327.

Berenson calls it a late work. L. Venturi dates it in the last years of the fifteenth century.

A. Venturi and Kristeller think it to be a studio work. The Cumaean Sibyl offered Tarquinius Superbus, last of the legendary Kings of Rome (534–510 B.C.), nine books of prophecies for which she demanded 300 pieces of gold. Upon his refusal to buy them, she burned all but three of the books, for which he finally paid the original price.

NEROCCIO DI BARTOLOMEO, Sienese, 1447–1500

*121. Portrait of a Woman (Pl. XIV)

Oil on panel, 18⅞ x 12¾ in.

Lent by Mr. Joseph Widener, Elkins Park, Philadelphia, Pennsylvania.

Lit.: F. M. Perkins, *Rassegna d'Arte,* XIII (1913), opp. 121 (repr.), 124–6; W. R. Valentiner, *Paintings in the Coll. of J. E. Widener,* 1923, 75 (repr.); R. Offner, *Italian Primitives at Yale,* 1927, 41 and Fig. 33c; L. Dussler, *Pantheon,* II (1928), 379, 381 (repr.); L. Venturi, *Pitt. Ital.,* 1931, Pl. CCXXVII; Berenson, *Ital. Pict.,* 1932, 390; G. M. Richter, *Burlington Magazine,* LIX (1931), 251, No. 237.

On the tablet is written: QUANTUM. HOMINI. FAS. EST. MIRA. LICET. ASSEQUAR. ARTE. NIL. AGO. MORTALIS. EMULOR. ARTE. DEOS ("Although by wondrous dexterity I may reach the summit of human achievement, yet am I doomed to failure. A mortal, I am pitting my art against that of the Gods.") In the handles at either side of the tablet, the initials A. P. (perhaps the name of the sitter, Alessandra Piccolomini of the famous Sienese family), and NER. (perhaps for Neroccio). Richter attributes it to Francesco di Giorgio.
In the original frame.

PIERO DI COSIMO, Florentine, 1462–1521

*122. A Lady Holding a Rabbit (Pl. XV)

Tempera on panel, 23 x 17⅝ in.

Lent by Yale University, Gallery of Fine Arts, New Haven, Conn.

Coll.: Vitelli, Città di Castello; Giovagnoli; J. J. Jarves (Sold 1871).

Exh.: Derby Gall., N. Y., 1860, No. 92; Historical Society, N. Y., 1863; Yale Art School, 1867–1871 (bought by Yale).

Lit.: R. Sturgis, *Manual of the Jarves Coll.,* 1868, 64, No. 68; W. Rankin, *American Journal of Archaeology,* S. I., X (1895), 146; Berenson, *Flor.,* 1909, 165; O. Sirèn, *Cat. of the Jarves Coll.,* 1916, 185–188 (repr.); R. Offner, *Italian Primitives at Yale University,* 1927, 8, 36 (fig. 25); *Van Marle,* XIII, 1931, 360 (repr. oppos.); L. Venturi, *Pitt. Ital.,* 1931, Pl. CCCXXXVII; Berenson, *Ital. Pict.,* 1932, 454.

Berenson, Sirèn, and Offner consider it a late work of Piero di Cosimo; L. Venturi attributes it to Mariotto Albertinelli (Florentine, 1474–1515).

PIETRO PERUGINO, Umbrian, 1445–1523

123. a. The Nativity
b. The Baptism of Christ
c. Christ and the Woman of Samaria
d. Noli Me Tangere

Oil on panel (transferred to canvas), each 10 x 16¾ in.

Owned by The Art Institute of Chicago (Mr. and Mrs. Martin A. Ryerson Collection).

COLL.: Alex. Barker, London (Sale, 1874); Earl of Dudley (Sale, 1892, Nos. 76–80 repr. in cat.); M. A. Ryerson, Chi. (1897).

EXH.: British Institution, 1852; Manchester, 1857, Nos. 70–74; Royal Academy, Lond., 1871, and 1892, Nos. 146–48, 155.

LIT.: Crowe and Cavalcaselle (Borenius), V, 365; G. Williamson, *Perugino,* 1903, 126; B. Berenson, *Cent. Ital.,* 1909, 218; W. Bombe, *Perugino,* 1914, 256 (repr.); M. Gnoli, *Perugino,* 1923, 58; B. Berenson, *Ital. Pict.,* 1932, 436.

These four panels formed part of a predella to an altarpiece belonging to the later period of the artist (c. 1510). A fifth painting of the same series, representing "The Resurrection," is in the Met. Mus., N. Y.

A drawing attributed to Perugino for the "Christ and the Woman of Samaria" is in the Oxford University Gall.

ANTONIO POLLAIUOLO, FLORENTINE, 1429–1498

*124. RAPE OF DEIANIRA (Pl. XIII)

Tempera on wood, transferred to canvas, 21½ x 31⅝ in.

Lent by Yale University, Gallery of Fine Arts, New Haven, Connecticut.

COLL.: J. J. Jarves (1871).

EXH.: Derby Gall., N. Y., 1860, No. 75; Historical Society, N. Y., 1863; Yale Art School, 1867–1871 (bought by Yale); Fogg Art Mus., Cambridge, Mass., 1927–28; Royal Academy, Lond., 1930, No. 123.

LIT.: R. Sturges, *Manual of the Jarves Coll.,* 1869, 61, No. 64; W. Rankin, *American Journal of Archaeology,* S. I., X (1895), 148; F. Mather, Jr., *Burlington Magazine,* VIII (1906), 440–1 (repr.); H. Cook, *Burlington Magazine,* IX (1906), 52–3; B. M. Howland, *Burlington Magazine,* IX (1906), 63–4; M. Cruttwell, *Antonio Pollaiuolo,* 1907, 78 (repr.); Berenson, *Flor.,* 1909, 173; A. Venturi, *Storia,* VII, 1, 1911, 562; F. Mather, Jr., *Yale Alumni Weekly* (May 22, 1914), 977 (repr.); O. Sirèn, *Cat. of the Jarves Coll.,* 1916, 111–117 (repr.), No. 42; B. Burroughs, *Met. Mus. of Art Bull.,* XVIII (1923), 198–9 (repr.); L. Dami, *Dedalo,* IV (1924), 703 (repr. detail), 706; R. Offner, *Ital. Primitives at Yale,* 1927, 6, 30–4 (fig. 23, 23b); M. Gilman, *Yale Alumni Weekly* (March, 1928), 747–8 (repr.); R. van Marle, XI (1929), 362, 363 (repr.); W. G. Constable, *Gazette des Beaux-Arts,* Per. 6, III (1930), 287–8 (repr. opp. 288); T. Borenius, *Apollo,* XI (1930), 157, 159, 162 (repr.); M. Brockwell, *The Connoisseur,* LXXXV (1930), 82 (by Piero); L. Venturi, *Pitt. Ital.,* 1931, Pl. CLXXIV; Berenson, *Ital. Pict.,* 1932, 466.

L. Venturi calls it a work of the artist's maturity.

"When purchased, the figure of Deianira was painted out; possibly, it is suggested, as the result of Savonarola's attack on the representation of the nude. Sirèn suggests that the figures of Nessus and Deianira are the work of Piero Pollaiuolo. The figure of Hercules was probably derived from a Roman sarcophagus. A drawing copied from this figure in the Berlin Print Room, and probably not the painting itself, served as a model to Dürer for the figure of Hercules in the 'Combat with the Stymphalides' in the Nuremberg Museum." (*Cat. of the Exh. of Italian Art, Royal Academy,* Lond., 1930, 90.)

The centaur, Nessus, attempted to kidnap Hercules' wife, Deianira, while ferrying her across a stream. Hercules came to her rescue, mortally wounding Nessus with one of his poisoned arrows.

RAPHAEL, ROMAN, 1483–1520

125. PORTRAIT OF A MAN

Oil on panel, 29¼ x 25⅛ in.

Lent anonymously.

COLL.: Pallavicini family; E. and A. Silberman Gall. N. Y.

EXH.: The Art Inst. of Chi., 1930–

LIT.: D. C. Rich, *Bull.,* XXIV (1930), 57–59 (repr.).

According to Raimond van Marle, Adolfo Venturi and Wilhelm Suida, painted c. 1509. Suida suggests that this may be the lost portrait of Evangelista Tarascono Parmigiano mentioned by the "Anonimo" of Morelli (see translation by Mussi, edited by G. C. Williamson, with Frizzoni's notes abridged, 1903, 107) as being in the house of "Messer Antonio Foscarini in Venice in 1530." "The Parmesan" was papal secretary to Pope Leo X (not Julius II as stated by the "Anonimo").

ITALIAN PAINTING

Sixteenth Century

GALLERY 32

JACOPO BASSANO DA PONTE, VENETIAN, 1510–1592

*126. ADORATION OF THE MAGI (Pl. XXI)

Oil on canvas, 39½ x 51¾ in.

Lent by The Fogg Art Museum of Harvard University, Cambridge, Massachusetts.

COLL.: E. Ventura (Sale, Milan, 1932, No. 38, Pl. V).

Painted c. 1565. Replicas are in the coll. F. A. Konig, Tyringham, Bucks., Eng., and in the Vienna Gall.

Attribution by Suida; Van Marle thinks it may be a youthful work of El Greco.

ANGELO BRONZINO, FLORENTINE, 1503–1572

127. YOUNG FLORENTINE NOBLEWOMAN

Oil on panel, 21⅝ x 17 in.

Lent by Mr. and Mrs. Charles H. Worcester, Chicago.

COLL.: Van Diemen, N. Y.

Early period and strongly Pontormesque in quality. May possibly be by Pontormo, though Lionello Venturi tentatively suggests Niccolò l'Abbate.

LORENZO LOTTO, VENETIAN, 1480–1556

128. PORTRAIT OF A YOUNG BARBERINI

Oil on canvas, 41½ x 34½ in.
Inscribed: 35
Lent by a Southern California Collector.

COLL.: Duke of Richmond-and-Gordon (1931).

LIT.: G. M. Richter, *Internatl. Stu.*, XCIX (1931), 26–7 (repr.).

Richter dates it 1535.
The identification with the Barberini is traditional.

GIOVANNI BATTISTA MORONI, BRESCIAN, 1510/25–1578

*129. LUDOVICO MADRUZZO (Pl. XXII)
Oil on canvas, 79½ x 46 in.
Owned by The Art Institute of Chicago (Mr. and Mrs. Charles H. Worcester Collection).

COLL.: Madruzzi Castle of Buonconsiglio, Trent, 1658; Barons of Roccabruna, 1837; Barons I. and V. Salvadori, Trent; J. Stillman, N. Y. (1906) (Sale, N. Y., 1927, No. 27, repr. in cat.); C. H. Worcester, Chi. (1927).

EXH.: Metro. Mus., N. Y., 1921–26.

LIT.: G. Morelli, *Italian Painters,* II, 1893, 65; L. Oberziner, *Rassegna d'Arte,* II (1902), 88–89 (repr.); Berenson, *North Ital.,* 1907, 272; G. Lafenestre, *Revue de l'Art,* XII (1907), 358; A. Locatelli-Milesi, *Emporium,* XLIV (1916), 380; Gino Fogolari, *Trento* (1916), 142 (repr.), 158–161; R. M. F., *Bull.,* XXI (1927), 45 (repr.), 47–9; L. Venturi, *Pitt. Ital.,* 1931, Pl. CCCXCVIII; *Guide,* 1932, 5 (repr.).

Painted before 1561 in which year Ludovico was made cardinal. There are two companion portraits to this: the one, of Cristoforo Madruzzo, by Titian, belongs to the Stillman heirs, the other, by Moroni, of Gian Federico Madruzzo, belongs to Mrs. W. R. Timken, N. Y.
Ludovico Madruzzo, born in 1532, nephew of Cristoforo Madruzzo, Cardinal-Bishop of Trent, was papal legate to Diet of Augsburg, 1555. Created Cardinal of Trent, 1561, he played a part in the Council of Trent, which was reopened in 1562.

MORETTO (ALESSANDRO BONVICINO), BRESCIAN, 1498–1555

130. THE ALABASTER VASE
Oil on canvas, 64½ x 17¾ in.
Lent by Mr. and Mrs. William O. Goodman, Chicago.

EXH.: The Art Inst. of Chi., 1928–1933.

Possibly represents the allegorical figure of Faith.

PONTORMO (JACOPO CARRUCCI), FLORENTINE, 1494–1556/7

*131. THE HALBERDIER (Pl. XXII)
Oil on canvas, 37½ x 29 in.
Lent by Mr. Chauncey Devereux Stillman, New York.

COLL.: Cardinal Fesch, 1844; Leroy d'Etiolles, 1861; Princess Mathilde Bonaparte, Paris (Sale, 1904, No. 53); J. Stillman, N. Y.; C. C. Stillman, N. Y. (Sale, N. Y., 1927, No. 35, repr. in cat.).

EXH.: Met. Mus. of Art, N. Y., 1921–26; Fogg Art Mus., Cambridge, Mass., 1927–30.

LIT.: G. Vasari, *Opere* (ed. Sansoni), VI, 275; H. Voss, *Die Malerei der Spätrenaissance,* I, 1920, 175–7 (repr.); C. Gamba, *Pontormo,* 1921, Pl. XXXI; F. J. Mather, *Art in America,* X (1922), 66–9 (repr.); *Ibid., History of Ital. Painting,* 1923, 252–3 (repr.); F. Clapp, *Art Studies,* I (extra number), 1923, 65–6, Fig. 46; O. Giglioli, *Dedalo,* VII (1927), 788–91 (reproductions); L. Venturi, *Pitt. Ital.,* 1931, Pl. CCCXLV; A. Venturi, *Storia,* IX, Pt. V, 1932, 172–3 (fig. 102), 191; Berenson, *Ital. Pict.,* 1932, 466.

A. Venturi dates it c. 1528–30.
Drawings for the painting are in the Uffizi (463F) and in the Louvre (958).

PONTORMO (JACOPO CARRUCCI), FLORENTINE, 1494–1556/7

†132. PORTRAIT OF A LADY
Oil on panel, 40 x 31 in.
Lent by The Bottenwieser Galleries, New York.

COLL.: Dirksen, Berlin.

EXH.: Kaiser Friedrich Mus., 1906, No. 104; Detroit Inst. of Arts, 1933, No. 42.

LIT.: B. Berenson, *Flor.,* 1909, 174; F. Clapp, *Jacopo Carucci da Pontormo,* 1916, 85, and Fig. 128.

Painted c. 1534–1545.

SCHIAVONE (ANDREA MELDOLLA), VENETIAN, 1522(?)–1582

133. FLIGHT INTO EGYPT
Oil on canvas, 16¼ x 38⅛ in.
Lent by Mr. and Mrs. Charles H. Worcester, Chicago.

EXH.: Renaissance Society, U. of Chi., 1930; Toronto Art Gall., 1931.

TINTORETTO (JACOPO ROBUSTI), VENETIAN, 1518–1594

134. ALESSANDRO FARNESE
Oil on canvas, 24⅝ x 21 in.
Lent by The Museum of Fine Arts, Boston, Massachusetts.

COLL.: Sir R. Waldie-Griffith; Agnew and Son, Lond.

LIT.: A. C. J., *Bull. of the Mus. of Fine Arts,* Boston, XXVI (1928),1–3 (repr.); L. Venturi, *Pitt. Ital.,* 1931, Pl. CCCCIV; B. Berenson, *Ital. Pict.,* 1932, 558; P. Hendy, *Burlington Magazine,* LXII (1933), 130, Pl. IIA.

Alessandro Farnese, grandson of Emperor Charles V and great-grandson of Pope Paul III, was born Aug. 27, 1545. In 1556 (aged eleven) he was sent to Spain to be educated, not returning to Italy until after his marriage to Maria of Portugal in Brussels in 1565, when he was twenty years old. L. Venturi judges his age to be fifteen in the portrait, and suggests that it may possibly have been painted from a Spanish miniature. Hendy, however, maintains his age in the portrait to be twenty and thinks it was painted on his return to Italy in 1565 and that he is here costumed in his wedding dress.

TINTORETTO (JACOPO ROBUSTI), VENETIAN, 1518–1594

*135. CHRIST ON THE LAKE OF GALILEE (Pl. XXI)

Oil on canvas, 45¾ x 66¼ in.

Lent by Mr. Arthur Sachs, New York.

COLL.: Count J. Gallotti; Durlacher Bros., N. Y.

EXH.: Fogg Art Mus., Cambridge, Mass., 1927; Met. Mus. of Art, N. Y., 1932–33.

LIT.: T. Borenius, *Apollo,* II (1925), 249–250 (repr.); A. Venturi, *Storia,* IX, 1929, Pt. 4, 615, note; L. Venturi, *Pitt. Ital.,* 1931, Pl. CCCCXI; Berenson, *Ital. Pict.,* 1932, 562.

Borenius dates it 1562–6; L. Venturi considers it a work of the last period, c. 1591–4.

TINTORETTO (JACOPO ROBUSTI), VENETIAN, 1518–1594

136. MADONNA AND CHILD

Oil on canvas, 36¼ x 28½ in.

Lent by The Cleveland Museum of Art (J. Huntington Coll.), Cleveland, Ohio.

COLL.: Baron Alfred de Rothschild, Paris; Durlacher Bros., N. Y.; J. Huntington, Cleveland.

LIT.: W. M. Milliken, *Bull., Cleveland Mus. of Art,* XIV (1927), 29 (repr.), 31–33; *Ibid., Burlington Magazine,* LI (1927), 55 (repr.); *Handbook, Cleveland Mus.,* 1928, 30 (repr.); L. Venturi, *Pitt. Ital.,* 1931, Pl. CCCCV; B. Berenson, *Ital. Pict.,* 1932, 558.

L. Venturi dates it c. 1560, while Milliken says it was done during the same period as the "Four Allegories" in the Ducal Palace, Venice (1570–1580); Berenson says it is a late work.

TINTORETTO (JACOPO ROBUSTI), VENETIAN, 1518–1594

137. VENUS AND MARS WITH THREE GRACES IN A LANDSCAPE

Oil on canvas, 41 x 55¾ in.

Owned by The Art Institute of Chicago (Mr. and Mrs. Charles H. Worcester Collection).

COLL.: D. Heinemann, Munich; a London collection; Charles H. Worcester, Chi.

LIT.: D. C. Rich, *Bull.,* XXII (1928), 101–3 (repr.); L. Venturi, *Pitt. Ital.,* 1931, Pl. CCCCIX; Berenson, *Ital. Pict.,* 1932, 558; *Guide,* 1932, 4 (repr.).

L. Venturi dates it 1583–87.
A pendant, "Venus and Adonis" is in the possession of Frank T. Sabin, Lond.

TITIAN, VENETIAN, 1477–1576

*138. ADORATION OF THE MAGI (Pl. XX)

Oil on canvas, 55½ x 88 in.

Lent by Mr. Arthur Sachs, New York.

COLL.: Walshe-Porter (Sale, 1826); S. Rogers, Lond.; Munro, Lond.; B. Johnstone, Lond.; Brocklebank (Sale, Lond., 1922); Durlacher Bros., N. Y.

EXH.: Met. Mus., N. Y., 1930.

LIT.: Crowe and Cavalcaselle, *Titian,* 1881, II, 309; A. L. Mayer, *Pantheon,* V (1930), 60–3 (repr. and details); B. Burroughs, *Bull. of the Met. Mus. of Art,* XXV (1930), 268–71 (repr.); L. Venturi, *Pitt. Ital.,* 1931, Pl. CCCLXXXVI.

Vasari mentions that Titian painted an "Adoration of the Magi," and copied it for the Cardinal of Ferrara. In 1560 Titian sent an "Adoration" to Philip II of Spain (probably the one described by Vasari), which Burroughs identifies with the Sachs picture. Mayer calls it a late variant of the 1559 picture, judging from the style which seems to him no earlier than 1564. L. Venturi dates it in the late period. (The catalogue of the Walshe-Porter sale states that Philip IV of Spain gave this picture to Charles I of England.)
Numerous versions exist. Burroughs thinks the example in the Ambrosiana, Milan, is the copy painted for the Cardinal of Ferrara, though L. Venturi considers this a school piece. There is an inferior replica in the Prado, and a Spanish copy in the old church at the Escorial.

TITIAN, VENETIAN, 1477–1576

*139. DANAE (Pl. XX)

Oil on canvas, 47½ x 66¾ in.

Lent anonymously.

COLL.: Earl of Chesterfield; Annesley Gore, Lond.

EXH.: The Art Inst. of Chi., 1928; Van Diemen Gall., N. Y.

LIT.: D. v. Hadeln, *Burlington Mag.,* XLVIII (1926), 78, 82–83 (repr.); D. C. Rich, *Bull.,* XXII (1928), 61–3 (repr.); F. E. Washburn Freund, *International Studio,* XC (May, 1928), 40 (repr.); (June, 1928), 65–66.

According to Hadeln, painted in the 1540s. The earliest version (1545–6) is in the Naples Mus.
At least four other replicas exist:

1. The Prado, Madrid (sent to Philip II, 1554).
2. Leningrad (by Titian ?).
3. Vienna (Titian School).
4. Formerly Marczell von Nemes, Budapest (Sale, Munich, 1931, No. 33, repr. in cat.) (by Titian ?).

Zeus entered the brazen tower where Danaë was imprisoned, under the form of a shower of gold.

TITIAN, VENETIAN, 1477–1576

*140. VENUS AND THE LUTE PLAYER (Pl. XIX)

Oil on canvas, 65 x 82¼ in.

Lent by Duveen Brothers, Inc., New York.

COLL.: Earl of Leicester, Holkham Hall, Norfolk.

LIT.: A. Hume, *Life and Works of Titian,* 1829, 95; G. M. Richter, *Burlington Mag.,* LIX (1931), 52 (repr.), 53–59; D. v. Hadeln, *Pantheon,* X (1932), 273–8 (repr. and details).

Richter maintains it was painted c. 1560, while Hadeln says it was begun in the 1540s and finished c. 1560.
Two closely related compositions exist. One is in the Fitzwilliam Mus., Cambridge (called a seventeenth century copy by Richter, accepted as a replica in great part by Titian from c. 1560, by Gronau, Berenson, and Hadeln), the other in Dresden, regarded as a later copy, possibly by an artist of the Bolognese seventeenth century (Hadeln).

PAOLO VERONESE, VENETIAN, 1528–1588

141. CREATION OF EVE

Oil on canvas, 31½ x 40¼ in.

Owned by The Art Institute of Chicago (Mr. and Mrs. Charles H. Worcester Collection).

Coll.: Böhler and Steinmeyer; C. H. Worcester, Chi. (1930).

Lit.: D. C. Rich, *Pantheon,* VII (Jan., 1931), 20–3 (repr. and detail); Berenson, *Ital. Pict.,* 1931, 420; *Guide,* 1932, 7 (repr.).

Attributed to Paolo by Berenson and Hadeln and dated by the latter c. 1570.

PAOLO VERONESE, Venetian, 1528–1588

142. Marriage of Saint Catherine

Oil on canvas, 21¾ x 34¾ in.

Lent anonymously.

Coll.: Liechtenstein, Vienna.

Exh.: Art. Inst. of Chi., 1927; Van Diemen Gall., N. Y., 1931.

Lit.: G. Fiocco, *Paolo Veronese,* 1928, 23–4 (repr.).

Fiocco calls it a youthful work.

PAOLO VERONESE, Venetian, 1528–1588

*143. Rest on the Flight into Egypt (Pl. XVIII)

Oil on canvas, 92¹¹⁄₁₆ x 63³⁄₁₆ in.

Signed: PAVLI CALIARI VERONESI FACIEBAT.

Lent by The John and Mable Ringling Museum, Sarasota, Florida.

Coll.: Electoral Gall., Düsseldorf; Gall. in Castle, Schleissheim (1912); Alte Pinakothek, Munich (1912); J. Böhler, Munich (1928).

Exh.: Reinhardt Gall., N. Y., 1928, No. 8 (repr. in cat.).

Lit.: G. Karsch, *Designation des peintures à Düsseldorf,* 1719; J. von Gool, *De nieuwe Schouburg, s'Gravenhage,* II, 1751, 5. (*Katalog der Düsseldorfer Galerie beim Tode des Kurfürsten Johann Wilhelm,* 1716); N. de Pigage, *La Galerie Electorale de Düsseldorf,* 1778, No. 116, Pl. 12; *Ibid. La Galerie Electorale de Düsseldorf,* 1781, 125–6, No. 116; *Pietro Caliari, Veronese,* 1888, 384; *Galerie Schleissheim, Katalog,* 1905, No. 517 (985); *Katalog der alten Pinakothek,* München, 1925, No. 921 (1593); A. Venturi, *P. Veronese,* 1928, 116; W. Valentiner, *Das Unbekannte Meisterwerk,* I, 1930, 30 (repr.); B. Berenson, *Ital. Pict.,* 1932, 425.

Hadeln dates it in the first half of the 1570's, basing his judgment on stylistic evidence and a document containing notices in Veronese's own writing from the years 1570–72, in the Coll. J. Böhler.

ITALIAN PAINTING

Seventeenth and Eighteenth Centuries

GALLERY 35

FRANCESCO GUARDI, Venetian, 1712–1793

144. Arch and Other Ruins

Oil on canvas, 11½ x 19½ in.

Owned by The Art Institute of Chicago (Mr. and Mrs. Martin A. Ryerson Collection).

Coll.: M. A. Ryerson, Chi. (1913).

From the artist's later period.

FRANCESCO GUARDI, Venetian, 1712–1793

145. Ruined Archway

Oil on canvas, 11⅜ x 19½ in.

Owned by The Art Institute of Chicago (Mr. and Mrs. Martin A. Ryerson Collection).

Coll.: M. A. Ryerson, Chi. (1913).

Pendant to No. 144.

FRANCESCO GUARDI, Venetian, 1712–1793,

*146. Ruins with Figures (Pl. XXIV)

Oil on canvas, 41 x 49 in.

Signed on fallen slab: FRANCESCO GUARDI.

Lent by The National Gallery of Art, Smithsonian Institution, Washington, D. C.

Coll.: Sale, Paris, 1909; Ralph Cross Johnson, Washington.

Lit.: W. Holmes, *The National Gallery of Art, Washington—Cat. of Collections,* 1922, I, No. 6, (repr. 56); *International Studio,* LXXVI (1922), 126 (repr.); I. Haumann, *Das Oberitalienische Landschaftsbild des Settecento,* 1927, 57–8, Fig. 63; L. Venturi, *Pitt. Ital.,* 1931, Pl. CCCCXXXIV.

Haumann points out that this is a copy with few variations of a composition of Sebastiano and Marco Ricci in Vicenza.

PIETRO LONGHI, Venetian, 1702–1783

147. The Dance

Oil on canvas, 24½ x 19½ in.

Owned by The Art Institute of Chicago (Mr. and Mrs. Charles H. Worcester Collection).

Coll.: J. Wanamaker, Phil.; J. Weitzner, New York; C. H. Worcester, Chi. (1931).

Lit.: A. Ravà, *Pietro Longhi,* 1909, 149 (repr. from engraving).

Engr.: By Alessandro Longhi (Rome, Gab. Stampe).

One of a series of rustic scenes of which others are in the Correr Mus. in Venice.

PIETRO LONGHI, Venetian, 1702–1783

148. Blind Man's Buff

Oil on canvas, 19¼ x 24 in.

Lent by Mr. Samuel H. Kress, New York.

Coll.: Prince Giovanelli, Venice; Gallery Salom, Venice.

Lit.: A. Ravà, *Pietro Longhi,* 1909, 33; A. M. Frankfurter, *The Fine Arts,* XIX (Dec., 1932), 8, 10 (repr.).

PIETRO LONGHI, VENETIAN, 1702–1783

149. THE SIMULATED FAINT

Oil on canvas, 19¼ x 24 in.

Lent by Mr. Samuel H. Kress, New York.

COLL.: Prince Giovanelli, Venice; Gallery Salom, Venice.

LIT.: A. Ravà, *Pietro Longhi,* 1909, 37 (repr.); A. M. Frankfurter, *The Fine Arts,* XIX (Dec. 1932), 9, 10 (repr.).

Pendant to No. 148.

ALESSANDRO MAGNASCO, GENOESE, 1681–1747

150. ARCADIAN LANDSCAPE

Oil on canvas, 28 x 37¼ in.

Owned by The Art Institute of Chicago (Mr. and Mrs. Charles H. Worcester Coll.).

COLL.: Charles H. Worcester, Chi.

LIT.: D. C. Rich, *Bull.,* XXIII (1929), 42–3 (repr.); *Guide,* 1932, 10 (repr.).

EXH.: Wadsworth Atheneum, Hartford, Conn., 1930, No. 24 (repr. in cat.).

PIERFRANCESCO MOLA, ROMAN, 1612–1666

*151. HOMER DICTATING (Pl. XXIII)

Oil on canvas, 28 x 38 in.

Owned by The Art Institute of Chicago (Mr. and Mrs. Charles H. Worcester Collection).

COLL.: Metropolitan Art Gall., New York; C. H. Worcester, Chi.

EXH.: Durlacher Bros., N. Y., 1931.

LIT.: D. C. Rich, *Bull.,* XXIV (1930), 69–71 (repr.).

Painted 1660–65.
A replica with variations is in the Rumyantsev Museum, Moscow. The subject was a favorite one with the artist.

GIOVANNI BATTISTA PIAZZETTA, VENETIAN, 1682–1754

152. THE BEGGAR BOY

Oil on canvas, 26 x 20½ in.

Owned by The Art Institute of Chicago (Mr. and Mrs. Charles H. Worcester Collection).

COLL.: Fischer, Viroflay, France (1929); C. H. Worcester, Chi. (1930).

EXH.: Venice, 1929, No. 17 (*Cat. Settecento Italiano,* 46, 49, repr.).

LIT.: D. C. Rich, *Bull.,* XXVI (1932), 53 (repr.), 55–6.

Painted in Piazzetta's later period. The model is a favorite one, appearing many times in the artist's work.

FRANCESCO SOLIMENA, NEAPOLITAN SCHOOL, 1657–1747

*153. ERMINIA AND THE SHEPHERDS (Pl. XXIII)

Oil on canvas, 39 x 50 in.

Lent by Mr. August Bontoux, Chicago.

LIT.: De Dominici, *Vita dei Pittori,* 1846, IV, 447.

Voss identifies it as the picture mentioned by De Dominici. The subject is taken from Tasso, *Gerusalemme Liberata,* Canto VII, Stanzas 5ff. Above the maiden (according to De Dominici) hovers the figure of Constancy.

GIANBATTISTA TIEPOLO, VENETIAN, 1696–1770

154. INSTITUTION OF THE ROSARY BY ST. DOMINIC

Oil on canvas, 38 x 19 in.

Owned by The Art Institute of Chicago (Mr. and Mrs. M. A. Ryerson Collection).

COLL.: M. A. Ryerson, Chi. (1913).

A study for the central panel of the ceiling of the Church of the Gesuati in Venice, for which Tiepolo was commissioned in 1737. Another, possibly earlier, study is in the Kaiser Friedrich Mus., Berlin.

GIANBATTISTA TIEPOLO, VENETIAN, 1696–1770

155. MADONNA AND CHILD WITH ST. DOMINIC AND ST. HYACINTH

Oil on canvas (arched top), 108 x 54 in.

Owned by The Art Institute of Chicago (Mr. and Mrs. M. A. Ryerson Collection).

COLL.: Morselli, Florence; Ladislaus Bloch, Vienna, (Sale, 1905, No. 66, repr. in cat.); M. A. Ryerson, Chi. (1913).

EXH.: Burlington Fine Arts Club, Lond., 1911, No. 45; Kleinberger Gall., N. Y., 1911, No. 138 (repr.); Panama-Pacific Exh., San Francisco, 1915, No. 3432.

LIT.: E. Sack, *Tiepolo,* 1910, 86, Pl. 71a, 88–9, 205, No. 411 (S. Januarius); P. Molmenti, *Tiepolo,* 1911, 201, Pl. 205.

Painted c. 1745.

GIANBATTISTA TIEPOLO, VENETIAN, 1696–1770

156. RINALDO ENCHANTED BY ARMIDA

Oil on canvas, 73½ x 102⅛ in.

Owned by The Art Institute of Chicago (James Deering bequest).

COLL.: Serbelloni, Venice; A. P. Cartier, Genoa; C. Sedelmeyer, Paris; J. Deering, Chi.

EXH.: Gall. Sedelmeyer, Paris, 1912 (Cat. 1913, Nos. 57–60, repr.).

LIT.: F. Malaguzzi-Valeri, *Rassegna d' Arte,* VIII (1908), 179 (repr.); E. Sack, *Giambattista und Domenico Tiepolo,* 1910, 236, Nos. 622–5; P. Molmenti, *Tiepolo,* 1911, 188–9, Pl. 84 (Fr. transl. 187, repr., 188); *Ten Masterpieces by Tiepolo,* 1913, (Translation of C. Mauclair's article in *Le Journal des Arts,* June, 1912), 16–24 (repr.); R. M. F., *Bull.,* XX (1926) 5–8; L. Venturi, *Pitt. Ital.,* 1931, Pls. CCCCXXII–CCCCXXV; *Guide,* 1932, 8–9, (repr.).

Lorenzo Tiepolo engraved the composition of "Rinaldo and Armida in the Garden."
L. Venturi dates the series 1737–1751. Several other versions exist: the frescoes of the Villa Valmarana near Vicenza (1737); the frescoes of the Castle of Würzburg (1751–3); a sketch of one of the Würzburg scenes in the K.-Friedrich Mus.; and an example in the Brera, Milan. Illustrate episodes from Torquato Tasso's "Gerusalemme Liberata." The first scene is taken from Canto XIV, Verses 65–8; the second is from XVI, 17–19; the third, XVI, 42; and the fourth, XVII, 64–5.

GIANBATTISTA TIEPOLO, VENETIAN, 1696–1770

157. RINALDO AND ARMIDA IN THE GARDEN
Oil on canvas, 73½ x 102⅛ in.
Owned by The Art Institute of Chicago (James Deering Collection).
See No. 156

GIANBATTISTA TIEPOLO, VENETIAN, 1696–1770

*158. ARMIDA ABANDONED BY RINALDO (Pl. XXIV)
Oil on canvas, 73½ x 84½ in.
Owned by The Art Institute of Chicago (James Deering Collection).
See No. 156

GIANBATTISTA TIEPOLO, VENETIAN, 1696–1770

159. RINALDO AND THE OLD HERMIT
Oil on canvas, 73½ x 84½ in.
Owned by The Art Institute of Chicago (James Deering Collection).
See No. 156.

GIANBATTISTA TIEPOLO, VENETIAN, 1696–1770

160. ST. JEROME IN THE DESERT
Oil on panel, 13½ x 9⁵⁄₁₆ in.
Owned by The Art Institute of Chicago (Mr. and Mrs. Charles H. Worcester Collection).

COLL.: G. Palumbo, Rome; J. Weitzner, N. Y.; C. H. Worcester, Chi. (1928).

EXH.: Wadsworth Atheneum, 1930, No. 48 (repr. in cat.).

LIT.: H. Voss, *Kunst und Künstler,* XX (1922), 431–32 (repr.); D. C. Rich, *Bull.,* XXIII (1929), 37 (repr.).

Voss attributes it to Tiepolo, connecting it with certain Tiepolo drawings (cf. "St. Jerome," Berlin Print Room) from the artist's early sketch books.

SPANISH PAINTING

Fourteenth, Fifteenth, Sixteenth, Seventeenth, Eighteenth and Nineteenth Centuries

GALLERY 50

FRANCISCO GOYA, SPANISH, 1746–1828

*161. BOY ON A RAM (Pl. XXXII)
Oil on canvas, 50 x 44 in.
The Charles Deering Collection. Lent by Mr. and Mrs. Chauncey McCormick, Chicago.

COLL.: G. Stuyck, Madrid; M. Knoedler and Co., Lond.; Ch. Deering, Chi.

EXH.: Art. Inst. of Chi., 1922–1931.

LIT.: P. Lafond, *Goya,* 1902, 148, No. 45; V. von Loga, *Francisco de Goya,* 1903, 223, No. 598; A. E. Calvert, *Goya,* 1908, 174, No. 45 and Pl. 310; L. C., *Bull.,* XVII (1923), 77 (repr.), 79; A. L. Mayer, *Francisco de Goya,* 1923, 218, No. 722, and Pl. 26. (Eng. trans., 1924, 184, No. 722, Pl. 26.)

A cartoon (over-door) for one of four tapestries woven for the King's study in the Palace of the Escorial by the Royal Tapestry Factory of Santa Barbara in 1791. (See Cruzada Villaamil, *Los Tapices de Goya,* Madrid, 1870.) The tapestry itself is now in the Escorial.

FRANCISCO GOYA, SPANISH, 1746–1828

*162. BULL FIGHT (Pl. XXXI)
Oil on canvas, 28 x 43 in.
Lent by Mr. Arthur Sachs, New York.

COLL.: D. Francisco Azebal y Arratia, 1863; Piot; H. Rochefort; Ed. Kahn (Sale, Paris, 1895); S. Bardac (Sale, Paris, 1910); Gimpel and Wildenstein.

EXH.: Met. Mus. of Art, N. Y., 1928, No. 6 (repr. in cat.); Fogg Art Mus., Cambridge, Mass., 1927.

LIT.: F. Zapater, *Apuntes Historicos Biograficos . . .,* 1863, 39; P. Lafond, *Goya,* 1902, 107, No. 28; V. von Loga, *Francisco Goya,* 1903, 219, No. 546; A. E. Calvert, *Goya,* 1908, 161, No. 143; H. Stokes, *Francisco Goya,* 1914, 352, No. 534 or 535; A. L. Mayer, *Francisco de Goya,* 1923, 215, No. 666 (Eng. trans., 1924, 181, No. 666).

Painted at Bordeaux 1827–8. The pendant is in the collection of Oskar Reinhart, Winterthur, Switzerland (Mayer, No. 605).

FRANCISCO GOYA, SPANISH, 1746–1828

163. DUCHESS OF ALBA
Oil on canvas, 33½ x 27 in.
The Charles Deering Collection. Lent by Mr. and Mrs. Chauncey McCormick, Chicago.

COLL.: Knoedler and Co., N. Y.; Ch. Deering.

LIT.: *Bull.,* XVII (1923), 79 (repr.); A. L. Mayer, *Francisco de Goya,* 1923, 186, No. 193a (Eng. trans., 1924, No. 193a.).

Doña Maria del Pilar Teresa Cayetana de Silva, XIII Duchess of Berwick and Alba, Marchioness of Villafranca. Similar versions are in the possession of the Duke of Alba, Madrid, and the Marchioness of Caltabuturu, Madrid. Painted c. 1795.

FRANCISCO GOYA, SPANISH, 1746–1828

164. DUKE OF ALBA
Oil on canvas, 34 x 27 in.
The Charles Deering Collection. Lent by Mr. and Mrs. Chauncey McCormick, Chicago.

COLL.: Knoedler and Co., N. Y.; Ch. Deering.

LIT.: P. Lafond, *Goya,* 1902, 123, No. 61; A. L. Mayer, *Francisco de Goya,* 1923, 186, No. 192, Pl. 89 (Eng. trans., 1924, No. 192 and Pl. 89).

XIII. Duke of Berwick and Alba, Marquis of Villafranca. Another version is in a private coll., Madrid. Painted c. 1793.

FRANCISCO GOYA, Spanish, 1746–1828

165. Isidro Gonzales (1801)

Oil on canvas, 36¾ x 26¼ in.

Inscribed: dn. ysidro gonzales. pr. goya 1801.

The Charles Deering Collection. Lent by Mr. and Mrs. R. E. Danielson, Boston.

Coll.: M. Knoedler and Co., Lond.; Ch. Deering, Chi.

Lit.: L. C., *Bull.*, XVII (1923), 80, 81–2 (repr.); A. L. Mayer, *Francisco de Goya*, 1923, 193, No. 287, and Pl. 157 (Eng. trans., 1924, 156, No. 287 and Pl. 157).

FRANCISCO GOYA, Spanish, 1746–1828

Six Episodes in the Capture of the Bandit Margato by the Monk Pedro de Zaldivia:

166a. Margato Robs a Fat Purser
Oil on canvas, 11½ x 15⅛ in.

b. Margato Points his Gun at Fray Pedro de Zaldivia
Oil on canvas, 11½ x 15⅛ in.

c. Fray Pedro Wrests the Gun from the Bandit
Oil on canvas, 11¾ x 15½ in.

d. Fray Pedro Clubs Margato
Oil on canvas, 11½ x 15⅛ in.

*e. Margato Shot (Pl. XXXI)
Oil on canvas, 11½ x 15⅛ in.

f. Margato Bound
Oil on canvas, 11½ x 15½ in.

Owned by The Art Institute of Chicago (Mr. and Mrs. Martin A. Ryerson Collection).

Coll.: Lafitte, Madrid; J. Böhler, Munich; M. A. Ryerson, Chi. (1911).

Exh.: Met. Mus. of Art, N. Y., 1928, Nos. 7–12 (repr. in cat.).

Lit.: P. Lafond, *Goya*, 1902, 110, Nos. 64–9; V. v. Loga, *Francisco de Goya*, 1903, 110, 215, No. 485 and Pls. 51–3; A. E. Calvert, *Goya*, 1908, 152–3, No. 24–9; H. Stokes, *Francisco Goya*, 1914, 351, Nos. 501–6; A. de Beruete y Moret, *Goya: Composiciones y Figuras*, II, 1917, 95–6 and Pl. 38 ("Margato Bound"); A. L. Mayer, *Francisco de Goya*, 1923, 83, 211, No. 597 (a–f) and Pls. 185–90 (Eng. trans., 1924, 177, No. 597 [a-f] and Pls. 185–90); A. P. McMahon, *The Arts*, XIII (1928), 182 (repr. "Margato Shot"), 183.

The name of the bandit is usually misspelled. Mayer in 1924 discovered it to be "Margato" (the word "gato" being the Spanish for cat). Painted according to him c. 1806. The episode was well known and Goya's series became famous, woodcuts of it being published at the time. Mayer also mentions songs and stories having to do with Margato.

EL GRECO (DOMENICO THEOTOCOPULI), Spanish, 1541–1614

*167. Agony in the Garden (Pl. XXVII)

Oil on canvas, 41 x 45¾ in.

Signed (in Greek).

Lent by Mr. Arthur Sachs, New York.

Coll.: Private Coll., Madrid.

Exh.: Met. Mus. of Art, N. Y., 1928, No. 26; Wadsworth Atheneum, Hartford, Conn., 1930; Fogg Art Mus., Cambridge, Mass., 1932–3.

Lit.: A. L. Mayer, *El Greco*, 1926, 10, 11 (repr.), No. 55; Mayer, *El Greco*, 1931, 25, Pl. 11, 120.

According to Mayer painted between 1590–98. The replica in the Nat. Gall., Lond., he considers a workshop repetition. The composition is known in a number of adaptations, usually upright in size.

EL GRECO (DOMENICO THEOTOCOPULI), Spanish, 1541–1614

168. Annunciation

Oil on canvas, 32⅞ x 50½ in.

Lent by Mr. and Mrs. Ralph M. Coe, Cleveland, Ohio.

Coll.: S. Biron; Marquis de Cevera; Durand-Ruel, Paris.

Lit.: M. B. Cossio, *El Greco*, 1908, 599, No. 301; A. L. Mayer, *El Greco*, 1926, 3 (repr. 4, No. 7); M. Barrès and P. Lafond, *Le Greco*, n.d., 142.

One of a number of versions of this subject. Mayer dates this example 1597–1600.

EL GRECO (DOMENICO THEOTOCOPULI), Spanish, 1541–1614

*169. The Assumption of the Virgin (1577) (Pl. XXV)

Oil on canvas, 158 x 90 in.

Signed (in Greek): "domenikos theotokopoulos painted this picture a. d. 1577"

Owned by The Art Institute of Chicago. (A. A. Sprague Memorial).

Coll.: Santo Domingo el Antiguo, Toledo, 1577; Museo Nacional de Fomento, Madrid; Don Sebastian Gabriel de Bourbon, Pau; Infanta Doña Cristina of Spain; Durand-Ruel, Paris, 1904.

Exh.: Prado Mus., Madrid, 1902, No. 6; 1902–5.

Lit.: A. Lavice, *Revue des Musées d'Espagne*, 1864, (Museo Nacional de Fomento); P. Lafond, *Les Arts*, V (1906), No. 58, 4–5, (repr. w. det.); M. B. Cossio, *El Greco*, 1908, 132–141, 594, No. 279 and Pl. 16; A. F. Calvert and C. G. Hartley, *El Greco*, 1909, 79–81 and Pl. 29; A. L. Mayer, *El Greco*, 1911, 11 (repr.), 29; *L'Art et les Artistes*, XVI (1912), 3; L. M. Bryant, *What pict. to see in Amer.* (1915), 257–8 (fig. 167); Mayer, *El Greco*, 1916, Pl. 6; M. C., *Bull.*, XVIII (1924), 30–31 (repr.); E. Trapier, *El Greco*, 1925, 26–7 and Pl. 6; Mayer, *El Greco*, 1926, xii, 19, No. 114, Pl. VII; E. Waterhouse, *Art Studies*, VIII (1930), I, Pls. 30–33, 81, 88; Mayer, *El Greco*, 1931, 41–2, 54, and Pl. 32; *Guide*, 1932, 96 (repr.).

Painted for the reredos of the high altar of Santo Domingo el Antiguo, in Toledo, 1577.

EL GRECO (DOMENICO THEOTOCOPULI), Spanish, 1541–1614

*170. Cardinal Don Fernando Niño de Guevara (Pl. XXVI)

Oil on canvas, 67⅞ x 42½ in.

Signed (in Greek): "domenikos theotokopoulos, i painted it."

Lent by The Metropolitan Museum of Art, New York.

COLL.: Count de Nava; Countess of Oñate, Madrid; Marczell v. Nemes, Budapest; Mrs. H. O. Havemeyer, N. Y.
EXH.: Prado Mus., Madrid, 1902, No. 13; M. Knoedler and Co., N. Y., 1915, No. 2.
LIT.: P. Lafond, *Les Arts,* V (1906), No. 58, 21 (repr.), 28; M. B. Cossio, *El Greco,* 1908, frontispiece, 420–24, 595, No. 283; A. F. Calvert and C. G. Hartley, *An Account of El Greco,* 1909, 144 and Pl. 55; *L'Art et les Artistes,* XVI (1912), 5 (repr.), 4; XVII (1913), supplt. 2; M. Barrès and P. Lafond, *Le Greco,* n. d., repr. opp. 88; A. L. Mayer, *El Greco,* 1926, xxiv, 52, No. 331 and Pls. LXXIX and LXXX; *Bull. of the Met. Mus. of Art,* XXV (1930), 53, (repr.), 58; F. J. Mather, Jr., *The Arts,* XVI (1930), 458–9, 480 (repr.); *Pantheon,* V (1930), 210, 213 (repr.); A. L. Mayer, *El Greco,* 1931, 130–1, 132, 141 (Pl. 102).

According to Mayer painted 1596–1600. A study for the head is in the coll. of Oskar Reinhart, Winterthur. (M. de Nemes Coll. Sale, 1913, No. 32). The sitter was born in 1541; became Cardinal in 1596, Grand Inquisitor in 1600 and Archbishop of Seville, 1601, dying in 1609.

EL GRECO (DOMENICO THEOTOCOPULI), SPANISH, 1541–1614

*171. CORONATION OF THE VIRGIN (Pl. XXVII)

Oil on canvas, 21¾ x 29¼ in. (oval)
Lent by Mr. Max Epstein, Chicago.

COLL.: J. Böhler, Munich.
EXH.: The Art Inst. of Chi., 1930; 1932.
LIT.: A. L. Mayer, *El Greco,* 1931, 100, 119, Pl. 86.

One of a number of versions of the same subject. Mayer connects it most closely with the composition in the Hospital de la Caridad at Illescas, painted between July, 1603 and the close of 1605. A missing oval sketch of the same subject is mentioned in one of the El Greco inventories.

EL GRECO (DOMENICO THEOTOCOPULI), SPANISH, 1541–1614

*172. THE FEAST IN THE HOUSE OF SIMON (Pl. XXVIII)

Oil on canvas, 57 x 40⅜ in.
Lent by Mr. Joseph Winterbotham, Burlington, Vermont.

COLL.: Guinea, Bilbao; Plasencia, Bilbao; Prince de Wagram, Paris; Miethke, Vienna; Durand-Ruel, N. Y.
EXH.: Durand-Ruel, N. Y., 1924; The Arts Club, Chi., 1931; The Art Inst. of Chi., 1931.
LIT.: M. B. Cossio, *El Greco,* 1908, 353, 602, No. 325; H. Kehrer, *Die Kunst des Greco,* 1914, 41, No. 19 (repr.); A. L. Mayer, *El Greco,* 1926, 9, No. 46a and Pl. XLIV; J. F. Willumsen, *La Jeunesse du Peintre El Greco,* 1928, II, 657–8, Pl. CI; Mayer, *El Greco,* 1931, 117, 119 132, Pl. 97.

Mayer dates it 1608–13, noting that it closely resembles the slightly earlier version of the subject in the Hess Coll., Berlin.

EL GRECO (DOMENICO THEOTOCOPULI), SPANISH, 1541–1614

*173. HEAD OF A MAN (Pl. XXIX)

Oil on canvas, 15½ x 11½ in.
Lent by Dr. F. H. Hirschland, New York.

COLL.: Y. Perdoux, Paris; Gimpel and Wildenstein, Paris; Wildenstein, N. Y.
EXH.: Met. Mus. of Art, 1928, No. 36 (repr. in cat.).
LIT.: A. L. Mayer, *El Greco,* 1926, 54, No. 344a (repr.).

A study for the "Portrait of an Old Man" in the Prado, Madrid, which was painted, according to Cossio, 1584–94. A larger version (by El Greco?) was formerly in the Col. Friedsam Coll., N. Y., and bequeathed to the Met. Mus. of Art, N. Y.

EL GRECO (DOMENICO THEOTOCOPULI), SPANISH, 1541–1614

174. PARTING OF CHRIST AND MARY

Oil on canvas, 41¼ x 39 in.
The Charles Deering Collection. Lent by Mr. and Mrs. R. E. Danielson, Boston.

COLL.: Cloister of the Convent of S. Pablo Eremitano, Toledo, 1911; L. Harris, Lond.; M. Knoedler and Co., N. Y.; Ch. Deering, Chi.
LIT.: M. B. Cossio, *El Greco,* 1908, 325, 590, No. 259, 52bis (repr.); R. Ramirez de Arellano, *Catálogo di Artifices,* 1920, 299; M. C., *Bull.,* XVIII (1924), 32, 33 (repr.); A. L. Mayer, *El Greco,* 1926, 10, No. 48 and Pl. XVIII; F. Rutter, *El Greco,* 1930, 96, No. 69 and Pl. 84; Mayer, *El Greco,* 73 and Pl. 56.

According to Mayer executed 1582–5. First mentioned in an inventory of the Convent of S. Pablo Eremitano, 1670. Mayer thinks that it may possibly have been the gift of Cardinal Niño de Guevara who was buried there.

EL GRECO (DOMENICO THEOTOCOPULI), SPANISH, 1541–1614

175. ST. ILDEFONSO, WRITING

Oil on canvas, 44 x 26 in.
Signed (in Greek): "DOMENIKOS THEOTOKOPOULOS, I PAINTED IT"
Lent by The Hon. Andrew W. Mellon, Washington, D. C.

COLL.: J. F. Millet (Sale, Paris, 1894, No. 261); Z. Astruc; E. Degas (Sale, Paris, 1918, No. 2); M. Knoedler and Co., Lond.
EXH.: Met. Mus. of Art, N. Y., 1928, No. 31 (repr. in cat.).
LIT.: M. B. Cossio, *El Greco,* 1908, 334, 598, No. 299; M. Barrès and P. Lafond, *Le Greco,* n. d., 139; A. L. Mayer, *El Greco,* 1926, No. 287, and Pl. LXIII; F. Rutter, *El Greco,* 96, No. 67.

A reduced replica of the composition in the Hospital de la Caridad, Illescas.
According to Mayer executed c. 1605.
St. Ildefonso (d. 667), Archbishop of Toledo, was famous for his treatises, particularly one on the virginity of the Blessed Mary; the legend is that the Virgin, to reward him for his zeal, appeared to him in person and presented him with a priestly vestment.

EL GRECO (DOMENICO THEOTOCOPULI), SPANISH, 1541–1614

176. ST. MARTIN AND THE BEGGAR

Oil on canvas, 46¾ x 24½ in.
Signed (in Greek): "DOMENIKOS THEOTOKOPOULOS, I PAINTED IT"
The Charles Deering Collection. Lent by Mr. and Mrs. Chauncey McCormick, Chicago.

COLL.: M. Knoedler and Co., N. Y.; Ch. Deering, Chi.
EXH.: Art Inst. of Chi., 1922–30.

Lit.: M. C., *Bull.*, XVIII (1924), 29 (repr.), 32; A. L. Mayer, *El Greco*, 1926, 48, No. 298; F. Rutter, *El Greco*, 1930, 62, 98, No. 78 and Pl. LXIX.

According to Mayer, painted 1599–1604. A later version of a composition first painted 1597–99 and today in the Joseph Widener Coll., Philadelphia. Three other versions exist, in the Bucharest, Durand-Ruel (1926) and Andrew W. Mellon colls.

EL GRECO (DOMENICO THEOTOCOPULI), Spanish, 1541–1614

*177. View of Toledo (Pl. XXVIII)
Oil on canvas, 48 x 42¾ in.
Signed (in Greek): "DOMENIKOS THEOTOKOPOULOS, I PAINTED IT."
Lent by The Metropolitan Museum of Art, New York.

Coll.: Countesses of Añover y Castañeda, Oñate Palace, Madrid; Durand-Ruel, Paris; Mrs. H. O. Havemeyer, N. Y.

Exh.: M. Knoedler and Co., N. Y., 1915, No. 3; Met. Mus. of Art, N. Y., 1920.

Lit.: A. Ponz, *Viaje de España,* 1776, V, 50; Ceán Bermúdez, *Diccionario Histórico de los Más Ilustres Profesores de las Bellas Artes en España,* 1800; P. Lafond, *Les Arts,* V (1906), No. 58, 19, (repr.), 26–7; M. B. Cossio, *El Greco,* 1908, 453–5, 565, No. 83 and Pl. 137; A. F. Calvert and C. G. Hartley, *El Greco,* 1909, 156, Pl. 60; M. Barrès and P. Lafond, *Le Greco,* n.d., 180; A. L. Mayer, *El Greco,* 1926, 50, No. 315 and Pl. LXVIII; F. J. Mather, Jr., *The Arts,* XVI (1930), 459–60 (repr.); *Kunst und Künstler,* XXVIII (1930), 354 (repr.); Mayer, *El Greco,* 1931, 23, Pl. 9, 140.

Mayer considers it a work of the last period. He suggests that it is probably to be identified with the lost "View of Toledo" noted by Ponz and Bermúdez which, in the eighteenth century, was hanging in the Church of the Recoletos in Madrid.

MASTER OF ST. GEORGE, Catalan, early fifteenth century

*178. St. George and the Dragon (Pl. III)
Tempera (?) on panel, 56 x 38 in.
Owned by The Art Institute of Chicago (The Charles Deering Collection). Gift of Mrs. R. E. Danielson and Mrs. Chauncey McCormick.

Coll.: Roccabruna family; Vidal Ferrer y Soler, Barcelona; Ch. Deering, Chi.

Lit.: Sanpere y Miquel, *Los Cuatrocentistas Catalanes,* 1906, I, 193–4 (repr.); II, 276; E. Berteaux in André Michel, *Histoire de l'Art,* 1908, III, Pt. 2, 772–5 (repr.); M. A. Dieulafoy, *Art in Spain and Portugal,* 1913, 175, 179 (repr.); R. B. H., *Bull.,* XVI (1922), 17–21 (repr.); *International Studio,* LXXVI (1922), 59 (repr.); C. R. Post, *History of Spanish Painting,* II, 1930, 393–402, Fig. 223.

Sanpere brings forth evidence to connect it with four panels in the Louvre, depicting the Martyrdom of St. George. The whole probably formed an altar-piece with the Institute composition as the central panel. Originally the painting was attributed to Benito Martorell, but subsequent authorities believe it to be the work of an anonymous Catalan, whom Post has christened "The Master of St. George." Date c. 1430.

LUIS DE MORALES, Spanish, 1509–1586

*180. Pieta (Pl. XXIX)
Oil on panel, 25¾ x 18¼in.
Lent by Mr. George Harding, Chicago.

Coll.: Dr. J. E. Stillwell, N. Y. (Sale, Pt. I., N. Y., 1927, No. 480, repr. in cat.).

Exh.: The Art Inst. of Chi., 1928.

In Morales' later style. Numerous versions (with slight changes) exist; compare especially the "Pietà" in the Episcopal Palace, Madrid (composition reversed) and one in the Sota Coll., Bilbao.

ATTRIBUTED TO JUSEPE RIBERA, Spanish, 1588–1656

181. The Good Samaritan
Oil on canvas, 80 x 58 in.
Lent by Mr. Willitts J. Hole, Los Angeles, California.

Coll.: Prof. Ludwig Knaus, Berlin.

Exh.: National Gallery, Stockholm.

Lit.: A. L. Mayer, *Jusepe de Ribera,* 1908, 194.

"The invention," says Dr. Hermann Voss, "undoubtedly goes back to Ribera." On the basis of a photograph he finds the "execution" "feeble." A. L. Mayer, *supra,* calls it a school work; Joseph Pijoan attributes to Ribera.

SCHOOL OF NAVARRE (?)

*182. Scenes from the Lives of Christ and the Virgin (1396). The Lopez de Ayala Retable and Frontal (Details, Pl. IV)
Tempera on panel, 99¾ x 251¾ in. predella, 33½ x 102 in.
Owned by The Art Institute of Chicago (The Charles Deering Collection). Gift of Mrs. R. E. Danielson and Mrs. Chauncey McCormick.

Coll.: Until 1913 in the chapel of the De Ayala family in the Dominican Convent of San Juan at Quejana; Ch. Deering, Chi.

Lit.: *Boletín de la Sociedad Española de Excursiones,* XXIV (1916), 154ff; V. von Loga, *Die Malerei in Spanien,* 1923, 13 and Pl. 10; R. M. F., *Bull.,* XX (1926), 95ff (repr.); C. R. Post, *History of Spanish Painting* II, 1930, 126–133 (repr.).

Donated in 1396 by Don Pedro López de Ayala and his wife Leonor de Guzmán to a chapel in a Dominican nunnery at Quejana (Alava) founded 1374 by Don Pedro's father. The donor (1322–1407) was a Chancellor of Castile and one of the most famous men of his day, scholar, poet, statesman and soldier. He was the author of the "Chronicles of Castile."
For the inscriptions and their translation see *Bull., supra.*

Note: This altar-piece is installed in Gallery M6.

DIEGO SILVA Y VELASQUEZ, Spanish, 1599–1660

*183. Isabella of Bourbon, First Queen of Philip IV of Spain (Pl. XXX)
Oil on canvas, 49¾ x 40 in.
Lent by Mr. Max Epstein, Chicago.

Exh.: Art Inst. of Chi., 1927, 1930; Met. Mus. of Art, N. Y., 1928, No. 57 (repr. in cat.).

Lit.: A. L. M(ayer), *The Art News,* XXV (May 14, 1927), 67 (repr.); D. C. R., *Bull.,* XXI (1927), 91–2 (repr.); *Bull. of the Met. Mus. of Art,* N. Y., XXIII (1928), 69 (repr.); R. Cortissoz, *Internatl. Stu.,* XC (June 1928), 38, 45 (repr.); A. P. McMahon, *The Arts,* XIII (1928), 180, 182.

According to Mayer, painted c. 1631. A very similar picture is in the Art Historical Mus., Vienna; other portraits of the Queen, some of them full-length, and all disputed, are in the collections of the Prado, Madrid, National Gall., Copenhagen, Hampton Court Palace, Uffizi and (formerly) H. Huth.
Isabella of Bourbon [christened Elisabeth] (1603–1644), daughter of Henri IV of France and Marie de Médicis, married Philip IV of Spain, 1615.

DIEGO SILVA Y VELASQUEZ, Spanish, 1599–1660

*184. Man with a Wine Glass (Pl. XXX)
Oil on canvas, 30 x 25 in.
Lent by The Toledo Museum of Art (The Edward Drummond Libbey Collection), Toledo, Ohio.

Coll.: Sir Prior Goldney, Derriads, Chippenham, Wiltshire; Duveen Brothers, Inc., N. Y.

Exh.: Bristol Loan Exh., 1893; Fogg Art Mus., Cambridge, Mass., 1914; Cleveland Mus. of Art, 1916, No. 22; Met. Mus. of Art, N. Y., 1928, No. 58 (repr. in cat.).

Lit.: A. L. Mayer, *Art in America,* III (1915), 183–187 (repr.); *Toledo Mus. of Art News,* L (1926), 2 (repr.); R. Cortissoz, *Internatl. Stu.,* XC (June 1928), 38, 40 (repr.).

According to Mayer, painted c. 1623. The same model appears in a very similar pose in the so-called "Geographer" ("Buffoon" [?], "Democritus" [?]) in the Rouen Mus.

DIEGO SILVA Y VELASQUEZ, Spanish, 1599–1660

*185. St. John in the Wilderness (Pl. XXXII)
Oil on canvas, 69 x 60 in.
The Charles Deering Collection. Lent by Mr. and Mrs. R. E. Danielson, Boston.

Coll.: J. Williams, Seville; F. H. Standish, Duxbury Hall, Lincolnshire (until 1841); King Louis Philippe, 1841–1853; Sold at Standish Sale, Lond., 1853, No. 93 to Anthony; R. P. Nichols, 1857; H. Blaker, Islesworth-on-Thames, 1922; T. Agnew & Sons, Ltd.; Ch. Deering, Chi.

Exh.: Art Treasures Exh., Manchester, 1857, No. 795.

Lit.: F. H. Standish, *Seville and its Vicinity,* 1840, 185; R. Ford, *Athenaeum,* (June 4 and June 11, 1853); Head, *Foreign Quarterly,* XXVI, 257; Wm. Stirling, *Velasquez et ses Oeuvres,* 1865, 192; C. B. Curtius, *Velazquez and Murillo,* 1883, 12, No. 18; A. L. Mayer, *Burlington Mag.,* XL (1922), 3 (repr.), 4–9; M. C., *Bull.,* XVIII (1924), 13–16.

According to Mayer painted c. 1622.

FRANCISCO DE ZURBARAN, Spanish, 1598–1661

186. Saint Romanus, Martyr (1638)
Oil on canvas, 97 x 73 in.
Dated 1638.
The Charles Deering Collection. Lent by Mrs. R. E. Danielson and Mrs. Chauncey McCormick.

Coll.: Stchoukine Coll.; Dr. Carvallo, Paris; Grafton Gall., Lond.

Exh.: Grafton Gall., Lond., 1914, No. 98.

Lit.: H. Kehrer, *Francisco de Zurbarán,* 1918, 82 and Pl. 40; *Bull.,* XVI (1922), 58–59 (repr.); *Rev. de Arqui,* 1922, 54 (repr.).

Saint Romanus was a deacon of Caesarea, who in 303–4 suffered martyrdom for his teachings. Before his death at the hands of Diocletian, however, he had his tongue cut out and was subjected to fire. The child beside him is thought to be St. Barulas.

ENGLISH PAINTING

Eighteenth and Early Nineteenth Centuries

GALLERY 38

RICHARD PARKES BONINGTON, English, 1801–1828

187. Figures Crossing a Stream
Oil on canvas, 14 x 18 in.
Signed: RPB 18. .
Lent by Mr. Francis Neilson, Chicago.

Coll.: French private coll.; Wm. Permain, Lond.

RICHARD PARKES BONINGTON, English, 1801–1828

*188. Santa Maria della Salute (Pl. XLII)
Oil on canvas, 12¾ x 21¼ in.
Lent by The Worcester Art Museum, Worcester, Massachusetts.

Lit.: R. H.-H., *Bull. of the Worcester Art Mus.,* XIV (1923), 38–40 (repr.).

Many versions of the subject appear in the sales and inventories. Mrs. Ella Siple has shown it to be a free copy of a Canaletto in the Louvre (acquired 1818). It was probably painted before Bonington's Italian trip of 1826.

JOHN CONSTABLE, ENGLISH, 1776–1837

189. HAMPSTEAD HEATH

Oil on canvas, 32 x 25 in.

Lent by Mr. and Mrs. Cyrus H. McCormick, Chicago.

JOHN CONSTABLE, ENGLISH, 1776–1837

*190. STOKE-BY-NAYLAND (Pl. XLI)

Oil on canvas, 49 x 66 in.

Owned by The Art Institute of Chicago (W. W. Kimball Collection).

COLL.: Nield (Sale, 1879); Mrs. W. W. Kimball Coll., Chi.

LIT.: Letter to William Purdon, Feb. 6, 1836, in which Constable describes his first conception of the picture. (Quoted by C. R. Leslie, *Memoirs of the Life of John Constable,* 1843, 104, where it is erroneously stated that the picture was never painted); *Bull.,* XX, 1926, 51–3 (repr.); *Guide,* 1932, 89 (repr.).

In 1829 Lucas made a mezzotint from a similar subject; the oil sketches in the Victoria and Albert Mus., and in the Nat. Gall., Lond., and the sepia drawing (also Nat. Call., Lond.), were preparatory for this.
Painted 1836.
The steeple is that of the church of St. Mary's (XV C), Stoke-by-Nayland, Suffolk.

THOMAS GAINSBOROUGH, ENGLISH, 1727–1788

191. COUNTESS OF BRISTOL

Oil on canvas, 35 x 28 in.

Owned by The Art Institute of Chicago (W. W. Kimball Collection).

LIT.: *Guide,* 1932, 81 (repr.).

Painted 1765–70 (?).
Elizabeth Chudleigh (1720–88), one of the most notorious women of her day. The daughter of Colonel Thomas Chudleigh, she was appointed Maid of Honor to Augusta, Princess of Wales, in 1743, and secretly married August John Hervey (later 3rd Earl of Bristol) in 1744. After numerous scandals she separated from Hervey to marry her lover, the Duke of Kingston (d. 1773). In 1776 she was publicly tried for bigamy, and being found guilty, fled to the continent where she later died. Reynolds also painted her.

THOMAS GAINSBOROUGH, ENGLISH, 1727–1788

*192. LANDSCAPE WITH A BRIDGE (Pl. XLII)

Oil on canvas, 44½ x 52½ in.

Lent by Duveen Brothers, Inc., New York.

COLL.: Lord d'Abernon, Lond.

EXH.: Detroit Inst. of Arts, 1926, No. 9 (repr. in cat.); Musée Moderne, Brussels, 1929, No. 66; Fogg Art Mus., Cambridge, Mass., 1930, No. 185; Cincinnati Art Mus., 1931, No. 22 (Pl. 42 of cat.).

LIT.: J. Hope-Johnstone, *Art in America,* XIV (1926), 86 (repr.), 91; F. E. W. Freund, *Cicerone,* XVIII (1926), 253, 255 (repr.); Freund, *Internatl. Stu.,* LXXXIV (May, 1926), 57 (repr.); M. E. Gilman, *Fogg Art Mus. Notes,* II, No. 5 (1930), 234 (repr.); W. Heil, *Pantheon,* VIII (1931), 383 (repr.) 384; W. R. Valentiner, *Das Unbekannte Meisterwerk,* 1930, Pl. 98.

From the artist's last period.

THOMAS GAINSBOROUGH, ENGLISH, 1727–1788

*193. QUEEN CHARLOTTE OF ENGLAND (Pl. XLIII)

Oil on canvas, 24 x 17½ in.

Lent by Mr. Jules S. Bache, New York.

COLL.: The Dukes of Waldeck-Pyrmont; L. Hirsch.

LIT.: *Cat. of Paintings in the Coll. of Jules S. Bache,* 1929, 53.

According to Armstrong, Gainsborough painted the Queen 1782–4. He records the following replicas: (1) Windsor Castle, Private Audience Chamber; (2) Victoria and Albert Mus., Lond.; (3) Lawrie and Co., Lond. (1898).
Charlotte Sophia, Queen of George III of England (1744–1818), daughter of Charles Louis, brother of Frederick, 3rd Duke of Mecklenburg-Strelitz. She married the King of England, 1761, and was painted by all the leading artists of the day.

THOMAS GAINSBOROUGH, ENGLISH, 1727–1788

194. SKIRTS OF THE WOOD

Oil on canvas, 16⅜ x 21 in.

Owned by The Art Institute of Chicago (W. W. Kimball Collection).

COLL.: H. E. Pfungst, Lond.; De la Haye Moores, Clifton; L. Huth (1898); Ehrich Gall., N. Y.

W. Armstrong, *Gainsborough,* 1898, 206 (Edition, 1906, 287); *Guide,* 1932, 82 (repr.).

WILLIAM HOGARTH, ENGLISH, 1697–1764

195. MONAMY AND WALKER

Oil on canvas, 23¼ x 20½ in.

Owned by The Art Institute of Chicago.

COLL.: Thos. Walker; R. Bull; H. Walpole, Strawberry Hill (Sale, 1842, No. 96); Earl of Derby (1842); Sold at Christie's, 1902; Ernest Brown and Phillips, Lond.

LIT.: A. Dobson, *William Hogarth,* 1902, 172.

According to Dobson, painted c. 1740. The subject is the English painter Peter Monamy (1689[?]–1749), showing a seapiece to his patron, Thomas Walker. The figures are by Hogarth; the seapiece by Monamy, himself.

WILLIAM HOGARTH, ENGLISH, 1697–1764

†196. PORTRAIT OF SIR EDWARD WALPOLE

Oil on canvas, 30 x 25 in.

Inscribed: SIR EDWARD WALPOLE, K. B. BY HOGARTH

Lent by The Chester H. Johnson Gallery, Chicago.

COLL.: H. Walpole (brother of the sitter), Strawberry Hill; The Keppel Family, Lexham Hall, Norfolk; G. F. Lindsay (1868); Scott and Fowles, N. Y.

EXH.: National Portrait Exh., London, 1869.

LIT.: A. Dobson, *Hogarth,* 1907, 188.

JOHN JACKSON, English, 1778–1831

197. An English Gentleman
Oil on canvas, 27 x 23⅜ in.
Owned by The Art Institute of Chicago.

Coll.: G. P. A. Healy, Chi.

Lit.: Thieme-Becker, *Künstlerlexikon,* XVIII (1925), 223; *Guide,* 1932, 85 (repr.).

THOMAS LAWRENCE, English, 1769–1830

*198. Mrs. Wolff (Pl. XL)
Oil on canvas, 50 x 39 in.
Owned by The Art Institute of Chicago (W. W. Kimball Collection).

Exh.: Royal Academy, Lond., 1815; Fogg Art Mus., Cambridge, 1930, No. 47.

Lit.: G. S. Layard (ed.), *Sir Thomas Lawrence's Letter-Bag,* N. Y., 1906, opp. 147 (repr.), 147–150, 245, 246; W. Armstrong, *Sir Thomas Lawrence,* N. Y., 1913, 65, 172, Pl. XXXVII; *Bull.,* XIV (1920), 73 (repr.), 77; *Guide,* 1932, 88 (repr.).

Mezzotinted by Samuel Cousins, 1831.
A drawing for the head and shoulders of the figure is in the collection of Mrs. M. S. Danforth, Providence, R. I. Mrs. Wolff, wife of the Danish consul in Lond., was an intimate friend of the artist. Her house in Battersea was a gathering place for the artistic circles of the day; the book before her is appropriately open at a colored engraving of a figure from Michelangelo's Sistine frescoes.

THOMAS LAWRENCE, English, 1769–1830

199. Portrait of a Lady
Oil on panel, 9 x 12 in.
Lent by Mr. Frederick T. Haskell, Chicago.

HENRY RAEBURN, Scotch, 1756–1823

*200. The Honorable Mrs. Veitch (Pl. XLIII)
Oil on canvas, 48 x 28½ in.
Lent by Mr. Francis Neilson, Chicago.

Coll.: Miss Alice Graham Stirling (niece of the sitter), Palmerston Pl., Edinburgh. (The painting went directly to her from the Veitch residence in Eliock and has never been anywhere else); Scott and Fowles, N. Y.

Exh.: The Art Inst. of Chi., 1924.

Lit.: J. Greig, *Sir Henry Raeburn,* 1911, 62.

Painted c. 1807.
Syepherina Loughan, great-granddaughter of Annie Laurie, the lady of the Scotch song; was the daughter of Philadelphia Ferguson, the daughter of R. Ferguson of Craigdarrock, who was the son of Alexander Ferguson of Craigdarrock by Annie Laurie, daughter of Sir Robert Laurie of Maxwelton House, originally the castle of the Earls of Glencairn, bought in 1611 by Stephen Laurie, (the founder of the Laurie family) and where Annie Laurie was born. Syepherina married Colonel Henry Veitch of Eliock.

HENRY RAEBURN, Scotch, 1756–1823

*201. John Johnstone of Alva, his Sister, Dame Betty, and his Niece, Miss Wedderburn. (Pl. XLI)
Oil on panel, 39 x 43⅝ in.
Lent by Mr. Robert W. Schuette, New York.

Coll.: Miss Johnstone (descendant of sitters); Mrs. P. Nelke; Lewis and Simmons, N. Y.

Lit.: W. Armstrong, *Sir Henry Raeburn,* 1901, 106; J. Greig, *Sir Henry Raeburn,* 1911, 50.

Painted c. 1806.

HENRY RAEBURN, Scotch, 1756–1823

202. Mrs. Roderick MacNeill
Oil on canvas, 48 x 40 in.
Lent by Mr. and Mrs. Cyrus H. McCormick, Chicago.

Coll.: Wigzell, 1895.

Lit.: W. Armstrong, *Sir Henry Raeburn,* 1901, 108; J. Greig, *Sir Henry Raeburn,* 1911, 52.

Jean Cameron, daughter of Sir Ewen Cameron of Fassifern, and wife of Roderick MacNeill of Barra.

JOSHUA REYNOLDS, English, 1723–1792

*203. The Honorable Mrs. Watson (Pl. XL)
Oil on canvas, 45 x 34 in.
Lent by Mr. Arthur J. Secor and The Toledo Museum of Art, Toledo, Ohio.

Coll.: F. Kleinberger, Paris.

Lit.: W. Roberts, *Sir Joshua Reynolds's Portraits of the Hon. Mrs. Watson,* 1913, opp. 3 (repr.).

Painted c. 1789.
Roberts notes two replicas; the earliest version, painted in 1789, belonged in 1913 to the Rev. W. Watson, and was hanging in Rockingham Castle, Northamptonshire. Another, painted the same year, is in an American private coll.

The Hon. Mrs. Watson was Mary Elizabeth Milles (1767–1818) of North Elmham, Norfolk. In 1785 she married the Hon. Lewis Thomas Watson, who became Baron Sondes in 1795. Three years after Baron Sondes' death in 1806 she married Major General Sir Henry Tucker Montresor, K.C.B., G.C.H. Gainsborough painted her c. 1785.

GEORGE ROMNEY, English, 1734–1802

204. Mrs. Francis Russell
Oil on canvas, 50 x 40 in.
Owned by The Art Institute of Chicago (W. W. Kimball Collection).

Coll.: C. Wertheimer (Sale, Lond., 1897, No. 45, repr. in cat.); Mrs. W. W. Kimball, Chi.

Lit.: *Magazine of Art,* XXI (1898), 139, 140 (repr.); H. Ward and W. Roberts, *Romney,* 1904, II, 137; *Guide,* 1932, 84 (repr.).

Painted partly in 1785; finished in 1787.
"Anne Kershaw, daughter of the Vicar of Leeds and Canon of Ripon; married Francis Russell, cousin of the Duke of Bedford, and an Attorney of Red Lion Square, who held at the same time four appointments in the Duchy Court of Lancaster, Gray's Inn; he was Surveyor of Lands and Woods, South of Trent; Sworn Attorney in Court for the Crown; Receiver of the Rents for Yorkshire and Nottinghamshire and Secretary to the Chancellor of the County Palatinate." Ward and Roberts, *supra.*

JOSEPH M. W. TURNER, English, 1775–1851

205. Dutch Fishing Boats
Oil on canvas, 71 x 90 in.
Signed: J. M. W. TURNER.
Owned by The Art Institute of Chicago (W. W. Kimball Collection).

Coll.: J. Naylor, Leighton Hall (purchased direct from the artist); Mrs. W. W. Kimball, Chi.

Lit.: W. Armstrong, *Turner,* 1902, 229.

According to Armstrong, painted c. 1826, and a companion to the "Pas de Calais" (R. A., 1827).

JOSEPH M. W. TURNER, English, 1775–1851

206. Evening of the Deluge
Oil on canvas, 29¾ x 29¾ in.
Lent by Mrs. William R. Timken, New York.

Coll.: Rev. T. Judkins (bought at Christie's, 1872); M. Kann; H. Darrell-Brown; H. Young, N. Y.

Exh.: Detroit Inst. of Arts, 1926, No. 48.

Lit.: W. Armstrong, *Turner,* 1902, 147, 156–7, 220; F. E. W. Freund, *Internatl. Stu.,* LXXXIV (May, 1926), 62 (repr.), 90.

Painted c. 1843. Another version is in the Tate Gall., Lond.

RICHARD WILSON, English, 1713–1782

207. Italian Landscape with Cliffs and Castle
Oil on canvas, 20 x 24 in.
Owned by The Art Institute of Chicago (W. W. Kimball Collection).

Coll.: Scott and Fowles, N. Y.; Mrs. W. W. Kimball, Chi.

Exh.: Fogg Art Mus., Cambridge, 1930, No. 111.

Lit.: M. C., *Bull.,* XIX (1925), 91–2 (repr.); *Guide,* 1932, 80 (repr.).

Painted before 1755.

JOHANN ZOFFANY, English, 1725–1810

†208. The Dutton Family Group
Oil on canvas, 40½ x 50¼ in.
Lent by M. Knoedler and Co., New York.

Coll.: Lord Sherborne, Lond.; D. H. Farr, Lond.

Exh.: Royal Academy, Lond., 1907, No. 143; "English Conversation Pieces," Lond., 1931, No. 134; Rhode Island School of Design, Providence, R. I., 1932.

Lit.: Lady V. Manners and G. C. Williamson, *John Zoffany, R.A.,* 1920, 154 (repr.), 233; Williamson, *English Conversation Pictures,* 1931, 14–15, Pl. XL.

A painted sketch for the figure of Mrs. Dutton was in the possession of Goudstikker, Amsterdam, 1930.
From left to right the figures are: Jane Dutton (who married Thomas Coke of Holkham, later Earl of Leicester), her father, Mr. Dutton, her brother James (1st Lord Sherborne), and her mother, Mrs. Dutton. The scene is in the drawing-room at Sherborne Park, Gloucestershire.

Painted c. 1770 (?).

FRENCH PAINTING

Seventeenth, Eighteenth and Early Nineteenth Centuries

GALLERY 39

FRANÇOIS BOUCHER, French, 1703–1770

209. Bathing Nymph
Oil on canvas, 16¼ x 18⅜ in.
Owned by The Art Institute of Chicago (W. L. Mead Memorial).

Coll.: Private German Coll.; Van Diemen, N. Y. (1931).

Lit.: D. C. Rich, *Bull.,* XXVI (1932), 25–7, 33 (repr.).

Closely related to the "Bath of Diana" in the Louvre and painted c. 1742–5. The same model appears in both pictures.

JEAN BAPTISTE SIMEON CHARDIN, French, 1699–1779

*210. The Industrious Mother (Pl. XLVI)
Oil on canvas, 20¾ x 16¾ in.
Lent from a Private Collection, New York.

Coll.: Lord Leconfield, Petworth, Sussex; Sir Joseph Duveen, N. Y., 1920, 14, No. 561.

Lit.: J. Guiffrey, *Chardin,* 1908, No. 66; H. Collins Baker, *Cat. of the Petworth Coll.;* J. Guiffrey, *W. R. Valentiner, Das Unbekannte Meisterwerk,* 1930, No. 80.

According to J. Guiffrey (in *Das Unbekannte Meisterwerk*), Chardin repeated the subject very often. The earliest version (exhibited in the Salon of 1740) is today in the Louvre (No. 90); a replica is in the Stockholm Mus. (No. 784) and other pictures bearing the same title appeared in the La Roque (1754), Chardin (1780) and Brugard Sales.

JEAN BAPTISTE SIMEON CHARDIN, French, 1699–1779

211. The Little School Mistress
Oil on canvas, 23 x 29¼ in.
Lent anonymously.

Coll.: Watelet(?)(Sale, Paris, 1786); Marquis de Cypierre(?)(Sale, Paris, 1845); De Curel (Sale, Paris, 1918); M. Knoedler and Co., N. Y.

Exh.: Salon, 1740 (?).

Lit.: C. Holmes, *Burlington Magazine,* XLVII (1925), 33; T. Bodkin, *Ibid.,* 93.

Engraved by Lépicié (?), Simon Duflos (?), Gauchard (?).
Three other versions exist: (1) National Gall., Ireland (possibly the painting exhibited at the Salon of 1740, though the present painting may be that one). (24½ x 28¾ in.) (2) National Gall., Lond. (24½ x 26¼ in.) (3) H. de Rothschild, Paris. (9⅞ x 7⅜ in.), by Chardin (?).

JEAN BAPTISTE SIMEON CHARDIN, French, 1699–1779

212. Still Life: Eggs

Oil on canvas, 31½ x 35½ in.

Signed: CHARDIN.

Owned by The Art Institute of Chicago.

Coll.: M. X., Paris (1907); Ehrich Gall., N. Y. (Sale, 1924, No. 56, repr. in cat.).

Exh.: Chardin-Fragonard Exh., Paris, 1907, No. 69.

Lit.: *Bull.*, XIX (1925), 34 (repr.); E. S. Siple, *Burlington Magazine*, LI (1927), 244 (repr.); *Guide*, 1932, 40 (repr.).

In the late style of the painter. Possibly the canvas which appeared at the Houdelot Sale, Paris, 1859, No. 22.

JACQUES LOUIS DAVID, French, 1748–1825

*213. Mme. Jeanne de Richemont and her son, Eugene (Pl. XLVII)

Oil on canvas, 45¾ x 35½ in.

Lent by Mr. Edward J. Berwind, New York.

Coll.: S. Bardac, Paris; Vicomte Chabert, Paris; Wildenstein, N. Y.

Exh.: "Portraits of Women and Children," Paris, 1897, No. 45.

Lit.: *Gaz. des Beaux Arts*, Per. 6, VII (1932), 81 (repr.); W. R. Valentiner, *J. L. David and the French Revolution*, 1929, 26; Valentiner, *Das Unbekannte Meisterwerk*, 1930, Pl. 83; *Formes*, No. XX (1931), 166, Pl. IV.

According to Dr. Valentiner, painted c. 1800.
(This painting is in gallery 40).

JEAN-HONORE FRAGONARD, French, 1732–1806

†214. Portrait of Hubert Robert (?)

Oil on canvas, 16½ x 13¼ in.

Lent by Jacques Seligmann and Co., Inc., New York.

Coll.: Rudinoff.

Exh.: Royal Academy, Lond., 1932, No. 269.

Lit.: *La Renaissance*, XV (1932), 34 (repr.).

The identification is traditional. Hubert Robert, "Robert of the Ruins" (1733–1808), famous French landscape and architectural painter, particularly noted for his subjects drawn from classical buildings. He was a close friend of Fragonard's. (See Nos. 227 and 228.)
Painted c. 1780–90 (?).

JEAN-HONORE FRAGONARD, French, 1732–1806

215. Rest of the Holy Family

Oil on canvas, 21⅜ x 17¾ in.

Lent anonymously.

Coll.: Mme. Oger de Bréart (Sale, Paris, 1886, No. 19); Ch. Pillet; Wildenstein and Co., N. Y.

Exh.: E. Gimpel and Wildenstein Gall., N. Y., 1914, No. 20 (where picture is confused with replica).

Lit.: R. Portalis, *Honoré Fragonard*, 1889, II, 287; P. de Nolhac, *J. H. Fragonard*, 1906, 166.

Closely connected with a large altarpiece painted by Fragonard, today in St. Nizier at Troyes. (See M. A. Boutillier, *Annuaire de l'Aube*, 1912, II, 19, 23.) A larger replica (sold in the Le Prince sale of 1781) is in the coll. of Dr. and Mrs. H. B. Jacobs of Baltimore. In the George Blumenthal Coll., N. Y., is a water color study. It is possible that the present picture was the one sold in 1859 at the "M. A." sale in Paris, there referred to as "Rest of the Holy Family (sketch)."
Painted c. 1770-75 (?).

CLAUDE GELLEE, CALLED "LE LORRAIN," French, 1600–1682

216. Landscape with Reposing Huntsmen

Oil on canvas, 39 x 52 in.

Signed: CLADIO GELLE ROMI 16.

Lent by The Smith College Museum of Art, Northampton, Massachusetts.

Liber Veritatis, 40.

Coll.: M. Doby, Grenoble; Proly (Sale, 1787); Lord Methuen, near Perth, Scotland; Lt. Col. Lloyd-Ellis, Lond.; J. Weitzner, N. Y.

Lit.: J. Smith, VIII, 1837, Nos. 40 and 354 (the same picture); *Bull. of the Smith College Mus. of Art*, No. 13 (May, 1932), 1 (repr.); *Parnassus*, IV (Feb., 1932), 34 (repr.); *The Connoisseur*, LXXXIX (1932), 211 (repr.); *The Fine Arts*, XVIII (Mar., 1932), 41 (repr.).

Painted for M. Doby, Grenoble. A pendant is in the possession of Springfield Mus. of Fine Arts, Springfield, Massachusetts.

JEAN AUGUSTE DOMINIQUE INGRES, French, 1780–1867

*217. Mlle. Jeanne Gonin (1821) (Pl. XLVII)

Oil on canvas, 30⅛ x 23¼ in.

Signed: D. INGRES . . . FLOR. 1821.

Lent by The Taft Collection, Taft Museum, Cincinnati Institute of Fine Arts, Cincinnati, Ohio.

Coll.: A. Thomeguex (grandson of sitter); Scott and Fowles, N. Y.

Lit.: H. Delaborde, *Ingres*, 1870, 250, No. 124 (incorrectly as *Gouin.*); H. Lapauze, *Ingres, sa Vie et son Oeuvre*, 1911, 213; Lapauze, *La Renaissance*, VI (1923), 446 (repr.); W. H. Siple, *Bull. of the Cincinnati Art Mus.*, I (1930), 25 (repr.), 33–39; L. G. Burroughs, *Creative Art*, X (1932), 365ff.

Painted at Florence, 1821. Ingres made many portrait drawings and some painted portraits of members of the Gonin-Thomeguex families.
Jeanne Gonin lived with her brother, Jean Pierre Gonin, in Florence. She later married Pyrame Thomeguex.

NICOLAS LANCRET, French, 1690–1743

218. The Duet

Oil on canvas, 19¾ x 16¾ in.

Lent by Mr. E. J. Stehli, New York.

Coll.: Sir Wm. Knighton, Lond., 1885; Pitt Rivers, Lond.

Lit.: G. Wildenstein, *Lancret*, 1924, 79, No. 120 (?); E. Singleton, *Old World Masters in New World Collections*, 1929, 294–5 (repr.); W. R. Valentiner, *Das Unbekannte Meisterwerk*, 1930, No. 79 (repr.).

Valentiner notes a variant or replica (oval in shape) sold at the de Beurnonville auctions, 1883 and 1884. He is not inclined to identify this picture with one sold in Paris at an anonymous sale, May 28, 1850, No. 33.

NICOLAS LANCRET, French, 1690–1743

†219. Love in the Wood

Oil on canvas, 17½ x 19 in.

Lent by Wildenstein and Co., Inc., New York.

Coll.: Frederick II of Prussia; Kings of Prussia; New Palace, Potsdam, 1923.

Exh.: Salon, 1739 (?).

Lit.: Lady Dilke, *French Painters of the 18th Century,* 1899, 106 (repr.); Seidel, *Les Collections de sa Majesté l'Empereur d'Allemagne* (trans. by P. Vitry and J. J. M. de Vasselot), 1900, 98, No. 53; J. J. Foster, *French Art from Watteau to Prud'hon,* 1905, I, 136, Pl. XLIX; G. Wildenstein, *Lancret,* 1924, 100, No. 455 and Fig. 111.

Engraved by Larmessin.
Wildenstein records a drawing (sold, April 21, 1845) at an anonymous Paris sale, probably for the picture.

NICOLAS LANCRET, French, 1690–1743

†220. The Swing

Oil on canvas, 38 x 49½ in.

Lent by Wildenstein and Co., Inc., New York.

Coll.: Wynn Ellis.

One of a series of compositions on the same subject.

LOUIS LE NAIN, French, 1593–1648

*221. The Peasant Family at the Well (Pl. XLIV)

Oil on canvas, 38½ x 40 in.

Owned by The Art Institute of Chicago (1923).

Coll.: Ch. Sedelmeyer, Paris (Sale, I, 1907, No. 223, repr. in cat. I); O. Sirèn, Stockholm.

Lit.: *Bull.,* XVII (1923), 82–4 (repr.); *Guide,* 1932, 39 (repr.).

If by Louis, painted c. 1640–48. This picture is closely associated with a group of similar compositions (see, R. C. Witt in *Illustrated Cat. of Pictures by the Brothers Le Nain,* 1910, 15, for variants).

MATHIEU LE NAIN, French, 1607–1677

*222. The Card Players (Pl. XLIV)

Oil on canvas, 22¾ x 26⅞ in.

Lent by the Worcester Art Museum, Worcester, Mass.

Coll.: Count de Champfeu; R. Langton Douglas, Lond.

Lit.: E. S. S., *Worcester Art Museum Bull.,* XVII (1926), 68 (repr.), 69–74.

Two other versions exist. The first is probably the one in the Louvre, assigned by P. Jamot to Mathieu, and dated c. 1639–40; the present version is doubtless the second (the standing figure in the center is omitted); last is the one in Buckingham Palace, Lond. (the central figure and the standing figure to the left are omitted).

JEAN BAPTISTE JOSEPH PATER, French, 1695–1736

223. Fete Champetre

Oil on canvas, 27¾ x 39¼ in.

Lent by Mrs. Ralph Harman Booth, wife of the late Honorable Ralph Harman Booth, former Minister to Denmark.

Coll.: A. Wertheimer, Lond. (1902); Huthemann, St. Petersburg (1914).

Exh.: Guildhall, Lond., 1902, No. 134; Detroit Inst. of Arts, 1926, No. 43; Reinhardt Gall., N. Y., 1928, No. 14 (repr. in cat.).

Lit.: F. Ingersoll-Smouse, *Pater,* 1928, 40, No. 30 and Fig. 16.

Unfinished. A variant of a composition in the Museum of Valenciennes.
An unfinished replica was in the possession of J. Böhler, Munich (1928).

JEAN BAPTISTE JOSEPH PATER, French, 1695–1736

224. Pastoral Pleasures

Oil on canvas, 31½ x 38 in.

Lent by Mrs. William R. Timken, New York.

Coll.: Daupias (Sale, 1892, No. 46); E. R. Bacon, Lond. (Sale, 1923); Anonymous Sale (Lond., May 23, 1924); F. T. Sabin, Lond.

Exh.: Exh. of French Art of the Eighteenth Century, Brussels, 1904, No. 54.

Lit.: F. Ingersoll-Smouse, *Pater,* 1928, 41, No. 42.

Unfinished.

JEAN BAPTISTE JOSEPH PATER, French, 1695–1736

*225. Love and Jest (Pl. XLV)

Oil on canvas, 21½ x 26 in.

Signed: pater.

Lent by Mr. Edward J. Berwind, New York.

Coll.: L. Neumann, Lond.; Count Vitzthum, Dresden (?); Wildenstein, N. Y.

Lit.: F. Ingersoll-Smouse, *Pater,* 38, No. 13 and Fig. 8; E. Singleton, *Old World Masters in New World Collections,* 1929, 298–9 (the repr. is not the Berwind picture).

Engraved by Filleoul.
Variant of a composition in the Baron Maurice de Rothschild Coll., Paris. A pendant is in the collection of Mr. Berwind.

NICOLAS POUSSIN, French, 1594–1665

*226. St. John on Patmos (Pl. XLV)

Oil on canvas, 40 x 52½ in.

Owned by The Art Institute of Chicago (Munger Collection).

Coll.: M. Robit (Sale, Paris, 1801, No. 91); Mr. Bryan, 1802 (Cat., No. 29); Sir S. Clarke, Lond.; Sir Thos. Baring, Lond. (1837).

Lit.: W. Buchanan, *Memoirs of Painting,* 1824, II, 59, No. 91; J. Smith, VIII, 1837, No. 316; A. Andresen, *Nicolas Poussin,* 1863, No. 455; O. Grautoff, *Poussin,* II, 1914, 259; H. Posse, *Pantheon,* V (1930), 62, 64, 65 (repr.); W. R. Valentiner, *Das Unbekannte Meisterwerk,* 1930, No. 74 (repr.); D. C. Rich, *Bull.,* XXIV (1930), 113–17 (repr.); *Guide,* 1932, 38 (repr.).

Engraved by Châtillon, etc. (see Valentiner, *supra,* for list of reproductions).
Closely related to the "St. Matthew with the Angel" in the Kaiser-Friedrich Mus., Berlin. H. Posse believes it to be a pendant to this composition, executed 1648–50. W. Friedländer (in *Das Unbekannte Meisterwerk*) calls it the earliest of the six Poussin landscapes engraved by Châtillon for N. Poilly, dating it 1645–50.

HUBERT ROBERT, French, 1733–1808

*227. The Fountains (Pl. XLVI)

Oil on canvas, 100 x 92 in.

Owned by The Art Institute of Chicago.

Coll.: Marquis de Laborde, Méréville (1788); Count de Saint Roman; L. François (Sale, Paris, 1900, No. 3, repr. in cat., p. 16).

Lit.: P. de Nolhac, *Hubert Robert,* 1910, 71, 154; T. Leclère, *Hubert Robert* (Les Grands Artistes), 1913, 92; *Guide,* 1932, 41 (repr.).

One of six great compositions, painted 1787–8, commissioned by the French financier, Marquis Jean Joseph de Laborde (1724–1794), for his Château de Méréville. Three of the others are also the possession of the Art Institute of Chicago.

HUBERT ROBERT, French, 1733–1808

228. Landscape with Figures

Oil on canvas, 26 x 19½ in.

Lent by Mr. Samuel H. Kress, New York.

Coll.: J. Groult, Paris.

Exh.: Exposition Centenale, Paris, 1900, No. 105 as "Les Pins Parasols."

Possibly the painting sold at an anonymous Paris sale (March 31–April 1, 1775), No. 17, "une belle étude de pins, cyprès et autres arbres."

FRENCH PAINTING

Nineteenth Century

GALLERY 40

THEODORE CHASSERIAU, French, 1819–1856

229. The Fisherman's Wife and Child

Oil on panel, 6¾ x 4¾ in.

Signed: th. chasseriau.

Lent by The Museum of Art, Rhode Island School of Design, Providence, R. I.

Exh.: Salon, 1851.

Coll.: Baron A. Chassériau, Paris.

Lit.: L. de Geoffroy, *Revue des Deux Mondes,* March, 1851; *L'Artiste* (Oct., 1852); P. Mantz, *L'Artiste,* 1856; H. Marcel, *Chassériau,* 1911, 91–2 (repr. opp. 92); L. E. Rowe, *Bull. of the R. I. School of Design,* XVII (1929), 40–2 (repr.); L. Bénédite (d. 1925), *Théodore Chassériau,* 1931, II, 368.

Lithographed by Lemoine.

CAMILLE COROT, French, 1796–1875

230. Arleux-Palluel, The Bridge of Trysts

Oil on canvas, 23½ x 28½ in.

Signed: corot.

Owned by The Art Institute of Chicago (Potter Palmer Collection).

Coll.: Arnold and Tripp (1882); G. Petit (1883); Durand-Ruel (1889); Mrs. Potter Palmer, Chi. (1892).

Lit.: A. Robaut, *L'Oeuvre de Corot,* III, 1905, No. 2210 (repr.).

Painted 1871–2. Robaut records a copy sold in 1876.

CAMILLE COROT, French, 1796–1875

*231. Interrupted Reading (Pl. LII)

Oil on canvas, 36 x 25¼ in.

Signed: corot.

Owned by The Art Institute of Chicago (Potter Palmer Collection).

Coll.: Larochenoire, Paris; Alex. Dumas I (Sale, Paris, 1882, No. 15); Alex. Dumas II (Sale, Paris, 1892, No. 24); Durand-Ruel, Paris (1892); Mrs. Potter Palmer, Chi.

Exh.: Ecole des Beaux-Arts, 1875, No. 93; Fogg Art Mus., Cambridge, Mass., 1929, No. 12; Mus. of Mod. Art, N. Y., 1930, No. 29 (repr. in cat.).

Lit.: A. Robaut, *L'Oeuvre de Corot,* III, 1905, 62, No. 1431 (repr. 64); J. Meier-Graefe, *Corot,* 1913, 107 (repr.); A. F. Jaccaci, *Art in America,* II (1913), (repr. 3, fig. 2), 5; Meier-Graefe, *Kunst u. Künstler,* XXVIII (1929), 51 (repr.); Meier-Graefe, *Corot,* 1930, Pl. CVII.

Painted 1865–70.

CAMILLE COROT, French, 1796–1875

232. Jumieges

Oil on canvas, 12 x 15½ in.

Signed: corot.

Lent by The Smith College Museum of Art, Northampton, Massachusetts.

Coll.: R. C. Vose, Boston.

Exh.: Mus. of Mod. Art, N. Y., 1930, No. 11 (repr. in cat.).

Lit.: A. V. Churchill, *Bull. of the Smith College Mus. of Art,* I, No. 9 (June 1928), 6–8 (repr.); H. A. Bull, *International Studio,* XCVIII (January, 1931), 56 (repr.); Churchill, *Bull. of Smith College,* No. 13 (May, 1932), 21 (repr.).

Painted 1829–30.

CAMILLE COROT, French, 1796–1875

233. St. Salvi Church, Albi

Oil on canvas, 14 x 11½ in.

Signed: corot.

Owned by The Art Institute of Chicago.

Coll.: Amer. Art Assn. Sale, Mar. 26, 1931, No. 115.

Lit.: D. C. Rich, *Bull.,* XXVI (1932), 30–31 (repr.).

Painted c. 1830.
Cf. C. Brossard, *France du Sud Est* (1903), 117.

CAMILLE COROT, French, 1796–1875

*234. View of Volterra (1838) (Pl. XLVIII)

Oil on canvas, 27¼ x 37⅜ in.

Signed: corot, 1838.

Lent from The Chester Dale Collection, New York.

Coll.: Baron Thenard (Sale, Paris, 1931, No. 22, repr. in cat.); P. Rosenberg, Paris.

Exh.: Salon, Paris, 1838, No. 342; Royal Academy, London, 1932, No. 298.

CAMILLE COROT, French, 1796–1875

235. Wounded Eurydice

Oil on canvas, 22 x 16¼ in.

Signed: corot.

Owned by The Art Institute of Chicago (Henry Field Collection).

Coll.: A. Sensier, Paris; Edwards (1878) (Sale, Paris, 1881); Tavernier, Paris; H. Field (1893).

Exh.: Durand-Ruel, Paris, 1878, No. 59; Knoedler, N. Y., 1929.

Lit.: A. Robaut, *L'Oeuvre de Corot,* III, 1905, 242, No. 2001 (repr. 243); A. F. Jaccaci, *Art in America,* II (1913), 6, 7 (repr. fig. 3 [not 4, as printed]).

Lithographed by Emile Vernier, 1870.
Two other versions exist. Robaut believes the first to be the painting now the property of Durand-Ruel (?), executed in 1868–70, the same period to which he gives the present example. The third (Lhiabasters Sale, 1885) he dates 1870.

GUSTAVE COURBET, French, 1819–1877

236. An Alpine Scene (1874)

Oil on canvas, 23⅞ x 28½ in.

Signed: '74 g. courbet.

Owned by The Art Institute of Chicago (Munger Collection).

Coll.: A. A. Munger, 1901.

Exh.: City Art Mus., St. Louis, 1930.

Lit.: T. Duret, *Courbet,* 1918, 149; *Guide,* 1932, 50 (repr.).

Painted in Switzerland, 1874.

GUSTAVE COURBET, French, 1819–1877

*237. Mere Gregoire (Mme Andler-Keller) (Pl. LI)

Oil on canvas, 50½ x 38 in.

Signed: g. c.

Owned by The Art Institute of Chicago.

Coll.: Prince de Wagram; Mme. de la Tour d' Auvergne; Alexander Reid & Lefèvre, Ltd., Lond.

Exh.: Courbet Exh., Paris, 1867, No. 96; Exh. of French Painting, St. Petersburg, 1911.

Lit.: D. C. Rich, *Bull.,* XXIV (1930), 41–3 (repr.); *Guide,* 1932, 49 (repr.).

Caricatured by G. Randon for *Le Journal Amusant,* 1867. Engraved on wood, for Dr. Blondon's *Les Misères des Gueux,* 1872, 145 (as "Mme. Gervais").
According to Ch. Léger painted c. 1855. A small canvas (sketch?) at the Museum of Morlaix reproduces the head. The sitter was Mme. Andler-Keller, wife of the proprietor of the Brasserie Andler, much frequented by Courbet and his artist friends.

GUSTAVE COURBET, French, 1819–1877

*238. The Toilet of a Bride (Pl. XLIX)

Oil on canvas, 74 x 99 in.

Lent by The Smith College Museum of Art, Northampton, Massachusetts.

Coll.: Zoubaloff, Paris; P. Rosenberg, Paris.

Exh.: Rosenberg Gall., Paris; Wildenstein Gall., N. Y., 1924; Fogg Art Mus., Cambridge, Mass., 1929, No. 15 (repr. in cat. Pl. XI); Albright Art Gall., Buffalo, N. Y., 1932, No. 11 (repr. in cat. Pl. VI).

Lit.: G. Eglington, *Internatl. Studio,* LXXIX (1924), 447–453 (repr. and det.); A. V. Churchill, *Bull. of the Smith College Mus. of Art,* No. 10 (April, 1929), 1–24 (repr. and det.); Ch. Léger, *Courbet,* 1929, 81–2 and Pl. 37; R. Fry, *The Characteristics of French Art,* 1932, 110–11 (repr. opp. 110).

Léger dates it c. 1859. Churchill believes it was painted 1856–70. The picture was never finished, forming part of Courbet's estate upon his death.

HONORE DAUMIER, French, 1808–1879

239. Don Quixote and the Windmills

Oil on panel, 13¾ x 27½ in.

Signed: h.d.

Owned by The Art Institute of Chicago (Mr. and Mrs. Charles H. Worcester Collection).

Coll.: Barbizon Hse., Lond.; R. C. Vose, Boston.

Exh.: Mus. of Mod. Art, N. Y., 1930, No. 53 (repr. in cat.).

Lit.: M. Sadlier, *Daumier,* 1924, Pl. I; R. M. F., *Bull.,* XIX (1925), 60–61 (repr.); *Guide,* 1932, 44 (repr.).

There are several variants. See Pls. 155–57 of E. Fuchs, *Der Maler Daumier,* 1927, and Pl. 306 of *Supplement,* 1930.

HONORE DAUMIER, French, 1808–1879

*240. The Drinkers (Pl. LI)

Oil on canvas, 14½ x 11⅛ in.

Signed: h.d.

Lent from The Adolph Lewisohn Collection, New York.

COLL.: Mme. Daubigny, Paris; H. Rouart, Paris (1912).

EXH.: Durand-Ruel, Paris, 1878, No. 49; Daumier Exh., Paris, 1901, No. 68; Manzi-Joyant Gall., Paris, 1912, No. 171; Mus. of Mod. Art, N. Y., 1930, No. 69 (repr. in cat.); Albright Art Gallery, Buffalo, 1932, No. 15 (repr. in cat. Pl. XI).

LIT.: A. Fontainas, *La Peinture de Daumier,* 1923, Pl. 37; E. Fuchs, *Der Maler Daumier,* 1927, Pl. 31; S. Bourgeois, *The Adolph Lewisohn Coll.,* 1928, 34 (repr.); G. Geffroy, *Daumier,* 26 (repr.); E. von Térey, *Kunst und Künstler,* XXVII (1929), 419 (repr.); S. A. Lewisohn, *Creative Art,* IX (1931), 191, 194 (repr.).

Fuchs (*Supplement,* 1930, Pl. 278) records a replica in the H. Fiquet Coll., Paris.

HONORE DAUMIER, FRENCH, 1808–1879

*242. THE UPRISING (Pl. XLIX)
Oil on canvas, 34½ x 44½ in.
Signed: H.D.
Lent by The Phillips Memorial Gallery, Washington, D. C.

COLL.: H. Fiquet, Paris; H. Bing, Paris.

EXH.: The Louvre; Leicester Gall., Lond.; Reinhardt Gall., N. Y., 1927, No. 18; Mus. of Mod. Art, N. Y., No. 61 (repr. in cat.).

LIT.: A. Alexandre, *Burlington Mag.,* XLIV (1924), 143–5 (repr.); M. Sadlier, *Daumier,* 1924, Pl. 53; E. Fuchs, *Daumier,* 1927, Pl. 91; F. J. Mather, Jr., *The Arts,* XI (1927), 77 (repr.), 78; D. Phillips, *Bull. of the Phillips Memorial Gallery,* 1927, 46 (repr.), 47; Phillips, *Art and Understanding,* I (Nov. 1929), 48 (repr., fourth fr. cover); Phillips, *Creative Art,* IV (1929), p. XIV (repr.), XXI; *Parnassus,* I (Nov., 1929), 13 (repr.); Phillips, *Formes,* No. IX (Nov. 1930), oppos. 8 (repr.); Phillips, *The Artist Sees Differently,* 1931, 20, 92, and Pl. XIV.

EUGENE DELACROIX, FRENCH, 1798–1863

243. ARAB RIDER ATTACKED BY A LION
Oil on canvas, 17½ x 15 in.
Signed: EUG. DELACROIX.
Owned by The Art Institute of Chicago (Potter Palmer Collection).

COLL.: M. D., Paris, 1862; Baron Trétaigne, 1872; Febvre, 1885; Mrs. Potter Palmer, Chicago, 1892.

EXH.: Delacroix Exh., Art Inst. of Chicago, 1930, No. 30.

LIT.: A. Robaut, *L'Oeuvre de Delacroix,* 1885, No. 1067.

Etched by Bracquemond; engraved on wood by Duvivier; lithographed by Dufourmantelle.
Painted in 1849.
A drawing for the composition is in the collection of Mr. Paul J. Sachs of Cambridge, Mass.

EUGENE DELACROIX, FRENCH, 1798–1863

244. DANTE'S BARK
Oil on canvas, 13½ x 15½ in.
Owned by The Art Institute of Chicago (Potter Palmer Collection).

COLL.: A. Royer; C. Narrey; S. Colman; J. T. Johnson; Mrs. Potter Palmer, Chicago.

EXH.: Delacroix Exh., The Art Inst. of Chi., 1930, No. 1 (repr. in cat.).

LIT.: A. Robaut, *L'Oeuvre de Delacroix,* 1885, No. 50; *Guide,* 1932, 43 (repr.).

One of several reductions of Delacroix' first successful entry in the Salon of 1822. The large version is today in the Louvre.

EUGENE DELACROIX, FRENCH, 1798–1863

*245. THE LION HUNT (1854) (Pl. XLVIII)
Oil on canvas, 18½ x 21½ in.
The Angell-Norris Collection (Lent to The Art Institute of Chicago).

COLL.: Doria; J. W. Gates, Chi.; Angell-Norris, St. Charles, Ill.

EXH.: Delacroix Exh., Art Inst. of Chi., 1930, No. 37 (repr. in cat.).

This sketch, another larger sketch, the property of Mme. Lauwick, and a variant formerly belonging to Heugel allow one to reconstruct the "Lion Hunt of 1854" which was purchased by the State and given to the city of Bordeaux where it was partially destroyed by fire in 1870. See Robaut, *L'Oeuvre de Delacroix,* 1885, Nos. 1230, 1242, and 1278. This present sketch may be the one catalogued as No. 1231, a painting which once belonged to M. Goldschmitt and is mentioned by Piron, after which it dropped out of sight.

EUGENE DELACROIX, FRENCH, 1798–1863

246. THE LION HUNT (1861)
Oil on canvas, 30 x 38½ in.
Signed, lower left: EUG. DELACROIX, 1861.
Owned by The Art Institute of Chicago (Potter Palmer Collection).

COLL.: Durand-Ruel, 1863; Count d'Aquila, 1868; Faure, 1885; A. Robinson, N. Y. (Sale, 1892); Mrs. Potter Palmer, Chi., 1893.

EXH.: École des Beaux-Arts, 1885, No. 76; Delacroix Exh., Art Inst. of Chi., 1930, No. 43 (repr. in cat.); Louvre, Paris, 1930, No. 191.

LIT.: A. Robaut, *L'Oeuvre de Delacroix,* 1885, No. 1350 (date given wrongly as 1858 and signature omitted).

See the *Journal de Eugène Delacroix* (New edition, edited by Joubin), 1928, II, 314, 317, 389, and 402 for important references to this work.

EUGENE DELACROIX, FRENCH, 1798–1863

247. SARACENS AND CRUSADERS
Oil on canvas, 23¼ x 30⅝ in.
Signed: EUG. D.
Owned by The Art Institute of Chicago.

COLL.: Roosevelt, Munich; M. Sterner Gallery, N. Y.

Painted c. 1840 (?). The subject is uncertain.

EUGENE DELACROIX, French, 1798–1863

†*248. Spring (Bacchus and Ariadne) (Pl. L)
Oil on canvas, 80 x 64¼ in.
Lent by Mr. Albert Gallatin, New York.

Coll.: Haro; Durand-Ruel; E. de Girardin (c. 1875).

Exh.: Am. Fine Arts Society, N. Y., 1904, No. 36; Albright Art Gall., Buffalo, 1932, No. 19.

Lit.: A. Moreau, *Delacroix Cat.,* 1873, 316; A. Silvestre, *Galerie Durand-Ruel,* 1873,12 and Pl. CXXV; A. Robaut, *L'Oeuvre de Delacroix,* 1885, 383, No. 1430 (as "Autumn"); J. Meier-Graefe, *Delacroix,* 1922, 235 (repr. as "Spring"); W. Pach, *The Masters of Mod. Art,* 1924, Pl. 4.

Etched by La Guillermie.
Painted 1862. One of a series of four decorations of "The Seasons" in Mr. Gallatin's collection.

JEAN FRANÇOIS MILLET, French, 1814–1875

*249. The Bather (Pl. LII)
Oil on canvas, 12⅝ x 9⅜ in.
Signed: J. F. MILLET.
Lent by the A. M. Barnhart Estate.

Coll.: A. Sensier, Paris.

Lit.: *Bull.,* XVIII (1924), 87–88 (repr.).

Painted c. 1846.

JEAN FRANÇOIS MILLET, French, 1814–1875

250. Bringing Home the New-Born Calf
Oil on canvas, 32 x 39⅜ in.
Signed: J. F. MILLET.
Owned by The Art Institute of Chicago (Henry Field Collection).

Exh.: Salon, 1864; International Exh., Paris, 1889; World's Columbian Expo., Chi., 1893, No. 3063.

Lit.: A. Sensier, *Jean-François Millet,* 1881, 258, 263–9 (Eng. trans., 1881, 170–2); J. Cartwright, *Jean François Millet,* 1902, 250–1, 264–5, 370; E. Moreau-Nélaton, *Millet, Raconté par Lui-Même,* II, 1921, 144, 154, 160–2 and Fig. 190; *Bull.,* XVIII (1924), 89 (repr.); *Guide,* 1932, 47 (repr.).

A drawing for the composition was formerly in the coll. of Mr. James Staats-Forbes. (See *Burlington Mag.,* V [1904], 145.)
This picture, begun in 1860 and exhibited in the Salon of 1864, aroused the wrath of the critics, who, with few exceptions, unmercifully attacked it. On its contemporary reception and Millet's defense see Moreau-Nélaton, *supra.*

JEAN FRANÇOIS MILLET, French, 1814–1875

251. The First Madame Millet (?)
Oil on canvas, 20 x 24 in.
Owned by The Art Institute of Chicago (Potter Palmer Collection).

Coll.: Mrs. Potter Palmer, Chi.

Painted c. 1844–5. The identification with Virginie Ono is traditional. The model resembles most closely the "Antoinette Hébert" in the portrait of 1845.

JEAN FRANÇOIS MILLET, French, 1814–1875

252. The Keeper of the Herd, Sunset
Oil on canvas, 28 x 36 in.
Signed: J. F. MILLET.
Owned by The Art Institute of Chicago (W. W. Kimball Collection).

Lit.: *Bull.,* XIV (1920), 68, 77 (repr.); XVIII (1924), 89.

Painted 1871–4.

JEAN FRANÇOIS MILLET, French, 1814–1875

253. In Auvergne
Oil on canvas, 31¼ x 38½ in.
Signed: J. F. MILLET.
Owned by The Art Institute of Chicago (Potter Palmer Collection).

JEAN FRANÇOIS MILLET, French, 1814–1875

254. The Little Shepherdess
Oil on canvas, 14 x 10 in.
Signed: J. F. MILLET.
Owned by The Art Institute of Chicago (Potter Palmer Collection).

Coll.: Mrs. Potter Palmer, Chi.

Exh.: G. Petit Gall., Paris, 1910.

Painted c. 1864–5.

JEAN FRANÇOIS MILLET, French, 1814–1875

255. The Rail-Splitter
Oil on canvas, 31½ x 25 in.
Signed: J. F. MILLET.
Owned by The Art Institute of Chicago (Potter Palmer Collection).

Coll.: Mrs. Potter Palmer, Chi., 1894.

Exh.: Art Institute of Chicago, 1910, No. 32.

Painted 1855–60. Another version in pastel and having practically the same composition dates from 1866. The subject was a favorite one with Millet and appears in many drawings and studies as well as in several completed works.

JEAN FRANÇOIS MILLET, French, 1814–1875

256. The Sheep-Shearers
Oil on canvas, 16 x 10 in.
Signed: J. F. MILLET.
Owned by The Art Institute of Chicago (Potter Palmer Collection).

Coll.: Mrs. Potter Palmer, Chi.

Exh.: G. Petit Gall., Paris, 1910.

Lit.: *Bull.*, XVIII (1924), 89 (repr.); E. Moreau-Nélaton, *Millet, Raconté par Lui-Même,* II, 1921, 74; P. Gsell, *Millet* (The Masters of Modern Art, Eng. trans.), 1928, Pl. 14 (confused with the Boston picture); *Guide,* 1932, 46–7 (repr.).

A very similar version is in the Mus. of Fine Arts, Boston, painted 1853. The Art Institute painting may be the one mentioned in the inventory of 1860, No. 20.

JEAN FRANÇOIS MILLET, French, 1814–1875

257. Woman Feeding Chickens
Oil on canvas, 18⅛ x 15 in.
Signed: J. F. MILLET.
Owned by The Art Institute of Chicago (Henry Field Collection).

Lit.: *Bull.*, XVIII (1924), 87–8.

An adaptation of the composition of 1854.

ADOLPHE MONTICELLI, French, 1824–1886

258. Garden Scene
Oil on panel, 11¾ x 24 in.
Lent by Mr. and Mrs. Charles H. Worcester, Chicago.

HENRI REGNAULT, French, 1843–1871

259. Young Woman's Portrait (1863)
Oil on canvas, 35½ x 28½ in.
Signed: HENRI REGNAULT, 1863.
Owned by The Art Institute of Chicago.

Lit.: *Guide,* 1932, 65 (repr.).

ALFRED STEVENS, Belgian, 1828–1906

260. At the Railway Station
Oil on panel, 26¼ x 19¼ in.
Signed: ALFRED STEVENS.
Owned by The Art Institute of Chicago (Munger Collection).

Coll.: A. A. Munger, Chi.

Painted c. 1860.

INTERNATIONAL PAINTING

Nineteenth and Twentieth Centuries

GALLERY 41

EUGÈNE CARRIÈRE, French, 1849–1906

261. Lady with a Dog (1885)
Oil on canvas, 45½ x 34½ in.
Signed: EUGENE CARRIERE, 1885.
Owned by The Art Institute of Chicago (Mr. and Mrs. Martin A. Ryerson Collection).

Coll.: M. A. Ryerson, Chi. (1913).

JEAN-LOUIS FORAIN, French, 1852–1931

262. George Moore Leaving the Opera
Gouache and oil on board, 12½ x 10¼ in.
Signed: FORAIN.
Lent by The Fogg Art Museum, Cambridge, Mass.

Coll.: Kraushaar, N. Y.; Mrs. L. L. Coburn, Chi., No. 11.

Exh.: The Art Inst. of Chi., 1932–3 (repr. in cat., 42).

Painted c. 1885. George Moore (1853–1933), Irish novelist and critic, friend and defender of the Impressionists.

JEAN-LOUIS FORAIN, French, 1852–1931

263. In the Wings (1899)
Oil on canvas, 23¼ x 28⅜ in.
Signed: FORAIN, 1899.
Owned by The Art Institute of Chicago (Mr. and Mrs. Martin A. Ryerson Collection).

Exh.: The Arts Club, Chi., 1922.

Lit.: D. C. Rich, *Bull.*, XXV (1931), 97 (repr.).

JEAN-LOUIS FORAIN, French, 1852–1931

264. Tight-Rope Walker
Oil on canvas, 18⅛ x 15 in.
Signed: FORAIN.
Lent by Mrs. Emily Crane Chadbourne, Chicago.

Lit.: D. C. Rich, *Bull.*, XXV (1931), 96–7, 99 (repr.).

Painted c. 1885.

WALTER GREAVES, English, 1841–1930

265. James McNeill Whistler (1869)
Oil on canvas, 32⅞ x 22⅞ in.
Signed: W. GREAVES, 1869.
Owned by The Art Institute of Chicago.

Coll.: Scott and Fowles, N. Y.

A portrait of the distinguished American artist James McNeill Whistler (1834–1903) in the thirty-fifth year of his life. Greaves painted several replicas with variations.

AUGUSTUS E. JOHN, English, 1879–

266. The Rogue (1923)
Oil on canvas, 29¼ x 24¾ in.
Signed: JOHN, 1923.
Owned by The Art Institute of Chicago (Mr. and Mrs. C. H. Worcester Collection).

JOHN LAVERY, Irish (English), 1857–

267. A Grey Day, Tangier
Oil on canvas, 24½ x 29½ in.
Signed: JOHN LAVERY.
Owned by The Art Institute of Chicago.

BRUNO LILJEFORS, Swedish, 1860–

268. Hawk and Partridge (1900)
Oil on canvas, 31 x 46 in.
Signed: Bruno Liljefors, 1900.
The Charles Deering Collection. Lent by Mr. and Mrs. Chauncey McCormick, Chicago.

ANTONIO MANCINI, Italian, 1852–1930

269. Girl Reclining
Oil on canvas, 23¾ x 38¾ in.
Signed: Venezia A. Mancini
The Charles Deering Collection. Lent by Mr. and Mrs. Chauncey McCormick, Chicago.

WILLIAM ORPEN, Irish, 1878–1931

270. The Old Cabman
Oil on canvas, 30 x 25 in.
Signed: WILLIAM ORPEN.
Owned by The Art Institute of Chicago (Mr. and Mrs. Charles H. Worcester Collection).

Coll.: J. Audley Harvey, 1924; Lord Leverhulme Sale, 1926, 154, No. 211.

WILLIAM ORPEN, Irish, 1878–1931

271. Myself and Venus
Oil on canvas, 36 x 34 in.
Lent by Carnegie Institute, Pittsburgh, Pennsylvania.

Exh.: Carnegie Inst., Pitts., 1910.

Lit.: *The Carnegie Magazine,* V (1931), 188 (repr.); P. G. Konody and S. Dark, *Sir William Orpen,* 1932, 240, appendix 268.

Painted in 1910.
A replica is in the Municipal Gallery, Dublin.

WILLIAM ORPEN, Irish, 1878–1931

272. A Woman in Grey
Oil on canvas, 74 x 49 in.
Signed: ORPEN.
Owned by The Art Institute of Chicago (1912).

Lit.: *Guide,* 1932, 94 (repr.); P. G. Konody and S. Dark, *Sir William Orpen,* 1932, 267.

Painted in 1908.
The model is the artist's wife.

PIERRE CECILE PUVIS DE CHAVANNES, French, 1824–1898

*273. The Fisherman's Family (1887) (Pl. L)
Oil on canvas, 32½ x 28 in.
Signed: P. PUVIS DE CHAVANNES, 1887.
Owned by The Art Institute of Chicago (Mr. and Mrs. Martin A. Ryerson Collection).

Coll.: Durand-Ruel (purchased directly from the artist); E. Aynard, Lyons (Sale, 1913, No. 12, repr. in cat.); M. A. Ryerson, Chi. (1915).

Exh.: Grosvenor Hse., Lond., 1914; Wadsworth Atheneum, Hartford, Conn., 1933, No. 55 (repr. in cat.).

Lit.: Vachon, *Puvis de Chavannes,* 1896, 51 (repr.); T. M. Wood, *Interntl. Stu.,* LIV (1914), 10 (repr.), 11; *Fine Arts Journal,* XXXV (1917), 174, 175 (repr.); L. C., *Bull.,* XVIII (1924), 119–20 [5–8] (repr.); F. J. Mather, Jr., *Modern Painting,* 1927, frontispiece; *Guide,* 1932, 51 (repr.).

The second version. The first painted in 1875, is of larger size, and in the Dresden Gallery. A drawing is No. 930 of the present catalogue.

DANTE GABRIEL ROSSETTI, English, 1828–1882

274. Beata Beatrix
Oil on canvas, 58 x 36⅛ in., predella, 27½ x 36 in.
Signed: GCDR, 1872.
Owned by The Art Institute of Chicago.

Coll.: Wm. Graham; Ch. L. Hutchinson, Chi. (1898).

Exh.: Burlington Fine Arts Club, Lond., 1883, No. 83; Louisiana Purchase Expo., St. Louis, 1904; Albright Art Gallery, Buffalo, 1905; Toledo Mus. of Art, 1912; Wadsworth Atheneum, Hartford, Conn., 1933, No. 61 (repr. in cat.).

Lit.: H. C. Marillier, *Dante Gabriel Rossetti,* 1899, 127, 252, No. 248; *Academy Notes,* I (1905–6), 62–64 (repr.); R. M. F., *Bull.,* XIX (1925), 102, 104 (repr.); *Guide,* 1932, 90 (repr.); F. J. Mather, Jr., *Modern Painting,* 1927, 74 (repr.).

A replica (with predella added) commissioned by Mr. William Graham, of the painting now in the Tate Gall., Lond. A pencil study of the predella was at one time in the coll. of Mr. Russell Rea. Another replica (retouched by F. Madox Brown) belongs to the Corporation Art Gall., Birmingham. For further versions see Marillier, *supra,* 127. According to Rossetti it illustrates Dante's *Vita Nuova,* "embodying symbolically the death of Beatrice as treated in that work. The picture is not intended at all to represent death, but to render it under the semblance of a trance in which Beatrice, seated at a balcony overlooking the city, is suddenly rapt from earth to heaven." On the top of the frame are the words: "Jan. Die 9 Anno 1290," the date of Beatrice's death and the phrase from *Lamentations* "Quomodo Sedet Sola Civitas!" ("How doth the city sit solitary . . ."). At the base: "Mart: Die 31. Anno 1300" (the date of Dante's death) and "Veni, Sponsa, de Libano" ("Come from Lebanon, my spouse." Song of Songs, IV, 8).

JOAQUIN SOROLLA, Spanish, 1863–1923

275. The Two Sisters, Valencia (1909)
Oil on canvas, 68½ x 44 in.
Signed: J. SOROLLA, 1909.
Owned by The Art Institute of Chicago.

EXH.: The Art Inst. of Chi., 1911, No. 7; Copley Society, Boston, 1912; Minneapolis Inst. of Arts, 1915, No. 285; Penn. Academy of the Fine Arts, 1919; Toledo Mus. of Art, 1928.

LIT.: R. Doménech, *Sorolla*, 1909, 84, Fig. 111; ***Bull.*, IV** (1911), 60, 61 (repr.); L. M. Bryant, *What pict. to see in America* (1915), 259 (fig. 168); *Guide*, 1932, 97 (repr.).

ANDERS LEONARD ZORN, SWEDISH, 1860–1920

276. INTERIOR WITH NUDES (1905)
Signed: ZORN, 1905.
Owned by The Art Institute of Chicago.

LIT.: F., *Bull.*, XX (1926), 82, 87 (repr.).

ANDERS LEONARD ZORN, SWEDISH, 1860–1920

277. MIDSUMMER DANCE (1897)
Oil on canvas, 45⅜ x 35⅛ in.
Signed: ZORN, 1897.
The Charles Deering Collection. Lent by Mrs. R. E. Danielson and Mrs. Chauncey McCormick.

LIT.: K. Asplund, *Anders Zorn, his Life and Work*, 1921, 43 and Pl. XVII.

IGNACIO ZULOAGA, SPANISH, 1870–

278. THE ACTRESS CONSUELO
Oil on canvas, 81 x 57½ in.
Signed: I. ZULOAGA.
Owned by The Art Institute of Chicago.

PAINTINGS BY DEGAS AND MONET

GALLERY 42

EDGAR DEGAS, FRENCH, 1834–1917

279. AT THE RACES: "THEY'RE OFF"
Oil on panel, 12 x 18½ in.
Signed: DEGAS.
Lent by The Fogg Art Museum, Cambridge, Massachusetts.

COLL.: Degas (Sale, Paris, 1918, Pt. 1, No. 91, repr. in cat.); E. Bignou, Paris; H. Young, N. Y.; Mrs. L. L. Coburn, Chi.

EXH.: The Art Inst. of Chi., 1932–3, No. 7 (repr. in cat. of the Coburn Coll.).

LIT.: J. B. Manson, *The Life and Works of Edgar Degas*, 1927, Pl. 26.

Painted c. 1870.

EDGAR DEGAS, FRENCH, 1834–1917

280. BALLET DANCER
Oil on canvas, 12 x 10 in.
Signed: DEGAS.
The Charles Deering Collection. Lent by Mr. and Mrs. Chauncey McCormick, Chicago.

COLL.: Durand-Ruel; Ch. Deering, Chi.

Painted c. 1875–8.

EDGAR DEGAS, FRENCH, 1834–1917

281. BALLET GIRLS ON THE STAGE
Pastel on paper, 22½ x 16 in.
Signed: DEGAS.
Owned by The Art Institute of Chicago (Potter Palmer Collection).

COLL.: Durand-Ruel; Mrs. Potter Palmer.

EXH.: The Art Inst. of Chi., 1910, No. 20.

LIT.: J. B. Manson, *The Life and Works of Edgar Degas*, 1927, 47.

Done in 1876.
A variant of the "Dancer on the Stage" in the Louvre; other studies exist, among them a pastel, formerly in the E. Bignou coll.

EDGAR DEGAS, FRENCH, 1834–1917

*282. CARRIAGE AT THE RACES IN PROVENCE (Pl. LIII)
Oil on canvas, 13¾ x 21⅜ in.
Signed: DEGAS.
Lent by The Museum of Fine Arts, Boston, Massachusetts.

COLL.: M. Faure, 1874; G. Durand-Ruel, Paris.

EXH.: First. Exh. of Impressionists, Paris, 1874, No. 63; Exh. of the Second Empire, Musée des Arts Décoratifs, 1922; G. Petit Gall., Paris, 1924, No. 40; Fogg Art Mus., Cambridge, Mass., 1929, No. 25 (repr. in cat. Pl. VII).

LIT.: G. Grappe, *Degas*, 1911, 18 (repr.); P. A. Lemoisne, *Degas* (L'Art de Notre Temps), 1912, Pl. XIX; M. Liebermann, *Degas*, 1912, 6 (repr.); P. Jamot, *Gazette des Beaux-Arts*, Per. 4, XIV (1918), 137, 138 (repr.); P. Lafond, *Degas*, I, 1918, 141 (repr.); J. Meier-Graefe, *Degas*, 1920, Pl. 21 (Eng. trans., 1923, Pl. XXI); Jamot, *Degas*, 1924, 141, Pl. 32; J. B. Manson, *The Life and Works of Edgar Degas*, 1927, 20, 46, Pl. 18; *Boston Mus. of Fine Arts Bull.*, XXV (Feb., 1927), 1 (repr.), 2; *Lettres de Degas*, 1931, No. XL, 65, Note 1; *Burlington Magazine*, LX (1932), 54 (repr.), 62.

The man sitting on the seat is M. Paul Valpinçon, life-long friend of Degas, who often painted him and his daughter.

EDGAR DEGAS, FRENCH, 1834–1917

283. DANCERS PREPARING FOR THE BALLET
Oil on canvas, 29 x 23¼ in.
Signed: DEGAS.
Lent by Mr. and Mrs. Potter Palmer, Chicago.

COLL.: Mrs. Potter Palmer, Chi.

EXH.: The Art Inst. of Chi., 1930.

LIT.: J. B. Manson, *The Life and Works of Edgar Degas*, 1927, 47.

Painted 1878–80.

EDGAR DEGAS, French, 1834–1917

284. The Laundresses

Oil on canvas, 18¼ x 24 in.

Signed: degas.

Lent by Mr. and Mrs. Howard J. Sachs, New York.

Coll.: Coquelin Cadet, Paris, 1879; Sir Wm. Eden.

Exh.: 4th Exh. of the "Impressionists," Paris, 1879, No. 64; M. Knoedler and Co., Lond., 1923, No. 15; "Painters of the 19th Century French School," Paris, 1924, No. 261; "Fifty Years of French Painting," Paris, 1925; Wadsworth Atheneum, Hartford, Conn., 1928, No. 28; Fogg Art Mus., Cambridge, Mass., 1930, No. 30 (repr. in cat. Pl. XX); Fogg Art Mus., 1931, No. 7.

Lit.: G. Grappe, *Degas,* 1911, 29 (repr. in color), 41; P. A. Lemoisne, *Degas* (L'Art de Notre Temps), 86 (repr.); C. B. Borgmeyer, *The Fine Arts Jl.,* XXVIII (1913), 338 (repr.); L. Binyon, *The New Statesman* (December 22, 1917); P. Lafond, *Degas,* I, 1918, 12 (repr.); J. Meier-Graefe, *Degas,* 1920, Pl. 58 (Eng. trans., 1923, Pl. LVIII; P. Jamot, *Degas,* 1924, 125, No. 64, also footnote 10; A. Vollard, *Degas* (Eng. trans., 1927, 73, repr.).

Associated drawings in crayon and pastel, 1st Degas Sale, 1918, Nos. 170 and 174; another, 1st Degas Sale, 1919, No. 319.

EDGAR DEGAS, French, 1834–1917

285. Mlle. Fiocre in the Ballet of "La Source"

Oil on canvas, 65 x 57 in.

Lent by The Brooklyn Museum, Brooklyn, New York.

Coll.: Degas (Sale, 1918, Pt. I, No. 8, repr. in cat.); J. Seligmann, N. Y. (Sale, N. Y., 1921, No. 68, repr. in cat.).

Exh.: Salon, 1868, No. 686; Luxembourg, 1918; Louvre (Orangerie), 1931, No. 37A; Royal Academy, Lond., 1932, No. 391.

Lit.: P. A. Lemoisne, *Degas* (L'Art de Notre Temps), 1912, 39; P. Lafond, *Degas,* I, 1918, 87 (repr.); P. Jamot, *Gaz. des Beaux-Arts,* Per. 4, XIV (1918), 148, 149 (repr.); *Brooklyn Mus. Quart.,* VIII (1921), 106 (repr.); H. E. Field, *The Arts,* I (Jan., 1921), 10 (repr.); Jamot, *Degas,* 1924, 57, 58, 123, 135–6 and Pl. 18; J. B. Manson, *The Life and Works of Edgar Degas,* 1927, 8; L. M. Sill, *The American Mag. of Art,* XXIII (1931), 433–4 (repr.).

Painted in 1868. Often wrongly credited to The Metropolitan Museum of Art.
A painted study of Mlle. Fiocre is in the coll. of Mme. Friedmann, Paris. Another study (pastel, head and shoulders) was in the 2nd Degas Sale of 1918 (No. 96). See Jamot, *Degas,* 136, for notices of other preliminary works. Studies for the hands are reproduced by M. Guérin, *Gazette des Beaux-Arts,* Per. 5, XVII (1928), 377–8.

EDGAR DEGAS, French, 1834–1917

*286. The Millinery Shop (Pl. LIII)

Oil on canvas, 39 x 43¼ in.

Owned by The Art Institute of Chicago (Mr. and Mrs. L. L. Coburn Collection).

Coll.: Durand-Ruel (purchased from the artist); Mrs. L. L. Coburn, Chi.

Lit.: D. C. Rich, *Bull.,* XXVI (1932), 69 (repr.).

A preliminary charcoal drawing, retouched with pastel, appeared in the 2nd Degas Sale, 1918, No. 251.
Painted c. 1882.

EDGAR DEGAS, French, 1834–1917

287. The Morning Bath (c. 1883)

Pastel on paper, 27¾ x 17 in.

Signed: degas.

Owned by The Art Institute of Chicago (Potter Palmer Collection), 1922.

Coll.: Durand-Ruel; Mrs. Potter Palmer, Chi. (1896).

Exh.: The Art Inst. of Chi., 1910.

Lit.: J. B. Manson, *The Life and Works of Edgar Degas,* 1927, 47; D. C. Rich, *Bull.,* XXIII (1929), 127 (repr.); Rich, *Pantheon,* XI (March, 1933), 76 (repr.).

Done about 1883.

EDGAR DEGAS, French, 1834–1917

288. Race Course; Before the Start (1884)

Oil on canvas, 18¼ x 21¾ in.

Signed: degas '84.

Lent by the Trustees of the Estate of Miss Lizzie P. Bliss and through The Museum of Modern Art, New York.

Coll.: Pope, Farmington, Conn.

Exh.: The Mus. of Mod. Art, N. Y., No. 59 (repr. in cat.); Addison Gall. of Amer. Art, Andover, Mass., 1931, No. 38; John Herron Art Inst., Indianapolis, Ind., 1932, No. 35 (repr. in cat. Pl. 6).

Lit.: J. Meier-Graefe, *Degas,* 1920, Pl. 78 (Eng. trans., 1923, Pl. LXXVII); G. Pène Du Bois, *The Arts,* XVII (1931), 606 (repr.).

A charcoal drawing for the right hand horseman appeared in the 2nd Degas Sale of 1919, No. 203-b.

EDGAR DEGAS, French, 1834–1917

*289. Uncle and Niece (Pl. LIV)

Oil on canvas, 38½ x 45½ in.

Owned by The Art Institute of Chicago (Mr. and Mrs. L. L. Coburn Collection).

Coll.: Bazzi, Naples; Wildenstein, N. Y.; Mrs. L. L. Coburn, Chi.

Exh.: XVth Biennial Expo., Venice, 1926, No. 1525; Fogg Art Mus., Cambridge, Mass., 1929, No. 34 (repr.); The Art Inst. of Chi., 1929–30, 1932, No. 6 (repr. in cat. of the Coburn Coll.).

Lit.: J. B. Manson, *The Life and Works of Edgar Degas,* 1927, 11–2, Pl. 5; D. C. Rich, *Bull.,* XXIII (1929), 125–7 (repr.); Rich, *Bull.,* XXVI (1932), 68; W. Hausenstein, *Pantheon,* VII (1931), 162 (repr.).

Painted in Italy c. 1862. The models are relatives of the artist: Edouard de Gas and his niece, Lucy de Gas. A study in pencil and charcoal, probably for the head of the child, was in the 2nd Degas Sale, 1919, No. 96c. Sketches in pencil for the head of Edouard de Gas appeared in the same sale, No. 131.

EDGAR DEGAS, French, 1834–1917

290. Woman with Boa

Pastel and oil on canvas, 33¼ x 29¼ in.

Lent by Mr. Joseph Winterbotham, Burlington, Vermont.

Coll.: Degas (Sale, Paris, 1918, Pt. I, No. 116, repr. in cat.); J. Seligmann, N. Y. (Sale, 1921, No. 34, repr. in cat.); Hughes, Philadelphia; Seligmann-Sharp Sale, N.Y., 1926, No. 171 (repr. in cat.).

Lit.: *The Arts,* XVI (1930), 328 (repr.), 333.

A portrait of Mme. D. M. .... done c. 1883–5.
A pastel study is in the coll. of A. Rouart, Paris; a pastel of the head was in the 2nd Degas Sale, 1918, No. 88; a drawing of the figure (charcoal retouched with white) was in the same sale, No. 348.

CLAUDE MONET, French, 1840–1926

290A. Antibes

Oil on canvas, 25½ x 32 in.

Signed: claude monet, '84.

Owned by The Art Institute of Chicago (Potter Palmer Collection).

Exh.: The Art Inst. of Chi., 1910, No. 33.

CLAUDE MONET, French, 1840–1926

*291. Argenteuil-on-the-Seine (1868) (Pl. LIV)

Oil on canvas, 32 x 39 in.

Signed: cl. monet, 1868.

Owned by The Art Institute of Chicago (Potter Palmer Collection).

Lit.: *Bull.,* XV (1921), 160 (repr.); *Ibid.,* XIX (1925), 18 (repr.); *Guide,* 1932, 59 (repr.).

CLAUDE MONET, French, 1840–1926

292. The Beach at Sainte-Adresse (1867)

Oil on canvas, 28 x 41¼ in.

Signed: claude monet '67.

Owned by The Art Institute of Chicago (Mr. and Mrs. L. L. Coburn Collection).

Coll.: Durand-Ruel (purchased from artist); Mrs. L. L. Coburn, Chi.

Exh.: The Art Inst. of Chi., 1932, No. 19 (repr. in cat. of the Coburn Coll.).

Lit.: G. Geffroy, *Monet,* 1922, opp. 40 (repr.); C. Mauclair, *Monet,* 1927, Pl. 6; X. Lathom, *Monet,* 1931, Pl. VI; D. C. Rich, *Bull.,* XXVI (1932), 66–7 (repr.).

CLAUDE MONET, French, 1840–1926

293. Boats in Winter Quarters, Etretat (1885)

Oil on canvas, 28½ x 36½ in.

Signed: claude monet '85.

Owned by The Art Institute of Chicago (Potter Palmer Collection).

Coll.: Durand-Ruel; Mrs. Potter Palmer, Chi. (1893).

Lit.: M. C., *Bull.,* XIX (1925), 21 (repr.); *Guide,* 1932, 60 (repr.); D. C. Rich, *Pantheon,* XI (March, 1933), 75 (repr.).

Several versions exist, painted from different angles.

CLAUDE MONET, French, 1840–1926

294. Charing Cross, London (1901)

Oil on canvas, 25 x 36 in.

Signed: claude monet, 1901.

Owned by The Art Institute of Chicago (Mr. and Mrs. Martin A. Ryerson Collection).

Coll.: Durand-Ruel; M. A. Ryerson, Chi. (1916).

Exh.: Durand-Ruel, Paris, 1904.

Lit.: G. Kahn, *Gazette des Beaux-Arts,* Per. 3, XXXII (1904), 88.

In 1904 Durand-Ruel exhibited twenty-seven paintings of the Thames, of which eight were of this subject.

CLAUDE MONET, French, 1840–1926

295. The Cliff Walk (1882)

Oil on canvas, 26½ x 32 in.

Signed: claude monet, '82.

Owned by the Art Institute of Chicago (Mr. and Mrs. L. L. Coburn Collection).

Coll.: Durand-Ruel; Mrs. L. L. Coburn, Chi.

Exh.: Grafton Gall., Lond., 1905; The Art Inst. of Chi., 1932, No. 22 (repr. in cat. of the Coburn Coll.).

Lit.: C. L. Borgmeyer, *The Fine Arts Journal,* XXVIII (1913), 328 (repr.); D. C. Rich, *Bull.,* XXVI (1932), 66.

CLAUDE MONET, French, 1840–1926

296. Coast Guard's Shack (1897)

Oil on canvas, 26 x 36½ in.

Signed: monet, '97.

Owned by the Art Institute of Chicago (Mr. and Mrs. Martin A. Ryerson Collection).

CLAUDE MONET, French, 1840–1926

296A. Coast Guard's Shack

Oil on canvas, 23 x 28½ in.

Signed: claude monet.

Lent by The Fogg Art Museum of Harvard University, Cambridge, Massachusetts.

Coll.: Durand-Ruel; Mrs. L. L. Coburn, Chicago.

Exh.: The Art Institute of Chi., 1932, No. 20 (repr. in cat.).

CLAUDE MONET, French, 1840–1926

297. Fruit: Apples and Grapes

Oil on canvas, 25¼ x 31⅞ in.

Signed: claude monet 1880.

Owned by the Art Institute of Chicago (Mr. and Mrs. Martin A. Ryerson Collection).

Coll.: Durand-Ruel; M. A. Ryerson, Chi. (1915).

Lit.: M. C., *Bull.,* XIX (1925), 19 (repr.).

One of a series of still-life compositions painted in 1880.

CLAUDE MONET, French, 1840–1926

298. The Artist's Garden at Argenteuil

Oil on canvas, 24 x 28½ in.

Signed: claude monet.

Owned by the Art Institute of Chicago (Mr. and Mrs. Martin A. Ryerson Collection).

Coll.: Durand-Ruel; M. A. Ryerson, Chi. (1915).

Painted in 1873.

CLAUDE MONET, French, 1840–1926
299. The Old St. Lazare Station: Train for Normandy (1877)
Oil on canvas, 31½ x 23½ in.
Signed: claude monet '77.
Owned by the Art Institute of Chicago (Mr. and Mrs. Martin A. Ryerson Collection).

Coll.: Durand-Ruel; M. A. Ryerson, Chi. (1913).

Lit.: G. Geffroy, *Claude Monet,* 1922, opp. 136 (repr.); *Bull.,* XIX (1925), 19 (repr.); C. Mauclair, *Monet* (The Masters of Modern Art), 1927, Pl. 20; F. Fels, *Monet* (Les Peintres Français Nouveaux, No. 22), 45 (repr.); X. Lathom, *Claude Monet,* 1931, Pl. XVI (repr.).

Several versions exist, among them the Louvre (Caillebotte Coll.) and the pictures in the collections of M. Donop de Monchy, Paris, and Herr J. Staub, Männedorf, Switzerland.

CLAUDE MONET, French, 1840–1926
300. Still Life: Pheasants and Partridge (1880)
Oil on canvas, 26¾ x 34¼ in.
Signed: claude monet.
Lent by Mr. and Mrs. Potter Palmer, Chicago.

Coll.: Mrs. Potter Palmer I, Chi.

Exh.: The Art Inst. of Chi., 1910, No. 39.

Lit.: F. Fels, *Monet* (Les Peintres Français Nouveaux, No. 22), 15 (repr.); C. Mauclair, *Monet* (Les Peintres Français Nouveaux, No. 22), Pl. 28.

Painted in 1880. An almost exact replica was exhibited at the Thannhauser Gall., Berlin, 1928, No. 29.

CAMILLE PISSARRO, French, 1831–1903
301. "Cafe-au-Lait" (1881)
Oil on canvas, 25 x 21½ in.
Signed: pissarro, 1881.
Owned by The Art Institute of Chicago (Potter Palmer Collection).

Coll.: Durand-Ruel; Mrs. Potter Palmer, Chi. (1892).

ALFRED SISLEY, French, 1839–1899
302. Sand Heaps (1875)
Oil on canvas, 21⅛ x 25⅝ in.
Signed: sisley '75.
Owned by the Art Institute of Chicago (Mr. and Mrs. Martin A. Ryerson Collection).

Coll.: Durand-Ruel; M. A. Ryerson, Chi.

ALFRED SISLEY, French, 1839–1899
303. Street in Moret
Oil on canvas, 24 x 29 in.
Signed: sisley.
Owned by The Art Institute of Chicago (Potter Palmer Collection).

Coll.: Durand-Ruel; Mrs. Potter Palmer, Chi. (1894).

Exh.: World's Columbian Expo., Chi., 1893, No. 3025; France, Cat. No. 48; Art Inst. of Chi., 1910.

Lit.: D. C. Rich, *Pantheon,* XI (March, 1933), 73 (repr.).

Painted c. 1890.

PAINTINGS BY CEZANNE

GALLERY 43

PAUL CEZANNE, French, 1839–1906
304. Auvers-sur-Oise, Village Panorama
Oil on canvas, 25½ x 31½ in.
Owned by The Art Institute of Chicago (Mrs. L. L. Coburn Collection).

Coll.: Chocquet, Paris (Sale, 1899); Durand-Ruel, Paris; Mrs. L. L. Coburn, Chi.

Exh.: Grafton Gallery, London, Jan.–Feb. 1905; The Art Inst. of Chi., 1932–3, No. 1 (repr. in cat. of the Coburn Coll.).

Painted in 1873.

PAUL CEZANNE, French, 1839–1906
305. The Basket of Apples
Oil on canvas, 24⅜ x 31 in.
Signed: p. cezanne.
Owned by The Art Institute of Chicago (Helen Birch Bartlett Memorial).

Coll.: J. Hessel, Paris (Sale, 1913).

Exh.: Fogg Art Mus., Cambridge, Mass., 1929, No. 6 (Pl. XXIV of cat.).

Lit.: C. Lewis Hind, The Post Impressionists, 1911, 74 (repr.); A. Vollard, *Cézanne,* 1914, opp. 102, Pl. 33. *The Fine Arts Journal,* XXXV (May, 1917), 335 (repr.); C. Coquiot, *Paul Cézanne,* 1919, 246; J. Meier-Graefe, *Cézanne und sein Kreis,* 1922, 185 (repr.); R. M. F., *Bull.,* XX (1926), 61–3 (repr.); F. Watson, *The Arts,* IX (1926), 304 (repr.), 310; *The Art News,* XXIV (June 12, 1926, supplement), 28 (repr.); M. D. Zabel, *Art and Archaeology,* XXVI (1928), 227 (repr.); *Cat. of the Helen Birch Bartlett Memorial,* 1929, 8–9 (repr.), 56.

Painted c. 1885. Reproduced by Maurice Denis in ceiling of Petit Palais, Paris.

PAUL CEZANNE, French, 1839–1906
306. The Bathers
Oil on canvas, 20 x 24¼ in.
Lent by Mrs. Robert Rutherford McCormick, Chicago.

Coll.: Zoubaloff, Paris; P. Rosenberg, Paris; Chester H. Johnson Gall., Chi.

Exh.: Mus. of Mod. Art, N. Y., Summer, 1930, No. 15; Renaissance Society, Univ. of Chi., 1931.

Painted c. 1890. A very similar composition is in the Vollard Coll., Paris.

PAUL CEZANNE, French, 1839–1906
*307. The Card Players (Pl. LX)
Oil on canvas, 25⅝ x 32½ in.
Lent by Mr. Stephen C. Clark, New York.

Coll.: Bernheim, Paris.

Exh.: Grosvenor Hse., Lond., 1914 (repr. in cat. Pl. 7); Bernheim Gall., Paris, 1926, No. 39.

Lit.: *Cézanne* (Bernheim-Jeune, Ed.), 1914, Pl. XLIII; *International Studio,* LIV (1914), 12 (repr.); A. Vollard, *Cézanne,* 1914, Pl. 18 (opp. 56); M. Denis, *L'Amour de l'Art,* I (1921), 281 (repr.); J. Meier-Graefe, *Cézanne und sein Kreis,* 1922, Pl. 237 (Eng. trans., 1927, Pl. XCVI); G. Rivière, *Le Maître Paul Cézanne,* 1923, 168 (repr.), 218; T. L. Klingsor, *Cézanne* (Masters of Modern Art), 1924, Pl. 32; J. Gasquet, *Cézanne,* 1926, opp. 18 (repr.); R. Fry, *Cézanne,* 1927, 72 and Fig. 36, Pl. XXVI; E. d'Ors, *Paul Cézanne,* 1930, Pl. 40.

Painted in 1892.
A painted study for the seated figure in the center is in the Worcester Art Museum, Worcester, Mass. Vollard (*supra*) reproduces a wash drawing for the seated figure to the left and a pencil study for the seated figure to the right.
Another version (with an additional figure and changes) was in the Vollard Coll., Paris and is now in The Barnes Foundation, Merion, Pa.

PAUL CEZANNE, French, 1839–1906
308. Chocquet in his Study
Oil on canvas, 18¼ x 15 in.
Signed: p. cezanne.
Lent by the Trustees of the Estate of Miss Lizzie P. Bliss, New York, through The Museum of Modern Art, New York.

Coll.: Chocquet; Durand-Ruel; Miss Lizzie Bliss, N. Y.

Exh.: Salon d'Automne, Paris, 1904; Mus. of Mod. Art, N. Y., 1929, No. 9 (repr. in cat.); John Herron Art Inst., Indianapolis, 1932, No. 6; Mus. of Mod. Art, N. Y., 1931, No. 6 (repr. in cat.); Addison Gall. of Am. Art, Andover, Mass., 1931, No. 6.

Lit.: A. Vollard, *P. Cézanne,* 1914, Fig. 15, opp. 46; J. Meier-Graefe, *Cézanne u. sein Kreis,* 1922, Pl. 128; G. Rivière, *Le Maître Paul Cézanne,* 1923, 204; G. Pène Du Bois, *The Arts,* XVII (1931), 603 (repr.).

Painted in 1877. A study (head) was in the coll. of Degas and sold in the 1918 Sale, No. 15. Chocquet was a famous *amateur* of pictures and an early friend and defender of Cézanne, who painted several portraits of him.

PAUL CEZANNE, French, 1839–1906
*309. L'Estaque (Pl. LXI)
Oil on canvas, 31½ x 38½ in.
Owned by the Art Institute of Chicago (Mr. and Mrs. Martin A. Ryerson Collection).

Coll.: M. A. Ryerson, Chi.

Exh.: Mus. of Mod. Art, N. Y., 1929, No. 18 (repr. in cat.).

Lit.: J. Gasquet, *L'Amour de l'Art,* I (1921), 263 (repr.); D. C. Rich, *Bull.,* XXIV (1930), 113–117 (repr.).

Painted c. 1886–8.

PAUL CEZANNE, French, 1839–1906
*310. Flowers and Fruit (Pl. LXII)
Oil on canvas, 23 x 16½ in.
Owned by the Art Institute of Chicago (Mr. and Mrs. L. L. Coburn Collection).

Coll.: Durand-Ruel, Paris; Mrs. L. L. Coburn.

Exh.: Grafton Gall., Lond., 1905; The Art Inst. of Chi., 1932–3, No. 3 (repr. in cat. of the Coburn Coll.).

Lit.: T. L. Klingsor, *Cézanne* (Masters of Modern Art), 1924, Pl. 20; D. C. Rich, *Bull.,* XXVI (1932), 65 (repr.). 70–1.

Painted c. 1885.

PAUL CEZANNE, French, 1839–1906
†311. The "Jas de Bouffan" (Aix-en-Provence)
Oil on canvas, 25½ x 32 in.
Lent by M. Knoedler and Co., New York.

Coll.: Baron D. Cochin, Paris.

Exh.: Knoedler Gall., N. Y., 1931, No. 23 (repr. in cat.).

Lit.: *Cézanne* (Bernheim-Jeune, Ed.), 1914, Pl. LV (as "Les Marronniers"); *L'Art Moderne,* 1919, I, Pl XXXVI.

Painted 1887.

PAUL CEZANNE, French, 1839–1906
†312. Madame Cezanne (?) in Blue
Oil on canvas, 29 x 24 in.
Lent by M. Knoedler and Co., New York.

Coll.: A. Vollard, Paris; H. Halvorsen, Oslo; Galerie Thannhauser, Berlin.

Exh.: Knoedler Gall., N. Y., 1930, No. 2 (repr. in cat.); Wilmington, Delaware, Fine Arts Society, 1931; Detroit Inst. of Arts, 1931, No. 16.

Lit.: E. d'Ors, *Paul Cézanne,* 1930, Pl. 4.

Painted c. 1890–5.

PAUL CEZANNE, French, 1839–1906
313. Man in Blue
Oil on canvas, 32 x 25 in.
Lent by Mr. A. Conger Goodyear, New York.

Coll.: A. Vollard, Paris; G. F. Reber, Lausanne; Wildenstein and Co., Inc., N. Y.

Exh.: Albright Art Gall., Buffalo, 1928, No. 3 (repr. in cat., 35); Fogg Art Mus., Cambridge, Mass., 1929, No. 7 (repr. in cat., Pl. XXV); Cleveland Mus. of Art, 1929; Wildenstein Gall., N. Y., 1928.

Lit.: J. Meier-Graefe, *Cézanne* (Eng. trans.), 1927, Pl. XCIV; E. B. Jones, *Parnassus,* I (Apr., 1929), 13 (repr.); F. Watson, *The Arts,* XVI (1930), 332 (repr.), 333; *Bull. of the Cleveland Mus. of Art,* XVI (1929), 154 (repr.).

Painted 1892–5.

PAUL CEZANNE, French, 1839–1906
*314. Portrait of a Girl (Pl. LXII)
Oil on canvas, 36 x 28 in.
Lent by Dr. and Mrs. Harry Bakwin, New York.

Coll.: A. Vollard, Paris.

Exh.: Mus. of Mod. Art, 1929, No. 8 (repr. in cat.).

Lit.: *CreativeArt,* IX (1931), 272 (repr.).

Painted c. 1888–90.

PAUL CEZANNE, French, 1839–1906

†315. Provençal Landscape

Oil on canvas, 26½ x 36 in.

Lent by Marie Harriman Gallery, New York.

Coll.: Hessel, Paris; G. F. Reber, Lausanne.

Exh.: Harriman Gall., N. Y., 1933.

Lit.: J. Meier-Graefe, *Cézanne und sein Kreis*, 1922, 216 (repr.).

Painted c. 1885.

PAUL CEZANNE, French, 1839–1906

*316. The Road that Turns (Pl. LXI)

Oil on canvas, 24½ x 29¾ in.

Lent by The Smith College Museum of Art, Northampton, Massachusetts.

Coll.: Auguste Renoir, Paris; Renou, Paris.

Lit.: *Bull. of the Smith College Mus. of Art*, No. 13 (1932), 31 (repr.); *Parnassus*, IV (Oct., 1932) 19, 20 (repr.); *The American Magazine of Art*, XXIV (1932), 224 (repr.).

Painted 1888–1890.

PAUL CEZANNE, French, 1839–1906

317. Road to Auvers

Oil on canvas, 18½ x 21¾ in.

Signed: P. CEZANNE.

Lent by Mr. John Nicholas Brown, Providence, Rhode Island.

Coll.: M. de Rochecouste, Paris.

Exh.: Knoedler Gall., N. Y., 1928, No. 23 (repr. in cat.); R. I. School of Design; Fogg Art Mus., Cambridge, Mass., 1929, No. 9 (repr. in cat., Pl. XXVI); Mus. of Mod. Art, 1929, No. 15 (repr. in cat.).

Painted 1880–2.

PAUL CEZANNE, French, 1839–1906

318. Seated Man

Oil on canvas, 21 x 17½ in.

Lent from The Adolph Lewisohn Collection, New York.

Coll.: A. Vollard, Paris; P. Cassirer, Berlin; Galerie Thannhauser, Berlin; W. Huber, Zurich.

Lit.: E. d'Ors, *Paul Cézanne*, 1930, Pl. 7.

Painted c. 1892–4.

PAUL CEZANNE, French, 1839–1906

†318A. Siesta

Oil on canvas, 21½ x 25¾ in.

Lent by Mr. Josef Stransky, New York, through The Worcester Art Museum, Worcester Massachusetts.

PAUL CEZANNE, French, 1839–1906

*319. Still Life with Apples (Pl. LX)

Oil on canvas, 27 x 36½ in.

Lent by the Trustees of the Estate of Miss Lizzie Bliss, New York, through The Museum of Modern Art, New York.

Coll.: Gangniat, Paris; Kelekian, N. Y. (Sale, 1920).

Exh.: Brooklyn Mus., 1926; The Mus. of Mod. Art, N. Y., 1929, No. 24 (repr. in cat.); John Herron Art Inst., Indianapolis, 1932, No. 11 (Pl. 1 of cat.); The Mus. of Mod. Art, N. Y., 1931, No. 11 (Pl. 11 of cat.); The Metro. Mus. of Art, N. Y., 1931, No. 18 (Pl. 18 of cat.); Addison Gall. of Am. Art, Andover, Mass., 1931, No. 11.

Lit.: E. Faure, *Cézanne*, 1923, Pl. 32; *Bull. of the John Herron Art Inst.*, XIX (1932), 10 (repr.).

PAUL CEZANNE, French, 1839–1906

†320. Still Life with Clock

Oil on canvas, 21¾ x 29¼ in.

Lent by Wildenstein and Co., Inc., New York.

Coll.: Baron Kohner, Budapest.

Exh.: Royal Academy, Lond., 1932, No. 441 (repr. in cat.).

Lit.: J. Meier-Graefe, *Cézanne und sein Kreis*, 1922, Pl. 117 (Eng. trans. 1927, Pl. V); G. Rivière, *Le Maître Paul Cézanne*, 1923, 199; K. Pfister, *Cézanne*, No. 199, and Pl. 25; *Formes*, No. XX (December, 1931), 187 (repr. opposite); *Gaz. des Beaux Arts*, Per. 6, VII (1932), 98, Fig. 1; *Apollo*, XV (1932), 72 (repr.); *Pantheon*, IX (1932), 90 (repr.).

Painted c. 1870.

PAINTINGS CHIEFLY BY MANET AND RENOIR

GALLERY 45

ALBERT ANDRE, French, 1869–

321. Portrait of Renoir (1914)

Oil on canvas, 26⅜ x 32½ in.

Signed: ALBERT ANDRE.

Owned by The Art Institute of Chicago.

HENRI FANTIN-LATOUR, French, 1836–1904

322. Portrait of Edouard Manet

Oil on canvas, 46 x 35½ in.

Signed: A MON AMI MANET, FANTIN, 1867.

Owned by The Art Institute of Chicago.

Coll.: Durand-Ruel, Paris.

Exh.: Salon, Paris, 1867, No. 571; Retrospective Expo., Paris, 1889; Retrospective, Paris, 1900; Fogg Art Mus., Cambridge, Mass., 1929, No. 40; Mus. of French Art, 1930, No. 32.

Lit.: A. Jullien, *Les Arts*, V (1906), No. 53, 30 (repr.), 31–2; F. Gibson, *Fantin-Latour*, n. d., 98 and Pl. 7; C. Mauclair, *Great French Painters*, n. d., 68 (repr.); *Catalogue de Mme. Fantin-Latour*, 1911, 42, No. 296; E. Moreau-Nélaton, *Manet*, I, 1926, Fig. 97; G. Kahn, *Fantin-Latour*, 1927, 45–6 (repr.); *Guide*, 1932, 58 (repr.).

Portrait of the leader of the Impressionists, Edouard Manet (1832–1883), in the thirty-fifth year of his life.

EDOUARD MANET, French, 1832–1883

323. Boulogne Roadstead

Oil on canvas, 28 x 35½ in.

Signed: MANET and E. M. (on sail).

Owned by The Art Institute of Chicago (Potter Palmer Collection).

For collections, exhibitions and literature see Tabarant, No. 107; Jamot-Wildenstein-Bataille, I, No. 92; II, Pl. 307.

Painted in 1865.

EDOUARD MANET, French, 1832–1883

324. Bull Fight

Oil on canvas, 18½ x 23¼ in.

Signed: MANET.

Lent by Mrs. Martin A. Ryerson, Chicago.

For collections, exhibitions and literature see Tabarant, No. 115 and Jamot-Wildenstein-Bataille, I, No. 121; II, Pl. 324. Add:

Exh.: Louvre (Orangerie), 1932, No. 24 (repr. in cat.).

Painted after Manet's return from Spain, 1866.

EDOUARD MANET, French, 1832–1883

*325. Departure of the Folkestone Boat (Pl. LV)

Oil on canvas, 23¼ x 28 in.

Signed: MANET.

Lent by Mr. Carroll Tyson, Philadelphia, Pennsylvania.

For collections, exhibitions and literature see Tabarant, No. 143 and Jamot-Wildenstein-Bataille, I, No. 163; II, Pl. 313. Add:

Exh.: Louvre (Orangerie), 1932, No. 36 (repr. in cat.).

Painted from the window of the Folkestone Hotel at Boulogne-sur-Mer, the summer of 1869. The figures of Mme. Manet and Léon Koëlla-Leenhoff (her son) may be made out in the crowd.
Another version (less complete) is in the Oskar Reinhart Coll., Winterthur.

EDOUARD MANET, French, 1832–1883

326. In the Garden

Oil on canvas, 17½ x 21¼ in.

Signed: MANET.

Lent by Mr. and Mrs. J. Watson Webb, New York.

For collections, exhibitions and literature see Tabarant, No. 139 and Jamot-Wildenstein-Bataille, I, No. 179; II, Pl. 174. Add:

Exh.: Louvre (Orangerie), 1932, No. 44 (repr. in cat.).

Painted in 1870–71. A wash drawing closely related is in the coll. of J. Seligmann and Co., New York.
Edma Morisot, and Mme. Himmes both posed for the figure of the young woman; Tiburce Morisot posed for the young man; the baby is the oldest daughter of Mme. Pontillon.

EDOUARD MANET, French, 1832–1883

*327. Jesus Mocked by the Soldiers (Pl. LVI)

Oil on canvas, 74 x 57 in.

Signed: MANET.

Owned by the Art Institute of Chicago (James Deering Collection).

For collections, exhibitions and literature see Tabarant, No. 101 (wrongly credited to The Deering Coll.) and Jamot-Wildenstein-Bataille, I, No. 113 (where the same error is repeated); II, Pl. 321. Add: *Guide,* 1932, 57 (repr.).

Janvier, a professional model, posed for the figure of the Christ.
Painted in 1865.

EDOUARD MANET, French, 1832–1883

328. Le Journal Illustré

Oil on canvas, 24 x 18¾ in.

Signed: MANET.

Owned by the Art Institute of Chicago (Mr. and Mrs. L. L. Coburn Collection).

For collections, exhibitions and literature see Tabarant, No. 293 (as "Liseuse à la Brasserie") and Jamot-Wildenstein-Bataille, I, No. 334 (name wrongly given as Mrs. Lewis C. Coburn); II, Pl. 334. Add:

Exh.: The Art Inst. of Chi., 1932–33, No. 17 (repr. in cat. of Coburn Coll., 43).

Lit.: D. C. Rich, *Bull.,* XXVI (1932), 67 (repr.).

Painted 1878–9. The model's nickname was Trognette, and the picture is sometimes known under this title.

EDOUARD MANET, French, 1832–1883

329. The Music Lesson

Oil on canvas, 55 x 67 in.

Signed: MANET.

The Charles Deering Collection.

Lent by Mr. and Mrs. R. E. Danielson, Boston.

For collections, exhibitions and literature see Tabarant, No. 155 and Jamot-Wildenstein-Bataille, I, No. 177 (wrongly credited to The Art Institute of Chicago); II, Pl. 168.

Painted 1869–70. The man is the poet and friend of Manet, Zacharie Astruc.
A study for the woman is in the Coll. of M. Emile Bernheim, Paris. (Jamot-Wildenstein-Bataille, No. 176.)

EDOUARD MANET, French, 1832–1883

330. The Philosopher

Oil on canvas, 73¾ x 42½ in.

Signed: MANET.

Owned by The Art Institute of Chicago (Arthur Jerome Eddy Collection).

For collections, exhibitions and literature, etc., see Tabarant, No. 104, and Jamot-Wildenstein-Bataille, I, No. 111; II, Pl. 29. Add:

Lit.: *The Eddy Collection of Modern Paintings and Sculpture,* 1930, 18, 20, 21 and No. 11 (repr.).

Etched by Manet (see E. Moreau-Nélaton, *Manet, Graveur et Lithographe,* No. 35).
Eugène Manet, brother of the artist, was the model.
Painted in 1865.

EDOUARD MANET, French, 1832–1883

331. The Philosopher

Oil on canvas, 74 x 43 in.

Signed: MANET.

Owned by The Art Institute of Chicago (Munger Collection).

For collections, exhibitions and literature see Tabarant, No. 105 and Jamot-Wildenstein-Bataille, I, No. 112; II, Pl. 30. Add: *Guide,* 1932, 55 (repr.).

Companion to No. 330. Painted 1865.

EDOUARD MANET, French, 1832–1883

332. The Race-Course at Longchamp

Oil on canvas, 17 x 32½ in.

Signed: MANET, 18. .

Owned by The Art Institute of Chicago (Potter Palmer Collection).

For collections, exhibitions and literature see Tabarant, No. 96, and Jamot-Wildenstein-Bataille, I, No. 202; II, 358. Add: *Guide,* 1932, 56 (repr.).

Tabarant believes it to have been done in 1864, the date of the version formerly in the Jules Strauss Coll., Paris; Jamot-Wildenstein-Bataille call it a re-handling of the subject, painted in 1872. In that year Manet made a lithograph of it (see E. Moreau-Nélaton, *Manet, Graveur,* 1906, No. 85). Compare a water color (with portion added to the left) today in the collection of Mr. Grenville Winthrop, N. Y.

EDOUARD MANET, French, 1832–1883

*333. The Railroad (1873) (Pl. LV)

Oil on canvas, 36¾ x 44⅛ in.

Signed: MANET, 1873.

Lent by Mr. Horace Havemeyer, New York.

For collections, exhibitions and literature see Tabarant, No. 185 (wrongly credited to the Metropolitan Museum) and Jamot-Wildenstein-Bataille, I, No. 231; II, Pl. 171.

Painted in the garden of the painter, Alphonse Hirsch, No. 58, Rue de Rome. Victorine Meurend, Manet's most famous model, posed for the figure of the young woman. See Jamot-Wildenstein-Bataille for notices of studies and drawings.

BERTHE MORISOT, French, 1841–1895

*334. Woman at Her Toilet (Pl. LIX)

Oil on canvas, 25¾ x 31¾ in.

Signed: BERTHE MORISOT.

Owned by The Art Institute of Chicago.

Coll.: P. Rosenberg, Paris; Wildenstein, N. Y.

Exh.: Durand-Ruel, Paris, 1896; Arts Club of Chi., 1932.

Lit.: R. M. F., *Bull.,* XVIII (1924), 50–1 (repr.); *Guide,* 1932, 62 (repr.); D. C. Rich, *Pantheon,* XI (Mar., 1933), 77 (repr.).

AUGUSTE RENOIR, French, 1841–1919

335. Algerian Girl (1883)

Oil on canvas, 15½ x 13 in.

Signed: A FOURNIER, A. RENOIR, '83.

Owned by the Art Institute of Chicago (Mr. and Mrs. L. L. Coburn Collection).

Coll.: Fournier, Paris; Durand-Ruel, N. Y.; Chester H. Johnson Gall., Chi.; Mrs. L. L. Coburn, Chi.

Exh.: The Art Inst. of Chi., 1932, No. 34 (repr. in cat. of the Coburn Coll.).

Lit.: A. Vollard, *Renoir* (Eng. trans.), 1925, 241; J. Meier-Graefe, *Auguste Renoir,* 1929, 174, No. 160.

Mlle. Fournier, who posed for the picture, was the daughter of a French official. She appears in the "Fillette au Faucon," in the Durand-Ruel Coll.

AUGUSTE RENOIR, French, 1841–1919

336. At the Milliner's

Oil on canvas, 12¾ x 9⅝ in.

Signed: RENOIR.

Lent by The Fogg Art Museum, Cambridge, Massachusetts.

Coll.: H. Young, N. Y.; Mrs. L. L. Coburn, Chi.

Exh.: The Art Inst. of Chi., 1932, No. 29 (repr. in cat. of Coburn Coll.).

Lit.: J. Meier-Graefe, *Auguste Renoir,* 1929, 92, No. 75 (repr.).

Painted c. 1876.

AUGUSTE RENOIR, French, 1841–1919

*337. At the Piano (Pl. LVI)

Oil on canvas, 35⅞ x 28⅛ in.

Signed: RENOIR.

Lent by Mrs. Martin A. Ryerson, Chicago.

Coll.: Durand-Ruel.

Exh.: The Renaissance Society, Univ. of Chi., 1931, 1933.

Painted c. 1879.

AUGUSTE RENOIR, French, 1841–1919

*†338. Bather (1885) (Pl. LVIII)

Oil on canvas, 36¼ x 28¾ in.

Signed: RENOIR '85.

Lent by Durand-Ruel, Inc., New York.

Coll.: Private Coll., Paris.

Exh.: Arts Club, Chi., 1931; Durand-Ruel Gall., N. Y., 1932, No. 15.

Lit.: J. Meier-Graefe, *Renoir* (French trans.), 1912, 115 (repr.); A. Vollard, *Renoir* (Eng. trans.), 1925, 242; Meier-Graefe, *Auguste Renoir,* 1929, 186, No. 17, (repr.).

AUGUSTE RENOIR, French, 1841–1919

339. Child in White

Oil on canvas, 23½ x 19 in.

Signed: RENOIR '83.

Owned by the Art Institute of Chicago (Mr. and Mrs. Martin A. Ryerson Collection).

Coll.: P. Bérard (Sale, Mme. Bérard, Paris, 1905, No. 20, repr. in cat.); Rivière Sale; M. A. Ryerson, Chi. (1913).

Lit.: *Renoir* (Bernheim-Jeune, Ed.), 1913, opp. 22 (repr.); M. C., *Bull.,* XIX (1925), 49 (repr.).

The model is the son of Paul Bérard, an early patron of the artist's.

AUGUSTE RENOIR, French, 1841–1919
340. Chrysanthemums
Oil on canvas, 21½ x 26 in.
Signed: renoir.
Owned by The Art Institute of Chicago (Mr. and Mrs. Martin A. Ryerson Collection).

Coll.: Durand-Ruel, Paris; M. A. Ryerson, Chi. (1915).

Lit.: M. C., *Bull.,* XIX (1925), 47–48 (repr.).

AUGUSTE RENOIR, French, 1841–1919
341. Diana, Huntress (1867)
Oil on canvas, 77 x 51¼ in.
Signed: renoir, 1867.
Lent from The Chester Dale Collection, New York.

Coll.: Dr. G. Viau, Paris, Prince de Wagram, Paris.

Exh.: Knoedler and Co., N. Y., 1928; Detroit Inst. of Arts, 1930.

Lit.: J. Meier-Graefe, *Renoir* (French trans.), 1912, 7 (repr.); *Renoir* (Bernheim-Jeune, Ed.), 1913, plate laid in after title-page; T. Duret, *Renoir,* 1924, Pl. 2, 23; Meier-Graefe, *Auguste Renoir,* 1929, 17, 21, No. 3 (repr.).

AUGUSTE RENOIR, French, 1841–1919
342. The Flower on the Hat
Oil on canvas, 21¼ x 25½ in.
Signed: renoir.
Owned by The Art Institute of Chicago (Mr. and Mrs. Martin A. Ryerson Collection).

Coll.: M. A. Ryerson, Chi. (1913).

Exh.: Carnegie Inst., Pitts., 1924–5.

Lit.: T. Duret, *Manet et les Impressionistes,* 1910, 198 (repr.); G. Rivière, *Renoir et ses Amis,* 1921, opp. 90 (repr.); A. Vollard, *Renoir* (Eng. trans.), 1925, 244; M. C., *Bull.,* XIX (1925), 47 (repr.); J. Meier-Graefe, *Auguste Renoir,* 1929, 260, No. 234 (repr.).

Painted 1893. Renoir also treated the subject in a pastel (Private Coll., U. S. A.), and in etching, lithography and color lithography. One of the girls is a daughter of Mme. Morisot Manet.

AUGUSTE RENOIR, French, 1841–1919
343. Fruits of the Midi (1881)
Oil on canvas, 20 x 27 in.
Signed: renoir '81.
Owned by The Art Institute of Chicago (Mr. and Mrs. Martin A. Ryerson Collection).

Coll.: Durand-Ruel; M. A. Ryerson, Chi. (1915).

Lit.: M. C., *Bull.,* XIX (1925), 49 (repr.); A. Vollard, *Renoir* (Eng. trans.), 1925, 240; J. Meier-Graefe, *Auguste Renoir,* 1929, 153, No. 134 (repr.).

AUGUSTE RENOIR, French, 1841–1919
344. Lady Sewing (1879)
Oil on canvas, 19½ x 24 in.
Signed: renoir '79.
Owned by The Art Institute of Chicago (Mr. and Mrs. L. L. Coburn Collection).

Coll.: Deudon, Nice; P. Rosenberg, Paris; H. Young, N. Y.; Mrs. L. L. Coburn, Chi.

Exh.: "100 Masterpieces," Gall. P. Rosenberg, 1922; The Art Inst. of Chi., 1932, No. 32.

Lit.: J. Meier-Graefe, *Auguste Renoir,* 1929, 122, No. 108 (repr.).

AUGUSTE RENOIR, French, 1841–1919
*345. Luncheon of the Boating Party (1881) (Pl. LVII)
Oil on canvas, 51 x 68 in.
Signed: renoir 1881.
Lent by The Phillips Memorial Gallery, Washington, D. C.

Coll.: Durand-Ruel, Paris.

Exh.: The Indépendants, Paris, 1882, No. 137; Durand-Ruel Gall., N. Y., 1923.

Lit.: J. Meier-Graefe, *Renoir* (French trans.), 1912, 106 (repr.); G. Rivière, *Renoir et ses Amis,* 1921, 138–140 (repr.); T. Duret, *Renoir,* 1924, oppos. 62 (fig. 22), 81; F. Watson, *The Arts,* V (1924), 203 (repr.); A. Vollard, *Renoir* (Eng. trans.), 1925, opp. 62 (repr.), 240; F. Fosca, *Renoir* (Masters of Modern Art), n. d., Pl. 20; D. Phillips, *A Collection in the Making,* 1926, 34 (repr.); D. Phillips, *Creative Art,* III (1929), xxi; Meier-Graefe, *Auguste Renoir,* 1929, 152–5, No. 137 (repr.); Phillips, *The Artist Sees Differently,* 1931, 19, 20, 67 (repr.).

See Meier-Graefe (*Renoir,* 1929, 152, N. 1) for comments on the scene and its personalities.

AUGUSTE RENOIR, French, 1841–1919
*346. Moulin de la Galette (1876) (Pl. LIX)
Oil on canvas, 31 x 45½ in.
Signed: renoir '76.
Lent by Mr. John Hay Whitney, New York.

Coll.: Chocquet, Paris (Sale of Mme. Chocquet, 1899, No. 88, repr. in cat.); Prince de Wagram, Paris; M. Knoedler and Co., N. Y.

Exh.: Royal Academy, Lond., 1906; Knoedler Gall., N. Y., 1929; Mus. of Mod. Art, N. Y., Summer, 1932.

Lit.: G. Rivière, *Renoir et ses Amis,* 1921, 136 (repr.); G. Coquiot, *Renoir,* 1925, 255 (repr.); J. Meier-Graefe, *Renoir,* 1929, 87, 90 (repr.), No. 68 (confused with the picture in the Louvre); *Apollo,* X (1929), 258–9 (repr.).

An almost completely finished study for the "Moulin de la Galette" in the Louvre (Caillebotte Coll.). (See Duret, *Renoir,* 1924, Pl. 12.) A painted sketch for a portion of the composition was formerly in the Marczell von Nemes Coll., Budapest. Toulouse-Lautrec painted the same cabaret. See No. 372.

AUGUSTE RENOIR, French, 1841–1919
347. Near the Lake
Oil on canvas, 18 x 22 in.
Signed: renoir.
Owned by The Art Institute of Chicago (Potter Palmer Collection).

Coll.: Durand-Ruel; Mrs. Potter Palmer, Chi. (1892).

Lit.: M. C., *Bull.,* XIX (1925), 32–3 (repr.).

AUGUSTE RENOIR, French, 1841–1919
348. On the Terrace (1881)
Oil on canvas, 39⅜ x 31½ in.
Signed: renoir '81.

Owned by The Art Institute of Chicago (Mr. and Mrs. L. L. Coburn Collection).

COLL.: Durand-Ruel, Paris; Mrs. L. L. Coburn, Chi.

EXH.: Grafton Gall., Lond., 1905; Burlington Hse., London, 1905; The Art Inst. of Chi., 1932, No. 33 (repr. in cat. of the Coburn Coll.).

LIT.: G. Lecomte, *L'Art Impressioniste* (etched by A. M. Lauzet), 1892, opp. 136; G. Rivière, *Renoir et ses Amis,* 1921, opp. 134 (repr.); F. Fosca, *Renoir* (Masters of Modern Art), 1924, Pl. 18; A. Vollard, *Renoir* (Eng. trans.), 1925, 240; J. Meier-Graefe, *Auguste Renoir,* 1929, 142, No. 119 (repr.).

AUGUSTE RENOIR, FRENCH, 1841–1919
349. PICKING FLOWERS
Oil on canvas, 20½ x 25¼ in.
Signed: RENOIR.
Owned by The Art Institute of Chicago (Mrs. L. L. Coburn Collection).

COLL.: M. Knoedler and Co., Lond.; H. Young, N. Y.; Mrs. L. L. Coburn, Chi.

EXH.: Knoedler Gall., Lond., 1923, No. 45; The Art Inst. of Chi., 1932–3, No. 30.

LIT.: J. Meier-Graefe, *Auguste Renoir,* 1929, 114, No. 94.

Painted in 1878.

AUGUSTE RENOIR, FRENCH, 1841–1919
350. THE ROWERS' LUNCH
Oil on canvas, 12½ x 25½ in.
Signed: RENOIR.
Owned by The Art Institute of Chicago (Potter Palmer Collection).

COLL.: Durand-Ruel; Mrs. Potter Palmer, Chi.

EXH.: Art Inst. of Chi., 1910.

LIT.: M. C., *Bull.,* XIX (1925), 33 (repr.); J. Meier-Graefe, *Auguste Renoir,* 1929, 124, No. 102 (repr.); *Guide,* 1932, 64 (repr.).

Painted c. 1879.

AUGUSTE RENOIR, FRENCH, 1841–1919
*351. TWO LITTLE CIRCUS GIRLS (Pl. LVIII)
Oil on canvas, 51 x 38½ in.
Signed: RENOIR.
Owned by The Art Institute of Chicago (Potter Palmer Collection).

COLL.: Durand-Ruel; Mrs. Potter Palmer, Chi. (1892).

EXH.: Fogg Art Mus., Cambridge, Mass., 1929, No. 80 (repr. in cat., Pl. XXXIII); Smith College Mus. of Art, 1932.

LIT.: G. Rivière, *Renoir et ses Amis,* 1921, 145 (repr.), as "Jongleuses au Cirque," 146; A. Vollard, *Renoir* (Eng. trans., 1925), 237; M. C., *Bull.,* XIX (1925), 32–3 (repr.); J. Meier-Graefe, *Auguste Renoir,* 1929, No. 6, 56, (repr.); *Guide,* 1932, 63 (repr.); D. C. Rich, *Pantheon,* XI (March, 1933), opp. 73 (repr.).

Dated too early (1868) by Meier-Graefe; executed 1875–6.

PAINTINGS BY GAUGUIN, ROUSSEAU, AND SEURAT

GALLERY 46

PAUL GAUGUIN, FRENCH, 1848–1903
†352. AT THE EDGE OF THE FOREST (PARAU NA TE VARUA INO) (1892)
Oil on canvas, 37 x 23½ in.
Signed: GAUGUIN '92 and inscribed: PARAU NA TE VARUA INO.
Lent by Marie Harriman Gallery, New York.

COLL.: Millet, Paris; P. Pluckett.

LIT.: Ch. Morice, *Paul Gauguin,* 1919, opp. 186 (repr. as "Paroles du Diable").

Drawings for the standing figure are reproduced in "Noa, Noa" and by A. Alexandre, *Paul Gauguin,* 1930, 233. Another version of the subject, with the squatting figure of the center retained, is also shown, *Ibid.,* 221.

PAUL GAUGUIN, FRENCH, 1848–1903
353. AUTREFOIS (MATA MUA) (1892)
Oil on canvas, 35½ x 26½ in.
Signed: PAUL GAUGUIN '92 and inscribed: MATA MUA.
Lent by Mr. and Mrs. Gilbert E. Fuller, Boston, Massachusetts.

COLL.: G. Fayet, Igny.

EXH.: Durand-Ruel, Paris, 1893; Fogg Art. Mus., Cambridge, Mass., 1929, No. 48; Mus. of Fine Arts, Boston, 1929; Fogg Art Mus., 1930.

LIT.: Ch. Morice, *Gauguin,* 1919, 128 (repr.); J. de Rotonchamp, *Paul Gauguin,* 1925, 137, 154.

PAUL GAUGUIN, FRENCH, 1848–1903
354. BEACH SCENE, TAHITI (TE TINÎ NA VE ITE RATA) (1899)
Oil on canvas, 29 x 37 in.
Signed: PAUL GAUGUIN '99 and inscribed: TE TINÎ NA VE ITE RATA.
Lent by Mr. A. Conger Goodyear, New York.

COLL.: Wildenstein and Co., N. Y.

EXH.: Albright Art Gall., Buffalo, 1928, No. 18; Reinhardt Gall., N. Y., 1928, No. 23 (repr. in cat.); Mus. of Mod. Art, N. Y., 1929, No. 51 (repr. in cat.); Wadsworth Atheneum, Hartford, Conn., No. 105 (repr. in cat.).

PAUL GAUGUIN, FRENCH, 1848–1903
355. THE DAY OF THE GOD (MAHANA NO ATUA) (1894)

Oil on canvas, 26 x 34¼ in.
Signed: GAUGUIN '94 and inscribed: MAHANA NO ATUA.
Owned by The Art Institute of Chicago (Helen Birch-Bartlett Memorial).

COLL.: G. Bernheim, Jeune, Paris; F. C. Bartlett, Chi.

EXH.: Boston Arts Club, 1925; Mus. of Mod. Art, N. Y., 1929, No. 46 (repr. in cat.).

LIT.: *Bull.,* XIX (1925), 77 (repr.), 81–2; M. Zabel, *Art and Archaeology,* XXVI (1928), 233–4 (repr.); *Cat. of the Helen Birch Bartlett Memorial,* 1929, 12–3 (repr.), 57–8. Gauguin reproduced the subject twice in two quite different woodcuts. (See M. Guérin, *L'Oeuvre Gravé de Gauguin,* 1927, I, Nos. 42 and 43.)

PAUL GAUGUIN, FRENCH, 1848–1903
356. LANDSCAPE (TE BURAO) (1892)
Oil on canvas, 26¼ x 35 in.
Signed: P. GAUGUIN '92 and inscribed: TE BURAO.
Owned by The Art Institute of Chicago.

COLL.: M. de Zayas, N. Y. (Sale, 1923, No. 83).

EXH.: Met. Mus. of Art, N. Y., 1921; Minneapolis Inst. of Arts, 1921.

LIT.: *Minn. Inst. of Arts Bull.,* X (Nov. 1921), 59 (repr.); *Bull.,* XVII (May, 1923), 51–2; *Guide,* 1932, 72 (repr.).

Described in Gauguin's "Noa Noa."

PAUL GAUGUIN, FRENCH, 1848–1903
357. MARTINIQUE (1887)
Oil on canvas, 37½ x 27¾ in.
Signed: PAUL GAUGUIN '87.
Lent by Mr. and Mrs. Charles H. Worcester, Chicago.

PAUL GAUGUIN, FRENCH, 1848–1903
358. MLLE. MARIE HENRY
Oil on canvas, 24½ x 20½ in.
Signed: P. GAUGUIN '90.
Owned by The Art Institute of Chicago (Joseph Winterbotham Collection).

COLL.: E. Brown & Phillips, London; Chester H. Johnson Gall., Chi.

LIT.: *Bull.,* XX (1926), 2 (repr.) as "Portrait of Mme. Gauguin"; A. Alexandre, *Paul Gauguin,* 1930, 29 (repr.); *Guide,* 1932, 71 (repr.).

Painted before his first trip to Tahiti. In the background is a still-life by Cézanne from Gauguin's collection.

PAUL GAUGUIN, FRENCH, 1848–1903
359. "OH, YOU'RE JEALOUS" (NO TE AHA OE RIRI) (1896)
Oil on canvas, 36⅜ x 50 in.
Signed: P. GAUGUIN '96 and inscribed: NO TE AHA OE RIRI.
Owned by The Art Institute of Chicago (Mr. and Mrs. Martin A. Ryerson Collection).

COLL.: Durand-Ruel, N. Y.; M. A. Ryerson, Chi. (1924).

EXH.: Exh. of "La Libre Esthétique," Brussels, 1904; Fogg Art Mus., Cambridge, Mass., 1929, No. 43 (repr. in cat. Pl. XXXV).

LIT.: R. Rey, *Gauguin* (Les Maîtres de l'Art Moderne), 1923, Pl. 26; *Ibid.* (Eng. trans.), 1924, Pl. 31; *L'Art et les Artistes,* N. S., XII (1925), 59 (repr.); A Alexandre, *Paul Gauguin,* 1930, 245 (repr.).

The picture also is known as "Devant La Case." Another version, inscribed TE RAAU RAHI is in the coll. of Mr. Frank Ginn, Cleveland.

PAUL GAUGUIN, FRENCH, 1848–1903
360. SEATED WOMAN (TE FAATURUMA) (1891)
Oil on canvas, 36 x 27 in.
Signed: P. GAUGUIN '91 and inscribed: TE FAATURUMA.
Lent by The Worcester Art Museum, Worcester, Massachusetts.

EXH.: Fogg Art Mus., Cambridge, Mass., 1929, No. 46 (repr. in cat. Pl. XXXVI); Mus. of Mod. Art, N. Y., 1929, No. 43 (repr. in cat.).

LIT.: R. W., *Bull. of the Worcester Art Mus.,* XIII (1922), 1, (repr.), 2–3; *Cat. of Paintings and Drawings, Worcester Art Mus.,* 1922, 154–5 (repr.).

PAUL GAUGUIN, FRENCH, 1848–1903
361. SUNFLOWERS (1901)
Oil on canvas, 25¾ x 30¼ in.
Signed: PAUL GAUGUIN, 1901.
Lent by Mrs. Robert Rutherford McCormick, Chicago.

COLL.: G. Fayet, Igny; P. Rosenberg, Paris; Chester H. Johnson Gall., Chi.

EXH.: Mus. of Mod. Art, N. Y., Summer, 1930, No. 40.

LIT.: R. Rey, *Gauguin* (Les Maîtres de l'Art Moderne), 1923, Pl. 18; *Ibid.* (Eng. trans.), 1924, Pl. 39; A. Alexandre, *Paul Gauguin,* 1930, 47 (repr.); B. Becker, *Gauguin, the Calm Madman,* 1931, 310.

PAUL GAUGUIN, FRENCH, 1848–1903
362. TAHITI WOMAN WITH CHILDREN (1901)
Oil on canvas, 37½ x 28½ in.
Signed: PAUL GAUGUIN, 1901.
Owned by The Art Institute of Chicago (Helen Birch Bartlett Memorial).

COLL.: Moderne Galerie, Munich; F. C. Bartlett, Chi. (1927).

EXH.: Mus. of Mod. Art, N. Y., 1929, No. 49 (repr. in cat.); Albright Art Gallery, Buffalo, 1932, No. 26 (repr. in cat. Pl. XX); Toronto Art Gallery, 1933.

LIT.: R. M. F., *Bull.,* XXI (1927), 74–75 (repr.); *Cat. of the Helen Birch Bartlett Memorial,* 1929, 14–15 (repr.), 57–8.

PAUL GAUGUIN, FRENCH, 1848–1903
363. TE RAAU RAHI (1891)
Oil on canvas, 28½ x 36 in.
Signed: P. GAUGUIN '91 and inscribed: TE RAAU RAHI.
Lent by Mr. and Mrs. Walter S. Brewster, Chicago.

COLL.: Mme. Gauguin, Copenhagen; Berwaldsen, Copenhagen; Perls, Berlin; Neusser, Breslau; Wildenstein, Paris; Chester H. Johnson Gall., Chi.

PAUL GAUGUIN, French, 1848–1903

*364. Two Tahitian Women (1899) (Pl. LXIV)

Oil on canvas, 37 x 38¾ in.

Signed: GAUGUIN '99.

Lent by Mr. William Church Osborn, New York.

Coll.: G. Fayet, Igny; Wildenstein, N. Y.

Exh.: Royal Academy, Lond., 1932, No. 536.

Lit.: Ch. Morice, *Paul Gauguin,* 1919, opp. 108 (repr.); Goulinat, *L'Amour de l'Art,* 1925, 141; A. Alexandre, *Paul Gauguin,* 1930, 184 (as "Et l'Or de leurs Corps."); Gauguin, *Noa, Noa* (Eng. trans.), n. d., opp. 12.

PAUL GAUGUIN, French, 1848–1903

365. Village Turkeys (1888)

Oil on canvas, 35½ x 28¼ in.

Signed: GAUGUIN '88.

Owned by The Art Institute of Chicago (Mr. and Mrs. Martin A. Ryerson Collection).

Coll.: G. Bernheim, Jne, Paris; M. A. Ryerson, Chi. (1924).

PAUL GAUGUIN, French, 1848–1903

*366. "We Greet Thee, Mary" (Ia Orana Maria) (1891) (Pl. LXIV)

Oil on canvas, 44¾ x 34½ in.

Signed: P. GAUGUIN '91 and inscribed: IA ORANA MARIA.

Lent from The Adolph Lewisohn Collection, New York.

Coll.: Manzi (Sale, Paris, 1919, No. 56, repr. in cat.).

Exh.: Durand-Ruel Gall., Paris, 1893, No. 1; Union League Club, N. Y., 1924; Knoedler Gall., 1928, No. 29 (repr. in cat.); Durand-Ruel Gall., N. Y., 1928; Mus. of Mod. Art, N. Y., 1930, No. 39 (repr. in cat.); Royal Academy, Lond., 1932, No. 540.

Lit.: J. de Rotonchamp, *Paul Gauguin,* 1906, 107, 118; Ch. Morice, *Paul Gauguin,* 1919, 183; S. Bourgeois, *Cat. of the Adolph Lewisohn Coll.,* 1928, 160 (repr.); E. von Térey, *Kunst und Künstler,* XXVII (1929), 418, 424 (repr.); A. Alexandre, *Paul Gauguin,* 1930, 133 (repr.).

Several drawings and prints of the figure of the mother with the child on her shoulder exist. A water-color (Frederic C. Bartlett), the large monotype (Fayet Coll.), and a lithograph on zinc are among these. In "Noa Noa" Gauguin pasted in a black-and-white reproduction of the picture and colored it with water-color.

HENRI-JULIEN ROUSSEAU, French, 1844–1910

*367. Exotic Landscape (1910) (Pl. LXV)

Oil on canvas, 51 x 64 in.

Signed: HENRI ROUSSEAU 1910.

Lent by Mrs. Robert Rutherford McCormick, Chicago.

Coll.: P. Rosenberg, Paris; Tetzen-Lund, Copenhagen; Chester H. Johnson, Chi.

Exh.: The Indépendants, Paris, 1910.

Lit.: Chr. Zervos, *Henri Rousseau,* Pl. 86; H. Kolle, *Henri Rousseau* (Junge Kunst), 1922, Pl. 35.

HENRI-JULIEN ROUSSEAU, French, 1844–1910

368. The Jungle (1908)

Oil on canvas, 66½ x 74½ in.

Signed: HENRI ROUSSEAU 1908.

Lent by Mrs. Patrick J. Hill to the Joseph Winterbotham Collection, The Art Institute of Chicago.

Coll.: J. Quinn, N. Y.; Mrs. J. A. Carpenter, Chi.

Exh.: Reinhardt Gall., N. Y., 1928, No. 27 (repr. in cat.).

Lit.: A. Basler, *Henri Rousseau,* 1927, Pl. XXXIX; Basler, *Henri Rousseau* (Les Peintres Français Nouveaux), 1929, No. 59 (repr.), as "Paysage Exotique."

HENRI-JULIEN ROUSSEAU, French, 1844–1910

369. The Waterfall (1910)

Oil on canvas, 45½ x 59 in.

Signed: HENRI ROUSSEAU 1910.

Owned by The Art Institute of Chicago (Helen Birch Bartlett Memorial).

Coll.: G. Bernheim, Paris; Frederic C. Bartlett, Chi. (1924).

Exh.: The Mus. of Mod. Art., N. Y., 1933.

Lit.: R. M. F., *Bull.,* XX (1926), 62–3 (repr.); F. Watson, *The Arts,* IX (1926), 310, 312 (repr.); M. D. Zabel, *Art and Archaeology,* XXVI (1928), 228 (repr.); *Cat of the Helen Birch Bartlett Memorial,* 1929, 10–11 (repr.), 57.

GEORGES SEURAT, French, 1859–1891

*370. Sunday on the Island of la Grande Jatte (Pl. LXIII)

Oil on canvas, 81 x 120⅜ in.

Owned by The Art Institute of Chicago (Helen Birch Bartlett Memorial).

Coll.: Mme. L. Cousturier, Paris; Galerie Vildrac, Paris; F. C. Bartlett, Chi. (1924).

Exh.: Exh. of the Impressionists, Paris, 1886; Exh. of the Indépendants, Paris, 1886, No. 363; Exh. of the "XX," Brussels, 1887; Exh. of the Indépendants, Paris, 1892; Exh. of the "Revue Blanche," Paris, 1900, No. 17; Boston Arts Club, 1926.

For literature on Seurat and the painting see the bibliography in R. Rey, *La Renaissance du Sentiment Classique,* 1931, 161–2. Add the following: A. Salmon, *Burlington Mag.,* XXXVII (1920), 115ff (repr. Pl. III-e); Chr. Zervos, *Cahiers d'Art,* III (1928), 361–75 (repr. and details); L. Cousturier, *Seurat,* 12, 17–18 (repr.); W. Pach, *The Arts,* III (1923), 165 (repr.), 168 as "In the Park"; IX (1926), 306–10 (repr.); Pach. *Georges Seurat,* N. Y., 1923, 22–3, and Pl. VI; *Bull.,* XXVIII (1924), 90–91 (repr.); G. Eglington, *Internatl. Stu.,* LXXXI (1925), 113ff (repr.); *Cat. of the Helen Birch Bartlett Memorial,* 1929, 30–31 (repr.), 61; *Maandblad voor Beeldende Kunsten,* VIII (1931), 163ff (repr. 175); *Guide,* 1932, 68–9 (repr.); F. Walter, *Revue de l'Art,* LXIII (1933), 165 (repr.).

Painted 1884–6. Numerous charcoal drawings and painted studies exist for various sections of the composition. Two of the final studies are in the colls. of Mrs. A. Chester Beatty, Lond., and Adolph Lewisohn, N. Y. The Island of La Grande Jatte is in the Seine at Neuilly.

PAINTINGS BY TOULOUSE-LAUTREC AND VAN GOGH

GALLERY 47

HENRI DE TOULOUSE-LAUTREC, French, 1864–1901

*371. At the Moulin-Rouge (Pl. LXIII)
Oil on canvas, 55¼ x 47¼ in.
Signed with Monogram.
Owned by The Art Institute of Chicago (Helen Birch Bartlett Memorial).

Coll.: Manzi-Joyant, Paris; Jean Laroche, Paris, 1926; Frederic C. Bartlett, Chi.

Exh.: Galerie Manzi-Joyant, Paris, 1914, No. 32; Barcelona, 1917, No. 2038; Art Inst. of Chi. (Arts Club), Dec. 1924–Jan. 1925, No. 7; Grand Palais, Paris, 1926, No. 3253; Amsterdam, April–May, 1928; Knoedler, N. Y., 1928, No. 34; Art Inst. of Chi., Dec., 1930–Jan., 1931, No. 19; Mus. of Mod. Art, N. Y., 1931, No. 19; Musée des Arts Décoratifs, Paris, 1931, No. 92 (repr. in cat., Pl. 5, wrongly credited to M. Seligmann).

Lit.: *Gazette des Beaux-Arts,* Per. 4, XII (1916), 100 (repr. opposite); M. Joyant, *Lautrec,* I, 1926, 137 (repr.), 275; *L'Art et les Artistes,* N. S., XIV (1927), 159–160; D. C. Rich, *Bull.,* XXIII (1929), 13–15 (repr.); P. de L'Apparent, *Toulouse-Lautrec,* 1928, Pl. 8; *Cat. of the Helen Birch Bartlett Memorial,* 1929, 36–37 (repr.).

Seated round the table from left to right: M. Edouard Dujardin, La Macarona, Paul Sescau, Maurice Guibert; in the foreground, Mlle. Nelly C....... In the background, La Goulue, doing up her hair, and silhouettes of Dr. Tapié de Celeyran and of Lautrec, the latter in his famous "melon" hat.

HENRI DE TOULOUSE-LAUTREC, French, 1864–1901

372. A Dance at the Moulin de la Galette (1889)
Oil on canvas, 35⅞ x 39⅝ in.
Signed: T-LAUTREC.
Owned by The Art Institute of Chicago (Mr. and Mrs. L. L. Coburn Collection).

Coll.: Montandon, Paris; Gallimard, Paris; Mrs. L. L. Coburn, Chi.

Exh.: Exh. of the Indépendants, Paris, 1889, No. 257; Gall. Goupil, Paris, 1893; Durand-Ruel, Paris, 1902, No. 71; Musée des Arts Décoratifs, Louvre, 1910, No. 2; Gall. Manzi-Joyant, Paris, 1914, No. 76; The Art Inst. of Chi. (Arts Club), 1924–1925, No. 6; the same, 1930–1931, No. 9 (repr. in cat. 62).

Lit.: T. Duret, *Lautrec,* 1920, opp. 16, Pl. VI; G. Coquiot, *Toulouse-Lautrec,* n. d., Pl. 22; M. Joyant, *Toulouse-Lautrec,* 1926, I, 125 (repr.), 266; *L'Art et les Artistes,* N. S., XIV (1927), 170 (repr.).

Painted in 1889. A drawing (reproduced in the *Courrier Français,* May, 19, 1889, 11, No. 20) is in the coll. of Mr. J. W. Barney, New York. Renoir painted the same subject, *see* No. 315. The man to the right is the painter Joseph Albert.

HENRI DE TOULOUSE-LAUTREC, French, 1864–1901

373. In the Circus Fernando: The Ring-Master
Oil on canvas, 38¾ x 63½ in.
Signed: T-LAUTREC.
Owned by The Art Institute of Chicago (Joseph Winterbotham Collection).

Coll.: Oller, Paris; Baron de Lafaurie, Paris.

Exh.: Moulin-Rouge, Paris, 1888; Musée des Arts Décoratifs, Paris, 1910, No. 4; Paul Rosenberg, Paris, 1914, No. 20; Galerie Manzi-Joyant, Paris, 1914, No. 45; Art Inst. of Chi. (Arts Club), Dec., 1924–Jan., 1925, No. 10; Fogg Art Mus., Harvard, 1929, No. 87 (repr. in cat. Pl. XLV); Art Inst. of Chi., 1930–31, No. 7 (repr. in cat.); Mus. of Mod. Art, N. Y., 1931, No. 7 (repr. in cat.); Musée des Arts Décoratifs, Paris, 1931, No. 52 (repr. in cat., Pl. 2); Albright Art Gall., 1932, No. 59 (repr. in cat. Pl. IX); Toronto Art Gallery, 1933.

Lit.: G. Coquiot, *Lautrec,* n. d., Pl. 46; Coquiot, *L'Art et les Artistes,* XIX (1914), 133 (repr.); M. Joyant, *L'Art et les Artistes,* N. S., XIV (1927), 168 (repr.); R. M. F., *Bull.,* XIX (1925), 94–5 (repr.); M. Joyant, *Toulouse-Lautrec,* I, 1926, 162 (repr.), 265; *Guide,* 1932, 74 (repr.).

Painted in 1888. The ringmaster is M. Loyal.

HENRI DE TOULOUSE-LAUTREC, French, 1864–1901

374. May Milton
Oil on cardboard, 25½ x 18¾ in.
Signed: T-LAUTREC.
Lent by Mr. and Mrs. Walter S. Brewster, Chi.

Coll.: E. Duplan, Paris; Th. Duret, Paris; J. Allard, Paris; Chester H. Johnson Gall., Chi.

Exh.: Goupil Gall., Lond., 1898, No. 13; Durand-Ruel Gall., Paris, 1902, No. 67; Manzi-Joyant Gall., Paris, 1914, No. 83; Art Inst. of Chi., 1930–1931, No. 26 (repr. in cat.); Mus. of Mod. Art, N. Y., 1931, No. 24 (repr. in cat.); Musée des Arts Décoratifs, Paris, 1931, No. 128.

Lit.: T. Duret, *Lautrec,* 1920, opposite 42 (repr.); M. Joyant, *Henri de Toulouse-Lautrec,* I, 1926; *L'Art et les Artistes,* N. S., XIV (1927), 153 (repr.); D. C. Rich, *The Arts,* XVII (1931), 314 (repr.).

Painted in 1895. May Milton, a singer of Irish origin, performed in London music halls in 1890, and made her debut in Paris in 1895. She sang at the *Cabaret des Décadents,* the *Eden-Concert,* the *Jardin de Paris* and the *Olympia.* Lautrec made a number of portraits of her, both in oil and lithography, often portraying her in her "baby" costume.

VINCENT VAN GOGH, Dutch, 1853–1890

†375. Banks of the River: La Grenouillere
Oil on canvas, 28⅞ x 35⅞ in.
Lent by M. Knoedler and Co., New York.

For collections, exhibitions and literature see J. B. de la Faille, No. 798.

Painted at Auvers, 1890.

VINCENT VAN GOGH, DUTCH, 1853–1890
376. THE BEDROOM AT ARLES
Oil on canvas, 29 x 36 in.
Owned by The Art Institute of Chicago (Helen Birch Bartlett Memorial).
For collections, exhibitions and literature see J. B. de la Faille, No. 484. Add:
EXH.: Mus. of Mod. Art, N. Y., 1929, No. 79.
LIT.: G. Coquiot, *Van Gogh* (1923), opp. 184 (repr.); R. M. F., *Bull.*, XX (1926), 92–4 (repr.); *Cat. of the Helen Birch Bartlett Memorial*, 1929, 22–3 (repr.), 59; *Guide*, 1932, 27 (repr.).
Painted at Arles, October 1888 or at St. Rémy, September, 1889. (See De la Faille for other versions.) Mentioned in Van Gogh's *Letters to his Brother*, III (Eng. trans., 1929), Nos. 554–55, and No. 604.
A pen-sketch of the composition is included in Letter No. 554.

VINCENT VAN GOGH, DUTCH, 1853–1890
377. LA BERCEUSE (MME. ROULIN) (1889)
Oil on canvas, 36 x 28 in.
Signed: VINCENT, ARLES '89 and inscribed: LA BERCEUSE.
Owned by The Art Institute of Chicago (Helen Birch Bartlett Memorial).
For collections, exhibitions and literature see J. B. de la Faille, No. 506. Add:
LIT.: M. D. Zabel, *Art and Archaeology*, XXVI (1928), 231 (repr.); *Cat. of the Helen Birch Bartlett Memorial*, 1929, 20–21 (repr.), 58.
See De la Faille for other versions. Mentioned in Van Gogh's *Letters to his Brother*, III (Eng. trans., 1929), Nos. 573, 578, and 592. The model was the wife of the postman, Marcel Roulin, whose portrait by Van Gogh is No. 384 of the present exhibition.

VINCENT VAN GOGH, DUTCH, 1853–1890
378. THE FIRST STEPS (AFTER MILLET)
Oil on canvas, 28⅞ x 35⅞ in.
Lent by Mr. Julius Oppenheimer, New York.
For collections, exhibitions and literature see J. B. de la Faille, No. 668. Add:
EXH.: Mus. of Mod. Art, 1929, No. 88 (repr. in cat.).
Painted at St. Rémy, 1890.

VINCENT VAN GOGH, DUTCH, 1853–1890
379. HOUSE ON THE CRAU
Oil on canvas, 25 x 21 in.
Signed: VINCENT.
Lent by Mr. A. Conger Goodyear, New York.
For collections, exhibitions and literature see J. B. de la Faille, No. 550. Add:
EXH.: De Hauke Gall., N. Y., 1927; Albright Art Gallery, 1928, No. 47 (repr. in cat. 36); Fogg Art Mus., Cambridge, Mass., 1929, No. 91; Mus. of Mod. Art, N. Y., 1929, No. 83 (repr. in cat.); Albright Art Gall., 1932, No. 62 (repr. in cat., Pl. XIX).
Painted at Arles, 1888–9.

VINCENT VAN GOGH, DUTCH, 1853–1890
380. MONTMARTRE
Oil on canvas, 17⅛ x 13 in.
Owned by The Art Institute of Chicago (Helen Birch Bartlett Memorial).
For collections, exhibitions and literature see J. B. de la Faille, No. 272. Add:
EXH.: Minneapolis Inst. of Arts, 1926; Boston Arts Club, 1925.
LIT.: *The Arts*, VI (1924), 294 (repr.); *Cat. of the Helen Birch Bartlett Memorial*, 1929, 16–17 (repr.), 59.

VINCENT VAN GOGH, DUTCH, 1853–1890
*381. PAVERS: STREET IN ST. REMY (Pl. LXV)
Oil on canvas, 29 x 36⅜ in.
Lent anonymously.
For collections, exhibitions and literature see J. B. de la Faille, No. 658. Add:
EXH.: French painting of XIX–XXC., Fogg Art Mus., 1929, No. 96, Pl. XLIII; Rhode Island School of Design, Providence, R. I., 1932.
Painted in December, 1889. A replica was formerly in the coll. of Mr. and Mrs. Gilbert E. Fuller, Boston. See *Letters to his Brother*, III, No. 618 and 621.

VINCENT VAN GOGH, DUTCH, 1853–1890
*382. Portrait of MLLE. GACHET (Pl. LXVI)
Oil on canvas, 29 x 24 in.
Lent from The Chester Dale Collection, New York.
For collections, exhibitions and literature see J. B. de la Faille, No. 431. Add:
EXH.: "Masterpieces by 19th Cent. French Painters," Lond., 1929, No. 3; Mus. of Mod. Art, N. Y., 1929, No. 75 (repr. in cat.); "Portraits of Women," Mus. of French Art, N. Y., 1931, No. 21; Met. Mus. of Art, N. Y., 1932.
Painted at Arles, July, 1888. Mentioned in Van Gogh's *Letters to his Brother*, III (Eng. trans., 1929), No. 514. (Cf. *Lettres à E. Bernard*, No. X.) Called "La Mousmé" here.
Drawings are in the collections of Dr. C. Hirschland, Essen, and the Mus. of Western Arts, Moscow.

VINCENT VAN GOGH, DUTCH, 1853–1890
383. PUBLIC GARDENS AT ARLES
Oil on canvas, 28 x 35½ in.
Lent by The Phillips Memorial Gallery, Washington, D. C.
For collections, exhibitions and literature see J. B. de la Faille, No. 566. Add:
COLL.: A. Sachs, N. Y.
EXH.: Mus. of Mod. Art, N. Y., 1929, No. 82 (repr. in cat.).
LIT.: D. Phillips, *The Artist Sees Differently*, I, 1931, 123–4 (repr.).
Painted at Arles, 1888–9.

VINCENT VAN GOGH, DUTCH, 1853–1890
*384. ROULIN, THE POSTMAN (Pl. LXVI)
Oil on canvas, 31¼ x 25 in.
Lent by Mr. Robert Treat Paine, 2nd, Boston, Massachusetts.

For collections, exhibitions and literature see J. B. de la Faille, No. 432. Add:
COLL.: M. Knoedler and Co., N. Y.
EXH.: Fogg Art Mus., Cambridge, Mass., 1929, No. 93 (repr. in cat., Pl. XLI); Mus. of Mod. Art, N. Y., 1929, No. 76 (repr. in cat.); Mus. of Fine Arts, Boston.

Painted in Arles, August, 1888. (See de la Faille for other versions.) Mentioned in Van Gogh's *Letters to his Brother*, III (Eng. trans., 1929), Nos. 516, 517, and 518. (Cf. *Lettres à E. Bernard*, No. IX.)
Marcel Roulin, the postman, was a faithful friend of Van Gogh's. He painted Mme. Roulin in "La Berceuse," No. 377.
Drawings for the portrait are in the colls. of H. Freudenberg, Nikolassee, and (formerly) Dr. A. Hahnloser, Winterthur.

VINCENT VAN GOGH, DUTCH, 1853–1890
385. SUNSET OVER PLOUGHED FIELDS
Oil on canvas, 28½ x 37 in.
Lent by Mr. Julius Oppenheimer, New York.

For collections, exhibitions and literature see J. B. de la Faille, No. 737. Add:
EXH.: Mus. of Mod. Art, N. Y., 1929, No. 87 (repr. in cat.).

Painted at St. Rémy, 1889–90.

VINCENT VAN GOGH, DUTCH, 1853–1890
386. WHITE ROSES
Oil on canvas, 29 x 36½ in.
Lent by Marie Harriman Gallery, New York.

For collections, exhibitions and literature see J. B. de la Faille, No. 681. Add:

EXH.: "Exh. of Impressionist Painting," Lucerne, 1929, No. 24; "Ten Masterpieces by 19th Cent. French Painters," N. Y., 1929, No. 3; M. Knoedler and Co., N. Y., 1932; Marie Harriman Gall., N. Y., 1933.

Painted in May 1890. See de la Faille for similar compositions. Mentioned in Van Gogh's *Letters to his Brother*, III (Eng. trans., 1929), No. 633.

VINCENT VAN GOGH, DUTCH, 1853–1890
†387. WOMEN OF THE FIELDS
Oil on paper on canvas, 12½ x 24 in.
Lent by the Chester H. Johnson Galleries, Chicago.

For collections, exhibitions and literature see J. B. de la Faille, No. 819.

Painted at Auvers, 1890.

PAINTINGS BY MATISSE AND PICASSO

GALLERY 48

HENRI MATISSE, FRENCH, 1869–
†388. PONT SAINT-MICHEL (1900)
Oil on canvas, 25½ x 31¾ in.
Signed: HENRI-MATISSE.
Lent by M. Knoedler and Co., New York.

HENRI MATISSE, FRENCH, 1869–
389. WOMAN ON ROSE DIVAN
Oil on canvas, 14⅞ x 18 in.
Signed: HENRI-MATISSE.
Owned by The Art Institute of Chicago (Helen Birch Bartlett Memorial).

HENRI MATISSE, FRENCH, 1869–
390. CARNIVAL AT NICE (1922)
Oil on canvas, 26½ x 37½ in.
Signed: HENRI-MATISSE.
Lent by Mr. and Mrs. Ralph M. Coe, Cleveland, Ohio.

HENRI MATISSE, FRENCH, 1869–
†391. DECORATIVE COMPOSITION (Odalisque with the Straight Back) (1926)
Oil on canvas, 51½ x 38⅜ in.
Signed: HENRI-MATISSE.
Lent by the Artist through Pierre Matisse, New York.

HENRI MATISSE, FRENCH, 1869–
†392. HARMONY IN YELLOW (1928)
Oil on canvas, 34⅝ x 34⅝ in.
Lent by the Artist through Pierre Matisse, New York.

HENRI MATISSE, FRENCH, 1869–
393. INTERIOR (1924)
Oil on canvas, 46 x 29½ in.
Signed: HENRI-MATISSE.
Lent by Miss Etta Cone, Baltimore, Maryland.

HENRI MATISSE, FRENCH, 1869–
†394. LARGE INTERIOR, NICE (1921)
Oil on canvas, 51½ x 35 in.
Signed: HENRI-MATISSE.
Lent by Pierre Matisse Gallery, New York.

HENRI MATISSE, FRENCH, 1869–
395. POPPIES (c. 1919)
Oil on canvas, 39¾ x 32 in.
Signed: HENRI-MATISSE.
Lent by Mr. Robert H. Tannahill, Detroit, Michigan.

HENRI MATISSE, French, 1869–
*396. Still Life: "Histoires Juives" (1924) (Pl. LXVII)
Oil on canvas, 31⅞ x 39⅜ in.
Signed: henri-matisse.
Lent by Mr. Samuel S. White, 3rd, Philadelphia.

HENRI MATISSE, French, 1869–
*397. White Plumes (1919) (Pl. LXVIII)
Oil on canvas, 24 x 29 in.
Signed: henri-matisse.
Lent by Mr. Stephen C. Clark, New York.
(See No. 1034).

HENRI MATISSE, French, 1869–
398. Woman before an Aquarium (Nice, 1921)
Oil on canvas, 31½ x 39 in.
Signed: henri-matisse.
Owned by The Art Institute of Chicago (Helen Birch Barlett Memorial).

PABLO PICASSO, Spanish, 1881–
*399. Blue Room (1901) (Pl. LXVII)
Oil on canvas, 20 x 24 in.
Signed: picasso.
Lent by The Phillips Memorial Gallery, Washington, D. C.

PABLO PICASSO, Spanish, 1881–
400. Figures (Pink) (1903–04)
Oil on canvas, 60¼ x 43¼ in.
Signed: picasso.
Lent by Mr. Leonard C. Hanna, Jr., Cleveland.

PABLO PICASSO, Spanish, 1881–
†401. Le Gourmet (1903)
Oil on canvas, 36 x 26⅝ in.
Signed: picasso.
Lent by Mr. Josef Stransky, through The Worcester Art Museum, Worcester, Massachusetts.

PABLO PICASSO, Spanish, 1881–
402. The Guitarist (1903)
Oil on panel, 47¾ x 32½ in.
Signed: picasso.
Owned by The Art Institute of Chicago (Helen Birch Barlett Memorial).

PABLO PICASSO, Spanish, 1881–
403. On the Upper Deck (1901)
Oil on canvas, 15½ x 24¼ in.
Signed: picasso.
Owned by The Art Institute of Chicago (Mr. and Mrs. L. L. Coburn Collection).

PABLO PICASSO, Spanish, 1881–
404. The Toilet (1906)
Oil on canvas, 58 x 39½ in.
Signed: picasso.
Lent by The Buffalo Fine Arts Academy (Albright Art Gallery), Buffalo, New York.

PABLO PICASSO, Spanish, 1881–
405. Woman and Child at a Fountain (1903)
Oil on canvas, 36½ x 29 in.
Signed: picasso.
Lent by Mr. and Mrs. Potter Palmer, Chicago.

PABLO PICASSO, Spanish, 1881–
†406. Woman Combing her Hair (c. 1906)
Oil on canvas, 49 x 35 in.
Signed: picasso.
Lent by Marie Harriman Gallery, New York.

PABLO PICASSO, Spanish, 1881–
407. Woman in White (c. 1923)
Oil on canvas, 39¼ x 32 in.
Signed: picasso.
Lent by the Trustees of the Estate of Miss Lizzie P. Bliss and through the Museum of Modern Art, New York.

PABLO PICASSO, Spanish, 1881–
*408. Woman with a Fan (1905) (Pl. LXVIII)
Oil on canvas, 39 x 31½ in.
Signed: picasso, 1905.
Lent by Marie Harriman Gallery, New York.

PABLO PICASSO, Spanish, 1881–
409. Woman with Loaves (1905)
Oil on canvas, 39 x 27½ in.
Signed: picasso, 1905.
Lent by The Pennsylvania Museum of Art, Philadelphia, Pennsylvania.

AMERICAN PAINTING
Eighteenth and Early Nineteenth Centuries
GALLERY 26

JOSEPH BLACKBURN, American, worked 1753–1763
410. Sir Jeffrey Amherst (1758)
Oil on canvas (oval), 31½ x 26 in.
Signed: i. blackburn pinxit 1758.
Lent by Mr. Herbert Lee Pratt, Glenn Cove, Long Island.

Coll.: Mrs. Scott, Boston, 1817, No. 16; Hale Family, Sherbrooke, Canada.

Exh.: Mus. of Fine Arts, Boston, 1930, No. 4 (repr.).

Lit.: L. Park, *Art in America,* VII (1919), 70, 71 (repr.), 77–9; *Brooklyn Mus. Quarterly,* VI (1919), 24, 33 (for signature); L. Park, *Joseph Blackburn,* 1923 (reprint from *The Proceedings of the American Antiquarian Society,* October, 1922), 11–12, No. 1; F. W. Bayley, *Five Colonial Artists of New England,* 1929, 57 (repr.); *The Antiquarian,* XV (August, 1930), 26 (repr); F. W. Coburn, *The Amer. Mag. of Art,* XXI (1930), 403–5 (repr.).

Park (*Blackburn, supra*), suggests that this may be the portrait mentioned in an advertisement of 1817. He thinks the picture was probably painted for Thomas Hancock, a wealthy Boston merchant.

Sir Jeffrey Amherst (1717–1797), born at Amherst of Riverhead, Kent. He acquired great military prestige as commander-in-chief of the British army in North America from 1758 to 1764. He came to Boston in September 1758, from Canada and encamped on Boston Common, taking up his march for Albany on September 16. It was during this period that Blackburn painted his portrait. After numerous military victories he was made Governor-General of British North America, and in 1776 elevated to Baron Amherst. There are portraits of him by Gainsborough (National Port. Gall., Lond.) and Reynolds (Earl Amherst).

JOHN SINGLETON COPLEY, American, 1737–1815

411. Brass Crosby, Lord Mayor of London

Oil on canvas, 88½ x 54½ in.
Indistinct signature.
Owned by The Art Institute of Chicago (Munger Collection).

Coll.: A. Ramsden; Ehrich Gall., N. Y.

Lit.: *Bull.*, XVI (1922), 66–7 (repr.); S. Lafollette, *Art in America*, 1929, opp. 54 (repr.); T. Bolton and H. L. Binesse, *The Antiquarian*, XV (December, 1930), 116; *Guide*, 1932, 101 (repr.).

Painted c. 1780–90.

Brass Crosby (1725–93), Lord Mayor of London (1770), was a conspicuous figure in English politics, championing the right of the press to publish parliamentary debates. Defeated in the elections of 1774 and 1784, Crosby was elected Governor of the Irish Society in 1785.

JOHN SINGLETON COPLEY, American, 1737–1815

*412. Dorothy Murray (Pl. LXXX)

Oil on canvas, 36¼ x 28⅛ in.
Lent by The Fogg Art Museum of Harvard University, Cambridge, Massachusetts.

Coll.: Mrs. Sarah Forbes Hughes, Milton, Mass.; Mrs. Dorthea Hughes Simmons.

Exh.: Mus. of Fine Arts, Boston, 1930, No. 38 (repr.) (the title is interchanged with that of Mrs. Ezekiel Goldthwait).

Lit.: F. W. Bayley, *J. S. Copley*, 1910, 37; Bayley, *The Life and Works of J. S. Copley*, 1915, 107–8; T. Bolton and H. L. Binesse, *The Antiquarian*, XV (December, 1930), 118.

The sitter (1743–1811), was born in Scotland. She married the Rev. John Forbes, Boston, 1769. Lived in Florida, 1769–73. Returned to Boston in 1773 and lived there until her death.

JOHN SINGLETON COPLEY, American, 1737–1815

*413. Master Augustus Brine (1782) (Pl. LXXX)

Oil on canvas, 50 x 40 in.
Signed: J. S. COPLEY PINXIT, 1782.
Lent from a Private Collection, New York.

Coll.: Brine Family, Boldre Hill, Lymington, England; Duveen Brothers, N. Y.

Exh.: Reinhardt Gall., 1929.

Repr.: *Internatl. Stu.*, XCVI (August, 1930), cover.

Augustus Brine (1770–1840), was the only son of Admiral James Brine (died at Blandford, Dorsetshire, 1814) of the Royal British Navy, by his first wife, Jane Knight. About the age of 12, in 1782, he entered the Navy as midshipman on board the Belliqueux, under the command of his father. In 1790 he was made a Lieutenant, and on Dec. 6, 1798, a Commander. His commission as Post-Captain bears the date, April 29, 1802. During the naval engagements, in 1805, against Napoleon's attempted invasion of England, he commanded the Medway. In July 1814, he captured the United States brig-of-war Syren, pierced for 18 guns, with a complement of 137 men. He received his commission as Rear-Admiral about 1822.

JOHN SINGLETON COPLEY, American, 1737–1815

414. Mrs. Seymour Fort

Oil on canvas, 50 x 40 in.
Lent by The Wadsworth Atheneum, Hartford, Connecticut.

Coll.: Dowdeswell, Lond., 1901.

Exh.: The Met. Mus. of Art, N. Y., 1910

Lit.: F. W. Bayley, *J. S. Copley*, 1910, 35; Bayley, *Life and Works of J. S. Copley*, 1915, 108; S. Isham, *History of American Painting* (New Edition), 1927, opp. 19 (repr.); Bayley, *Five Colonial Artists of New England*, 1929, 203 (repr.); T. Bolton and H. L. Binesse, *The Antiquarian*, XV (December, 1930), 83 (repr.).

Painted c. 1785–90.

RALPH EARL, American, 1751–1801

*415. Mother and Child (Pl. LXXIX)

Oil on canvas, 50 x 40 in.
Owned by The Art Institute of Chicago (Friends of American Art Collection).

Coll.: Ehrich Gall., N. Y.

Lit.: D. C. Rich, *Internatl. Stu.*, XCVI (August, 1930), 36 (repr.), 37; *Guide*, 1932, 104.

ROBERT FEKE, American, c. 1705–c. 1751

*416. Self-Portrait (Pl. LXXIX)

Oil on canvas, 29¾ x 26 in.
Lent by The Reverend Henry Wilder Foote, Belmont, Massachusetts.

Coll.: G. Flagg IV to M. F. Wilder to M. W. White to M. W. Foote to H. W. Foote I to H. W. Foote II to the present owner.

Exh.: Mus. of Fine Arts, Boston, 1930, No. 34 (repr. in cat.); Fogg Art Mus., Cambridge, Mass., Summer, 1931; Summer, 1932.

Lit.: W. Dunlap, *History of the Arts of Design in America*, 1918, I, opp. 28 (repr.); F. W. Bayley, *Five Colonial Artists of New England*, 1929, 299 (repr.); H. W. Foote, *Robert Feke*, 1930, frontispiece, 139; F. W. Coburn, *The American Mag. of Art*, XXI (1930), 490 (repr.) 494.

According to Foote painted c. 1725.

CHESTER HARDING, American, 1792–1866

417. Mr. George Hallett
Oil on panel, 28 x 23 in.
Owned by The Art Institute of Chicago.
Lit.: R. M. F., *Bull.*, XXI (1927), 40–41 (repr.).

CHESTER HARDING, American, 1792–1866

418. Mrs. George Hallett
Oil on panel, 28 x 23 in.
Owned by the Art Institute of Chicago.
Lit.: R. M. F., *Bulletin,* XXI (1927), 40–1 (repr.); *Guide,* 1932, 108 (repr.).
Pendant to No. 417.

JOHN HESSELIUS, American, 1728–1778

419. Charles Calvert of Maryland (1761)
Oil on canvas, 60 x 40 in.
Signed: j. hesselius, 1761.
Lent by General Lawrason Riggs, Baltimore, Maryland.
Coll.: Onorio Razzolini Coll., Asolo, Italy; Loredan.
Exh.: The Baltimore Mus. of Art, Baltimore, Md.
Lit.: The Art News, XXIV (April 3, 1926), 4.

One of eight paintings of the Calvert family of Maryland discovered in Asolo, Italy, the work of Gustave Hesselius and his son, John Hesselius. This portrait depicts Charles Calvert (1756–1777), son of Benedict (Swingate) Calvert, illegitimate son of Charles Calvert, Fifth Lord Baltimore (1699–1751). In 1748 Benedict married Elizabeth, daughter of the Hon. Charles Calvert, Governor of Maryland, who bore him thirteen children.

SAMUEL F. B. MORSE, American, 1791–1872

420. Susan Root Fitch
Oil on canvas, 30¾ x 25¼ in.
Lent by Mrs. Forbes Hawkes, New York.
Coll.: Descendants of Susan Root Fitch.
Exh.: Met. Mus. of Art, N. Y., Winter, 1932 (repr. in cat., Fig. 30); Syracuse N. Y., Gallery, Spring, 1932.

Susan Root Fitch (1800–1846) was the wife of Reverend Eleazer T. Fitch, Professor of Sacred Theology, Yale College.

EDWARD SAVAGE, American, 1761–1817

421. George Washington (1793)
Oil on panel, 17½ x 13¾ in.
Signed: e. savage, 1793.
Owned by The Art Institute of Chicago.
Coll.: C. H. Savage, Dartford, Wisconsin (descendant of the artist); Catherine Colvin (descendant of the artist).
Exh.: Washington Bi-centennial Expo.; Corcoran Gallery, Wash., D. C., 1932.
Lit.: C. H. Hart, *Edward Savage,* 1905, 8–9; *Guide,* 1932, 106 (repr.).

Mezzotinted by the artist (occasionally in color).
Painted from studies made directly from Washington in 1790. Finished in London, 1793, and Savage used this panel as the model for his highly successful engraving.

GILBERT STUART, American, 1755–1828

422. George Washington
Oil on canvas (oval), 19¾ x 16 in.
Lent by Mr. Samuel W. Weis, Chicago.
Coll.: G. Pollock, G. A. Pollock, J. Pollock, H. Levi, all of New Orleans, La.
Exh.: Isaac Delgado Mus. of Art, New Orleans, La.; The Art Inst. of Chi., since 1923.
Lit.: M. Fielding and J. H. Morgan, *Life Portraits of George Washington,* 1931, 299, Item 81.

One of the two replicas painted by Stuart of the Athenaeum George and Martha Washington, referred to in his memorandum, dated April 20, 1795, as: "Mess. Pollock, New York 2." George Pollock lived until 1804 in New York, removing at that date to New Orleans where he died in 1820. George Pollock probably presented the pair of Washington portraits to his nephew, George Augustus Pollock, from whose direct heirs the present picture was obtained. At the time it was found there was also a portrait of Martha Washington, subsequently destroyed because of bad condition. Mr. Henry Levi, who found the pictures, cut down and mounted the George Washington from a rectangular stretcher (c. 30 x 24 in.) to its present oval dimensions.

GILBERT STUART, American, 1755–1828

423. George Washington
Oil on canvas, 92 x 57½ in.
Owned by The Art Institute of Chicago.
Coll.: G. Baker, N. Y.; W. M. Tweed, N. Y.; Mrs. McGinnis and Mrs. Gilmore of New Orleans; Stan. V. Henkels Sale, Philadelphia, Dec. 17, 1915; Max Williams, Phil.
Exh.: Mus. of Society of St. Tammany, Tammany Hall, 1790–98; Chicago Historical Society, 1932.
Lit.: G. Mason, *Life and Works of Gilbert Stuart,* 1879, 101; A. Rosenthal, *Portrait of George Washington,* 1919, frontispiece; M. Fielding, *Gilbert Stuart's Portraits of George Washington,* 1923, oppos. 72 (repr.), 135, No. 19; *Bull.* XVIII (1924), 64 (repr.), 80–1; L. Park, *Gilbert Stuart,* 1926, II, 856–7, No. 21.

A replica of the "Lansdowne" portrait, the original of which was painted for Mr. William Bingham of Philadelphia, 1796.

GILBERT STUART, American, 1755–1828

*424. Major-General Henry Dearborn (Pl. LXXXI)
Oil on panel, 28$\frac{3}{16}$ x 22¾ in.
Owned by The Art Institute of Chicago (Friends of American Art Collection).
Coll.: The Dearborn Family (until 1886); Chicago Commercial Club; Calumet Club of Chicago; M. Knoedler and Co., N. Y. (1914).
Exh.: Exh. of Stuart's Portraits, Boston, Mass., 1828, No. 197; Bostonian Society, Boston, 1886; The Art Inst. of Chi., 1905.
Lit.: *Fine Arts Journal,* XXIX (1913), 718–9 (repr.); L. M. Bryant, *American Pictures and Their Painters,* 1920, opp. 30 (fig. 7), 32; L. Park, *Gilbert Stuart,* 1926, I, 268–9, No. 224, III, 137 (repr.).

Painted in Boston, 1812. Replicas are in the colls. of Mrs. Arthur Meeker, Chi., and Bowdoin College, Brunswick, Maine.
Major-General Henry Dearborn (1751–1829), born at North Hampton, New Hampshire, served in many important battles of the Revolution. He was Secretary of War from 1801–9; Major-General in 1812 and Minister to Portugal in 1822. Fort Dearborn (later Chicago) was named for him.

GILBERT STUART, American, 1755–1828

*425. Mrs. Perez Morton (Pl. LXXXI)
Oil on canvas, 28½ x 24½ in.
Lent by The Worcester Art Museum, Worcester, Mass.

Coll.: Jane Stuart (until 1862); E. Tuckerman, J. Tuckerman, both of Newport, R. I.; S. Salisbury, Worcester, Mass.

Exh.: Boston Athenaeum, 1855; Copley Hall, Boston, 1902.

Lit.: H. M. L., *Bull. of the Worcester Art Mus.*, VI (1915), 10 (repr.), 11; L. M. Bryant, *American Pictures and their Painters*, 1917, opp. 33 (fig. 9); L. Park, *Gilbert Stuart*, 1926, II, 534–6, No. 561, IV, 340 (repr.).

Painted in Philadelphia c. 1802. Unfinished. Other portraits of her by Stuart belong to the Misses Hannah M. and Grace Edwards of Boston and to Miss Mary Griselda Gray of Halifax.
Sarah Wentworth Apthorp (Mrs. Perez Morton) (1759–1846), was born in Braintree, Mass. A woman of great personal charm, she was likewise a well-known writer, being called "the American Sappho." Writing under the name of "Philemia," she published in 1790, *Ouabi, or the Virtues of Nature;* in 1797, a patriotic poem entitled *Beacon Hill;* in 1823, *My Mind and Its Thoughts,* a collection of verse and prose.

THOMAS SULLY, American, 1783–1872

426. Mrs. George Lingen
Oil on canvas (oval), 24½ x 24 in.
Owned by The Art Institute of Chicago (Friends of American Art Collection).

Coll.: Descendants of the sitter; Mrs. A. C. Lambdin, Philadelphia.

Lit.: C. H. Hart, *A Register of Portraits Painted by Thomas Sully,* 1909, 107, No. 1054; *100 Early American Paintings,* (Ehrich Gall., N. Y.), 130 (repr.); E. Biddle and M. Fielding, *Life and Works of Thos. Sully,* 1921, 213, No. 1098; *Guide,* 1932, 107.

Painted in Philadelphia. Begun September 29, 1842, and finished November 10, the same year. Mrs. Lingen (Maria Oldmixon) was the wife of a prominent Philadelphia doctor of the day.

SAMUEL LOVETT WALDO, American, 1783–1861

427. Major-General Andrew Jackson
Oil on canvas, 33¼ x 26¼ in.
Lent by Mr. and Mrs. William A. Fisher, Detroit.

Coll.: L. G. Bloomingdale, N. Y.; H. Young Gall., N. Y.

Lit.: F. C. Sherman, *Art in America,* XVIII (1930), 82, 83 (repr.).

Andrew Jackson (1767–1845), American general and seventh President of the United States. Fought as a youth in the Revolution, and became one of the chief heroes of the War of 1812, capturing and defending New Orleans; afterwards conducted a highly successful campaign in Florida, becoming its first Governor.
The portrait was probably painted at the height of Jackson's popularity as a General, c. 1816–7.

SAMUEL LOVETT WALDO, American, 1783–1861

428. Mrs. J. F. Mackie
Oil on canvas, 35½ x 29 in.
Owned by The Art Institute of Chicago (Friends of American Art Collection).

A companion portrait of Mr. Mackie is in the collection of the Institute.

BENJAMIN WEST, American, 1738–1820

429. Troilus and Cressida
Oil on panel, 13⅜ x 16⅞ in.
Owned by The Art Institute of Chicago

According to versions of the legend, Cressida was the daughter of a priest, Chalcas, and was betrothed to Troilus. Upon the exchange of prisoners she fell to the lot of one Diomed, to whom she transferred her affections, even giving him the sleeve which Troilus had bestowed upon her in token of their betrothal.

AMERICAN PAINTING
Nineteenth and Twentieth Centuries

GALLERIES 25 *and* 53

CECILIA BEAUX, American, 1863–

430. After the Meeting
Oil on canvas, 40 x 28 in.
Signed: cecilia beaux.
Lent by The Toledo Museum of Art (Maurice A. Scott Collection), Toledo, Ohio.

GEORGE W. BELLOWS, American, 1882–1925

431. Love of Winter
Oil on canvas, 32½ x 40½ in.
Signed: george bellows.
Owned by The Art Institute of Chicago (Friends of American Art Collection).

Lithographed as a Christmas card by the artist, 1923. Painted c. 1912–13.

GEORGE W. BELLOWS, American, 1882–1925

432. My Mother
Oil on canvas, 83 x 49 in.
Signed: geo. bellows.
Owned by The Art Institute of Chicago (Friends of American Art Collection).

EXH.: 36th Amer. Ptg. & Sculpt., The Art Inst. of Chi., 1923, No. 13 (repr. in cat.); The Met. Mus. of Art, N. Y., 1925.

LIT.: E. S. Bellows, *The Paintings of Geo. Bellows,* 1929, Pl. 113; G. W. Eggers, *Geo. Bellows* (American Artists Series), 1931, 48 (repr.); *Guide,* 1932, 135 (repr.).

Lithographed (with changes) by the artist, 1921.
The second version, painted in 1921. A pencil drawing of the figure is in the collection of the Institute (see No. 836). An oil study (preliminary?) is in the Columbus (Ohio) Gallery of Fine Arts.

GEORGE W. BELLOWS, AMERICAN, 1882–1925

433. THE PICNIC
Oil on canvas, 30 x 44 in.
Signed: GEO. BELLOWS.
Lent from The Adolph Lewisohn Collection, New York.

EXH.: Lamar Gall., N. Y., 1929; City Woman's Club, N. Y., 1930; Columbus Gall. of Fine Arts, 1931, No. 263; Mus. of Mod. Art, N. Y., 1932–3, No. 3 (as "Hills of Dream").

LIT.: *The Arts,* VII (1925), 166, 167 (repr.); E. S. Bellows, *The Paintings of George Bellows,* 1929, Pl. 135; G. W. Eggers, *George Bellows* (American Artists Series), 1931, 24 (repr.).

Painted in 1924.

GEORGE W. BELLOWS, AMERICAN, 1882–1925

*434. A STAG AT SHARKEY'S (Pl. LXXXVIII)
Signed and inscribed on back: "GEO. BELLOWS, 146 E. 19TH ST. N. Y. 'CLUB NIGHT' 67."
Lent by The Cleveland Museum of Art (Hinman B. Hurlbut Collection).

COLL.: Marie Sterner, N. Y.

EXH.: Cleveland Mus. of Art, 1922; Met. Mus. of Art, N. Y., 1925; Los Angeles Mus. of Hist., Science and Art, 1932; Mus. of Mod. Art, N. Y., 1932–1933, No. 1.

LIT.: *Bull., Cleveland Mus.* (1922), 106 (repr.); *Handbook, Cleveland Mus.,* 1928, 44 (repr.); E. S. Bellows, *The Paintings of George Bellows,* 1929, Pl. 20; *Bull. of the Columbus Gall. of Fine Arts,* I (1931), 15 (repr.); G. W. Eggers, *George Bellows* (American Artists Series), 1931, 42 (repr.).

Lithographed by the artist, 1917.
Painted in 1909.

RALPH A. BLAKELOCK, AMERICAN, 1847–1919

435. THE VISION OF LIFE
Oil on canvas, 21 x 39 in.
Signed: R. A. BLAKELOCK.
Lent by Mr. and Mrs. Charles H. Worcester, Chicago.

COLL.: J. G. Snydacker, Chicago (Sale, N. Y., 1922), Reinhardt Gall., N. Y.

LIT.: E. Daingerfield, *Ralph Albert Blakelock,* 1914, opp. 16 (repr. as "The Ghost Dance"); *The Arts,* II (1921), 248 (repr.).

EMIL CARLSEN, AMERICAN, 1853–1932

436. CONNECTICUT HILLSIDE
Oil on canvas, 29¼ x 27⅜ in.
Signed: EMIL CARLSEN.
Owned by The Art Institute of Chicago (Walter H. Schulze Memorial).

MARY CASSATT, AMERICAN, 1845–1926

437. AT THE OPERA
Oil on canvas, 32 x 26 in.
Signed: MARY CASSATT.
Lent by The Museum of Fine Arts, Boston, Massachusetts.

EXH.: The Art Inst. of Chi., 1926–7, No. 1.

LIT.: F. Watson, *Mary Cassatt* (American Artists Series), 1933, 29 (repr.).

Painted in 1880.

MARY CASSATT, AMERICAN, 1845–1926

*438. GIRL COMBING HER HAIR (Pl. LXXXV)
Oil on canvas, 29 x 24½ in.
Lent from The Chester Dale Collection, New York.

COLL.: E. Degas, Paris (Sale, 1918, No. 8); Mrs. H. O. Havemeyer, N. Y. (Sale, 1930, Pt. I, No. 75, repr. in cat.).

EXH.: Exh. of the Impressionists, Paris, 1886; Penn. Acad. of Fine Arts, Phil., 1920; The Art Inst. of Chi., 1926–7, No. 4 (repr. in cat.); Penn. Mus., Phil., 1927, No. 7; French Inst., N. Y., 1931, No. 7; Mus. of Mod. Art, N. Y., 1932–3, No. 13 (repr. in cat.).

LIT.: A. Segard, *Mary Cassatt,* 1913, opp. 20 (repr.); F. Watson, *The Arts,* XI (1927), 294 (repr.).

Painted in 1886.

MARY CASSATT, AMERICAN, 1845–1926

439. THE TOILET
Oil on canvas, 39 x 26 in.
Signed: MARY CASSATT.
Owned by The Art Institute of Chicago.

COLL.: Durand-Ruel, N. Y. (1910).

EXH.: The Art Inst. of Chi., 1927, No. 29 (repr. in cat.).

LIT.: A. Segard, *Mary Cassatt,* 1913, between 52 and 53 (repr.); F. Watson, *Mary Cassatt* (American Artists Series), 1933, 43 (repr.); *Guide,* 1932, 115 (repr.).

Painted in 1894.

WILLIAM M. CHASE, American, 1849–1916
440. Alice
Oil on canvas, 68¼ x 49⅝ in.
Signed: WM. M. CHASE.
Owned by The Art Institute of Chicago.
Coll.: Ernest A. Hamill, Chi. (1893).
Exh.: World's Columbian Expo., Chi., 1893, No. 769; Toledo Mus., 1912, No. 18 (repr. in cat.); Albright Art Gall., Buffalo, N. Y., 1928.
Lit.: K. M. Root, *The Life and Art of William Merritt Chase,* 1917, 165, opp. 166 (repr.); L. M. Bryant, *Amer. pict. and their painters,* 1917, 114–5 (fig. 75); *The Mentor,* XII (O. 1924), 33 (repr.); *Guide,* 1932, 118 (repr.).
The model is the artist's daughter, painted in 1893.

ARTHUR B. DAVIES, American, 1862–1928
441. Avatar
Oil on canvas, 17⅝ x 39¾ in.
Signed: A. B. DAVIES.
Owned by The Art Institute of Chicago (Mr. and Mrs. Martin A. Ryerson Collection).
Coll.: M. A. Ryerson, Chi., 1926.

ARTHUR B. DAVIES, American, 1862–1928
442. The Choral Sea
Oil on canvas, 17 x 39⅜ in.
Signed: A. B. DAVIES.
Owned by The Art Institute of Chicago (Mr. and Mrs. Martin A. Ryerson Collection).
Coll.: M. A. Ryerson, Chi., 1917.
Painted in 1915.

ARTHUR B. DAVIES, American, 1862–1928
443. Evening Among Ruins
Oil on canvas, 11 x 16 in.
Owned by The Art Institute of Chicago.
Coll.: Geo. F. Porter, Chi. (1927).
Lit.: R. Cortissoz, *Arthur B. Davies* (American Artists Series), 1931, 24.
Painted in 1902.

ARTHUR B. DAVIES, American, 1862–1928
444. Full-Orbed Moon
Oil on canvas, 20½ x 15½ in.
Owned by The Art Institute of Chicago (Mr. and Mrs. Martin A. Ryerson Collection).
Painted in 1901.

ARTHUR B. DAVIES, American, 1862–1928
445. Helen the Dawn Flower
Oil on canvas, 23¾ x 17¾ in.
Signed: A. B. DAVIES.
Owned by The Art Institute of Chicago (Mr. and Mrs. Martin A. Ryerson Collection).
Lit.: M. B. W., *Bull.,* XVI (1922), 54, 55 (repr.).

ARTHUR B. DAVIES, American, 1862–1928
*446. Italian Landscape (Pl. LXXXVII)
Oil on canvas, 26 x 39¾ in.
Lent by The Trustees of the Estate of Miss Lizzie P. Bliss through The Museum of Modern Art, New York.
Coll.: Miss L. P. Bliss, N. Y.
Exh.: Mus. of Mod. Art, N. Y., 1931, No. 46 (repr. in cat.); Addison Gall. of Amer. Art, Andover, Mass., 1931, No. 34; John Herron Art Inst., Indianapolis, 1932, No. 31 (repr. in cat., Pl. 5).
Lit.: R. Cortissoz, *Arthur B. Davies* (American Artists Series), 1931, 27.
Painted in 1925.

ARTHUR B. DAVIES, American, 1862–1928
447. Jewel-Bearing Tree of Amity
Oil on canvas, 18 x 40 in.
Owned by The Art Institute of Chicago (Mr. and Mrs. Martin A. Ryerson Collection).
Coll.: M. A. Ryerson, Chi., 1915.
Lit.: *Interntl. Studio,* LXXV (1922), 216 (repr.).
Painted in 1912.

ARTHUR B. DAVIES, American, 1862–1928
448. Maya, Mirror of Illusions
Oil on canvas, 26 x 40 in.
Owned by The Art Institute of Chicago (Friends of Amer. Art Collection).
Exh.: Carnegie Inst., Pitts., 1911; Detroit Inst. of Art, 1915; Albright Art Gall., Buffalo, N. Y., 1921; John Herron Art Inst., Indianapolis, 1924; Milwaukee Art Institute, 1925; Corcoran Gall., Washington, 1930; Met. Mus. of Art, N. Y.; Wadsworth Atheneum, Hartford, Conn., 1933, No. 61 (repr. in cat.).
Lit.: R. Cortissoz, *Arthur B. Davies* (American Artists Series), 1931, 29; *Guide,* 1932, 126 (repr.).
Painted in 1910.

ARTHUR B. DAVIES, American, 1862–1928
449. Pearl and Jet
Oil on canvas, 11¾ x 5¾ in.
Signed: A. B. DAVIES.
Owned by The Art Institute of Chicago (Mr. and Mrs. Martin A. Ryerson Collection).
Coll.: M. A. Ryerson, Chi. (1917).
Painted in 1899.

ARTHUR B. DAVIES, American, 1862–1928
450. Silver Springs
Oil on canvas, 17 x 39½ in.
Signed: A. B. DAVIES.
Lent by Mrs. Martin A. Ryerson, Chicago.
Coll.: M. A. Ryerson, Chi. (1915).
Lit.: R. Cortissoz, *Arthur B. Davies* (American Artists Series), 1931, 32.
Painted in 1910.

ARTHUR B. DAVIES, American, 1862–1928
451. Two Voices: Harmony and Discord
Oil on canvas, 17⅜ x 39½ in.
Signed: A. B. DAVIES.
Owned by The Art Institute of Chicago (Mr. and Mrs. Martin A. Ryerson Collection).
Coll.: M. A. Ryerson, Chi., 1923.

FRANK DUVENECK, American, 1848–1919
452. The Music Master (1875)
Oil on canvas, 20 x 16 in.
Signed with monogram and dated '75.
Lent by The Phillips Memorial Gallery, Washington, D. C.
Lit.: F. F. Sherman, *Art in America,* XVI (1928), 98, No. 71 (repr.).
Painted in Munich in 1875.

FRANK DUVENECK, American, 1848–1919
*453. The Whistling Boy (1872)
(Pl. LXXXVI)
Oil on canvas, 28 x 21 in.
Signed: FD, MUNICH, 1872.
Lent by The Cincinnati Art Museum, Cincinnati, Ohio.
Exh.: Royal Academy, Berlin, 1910; Panama-Pacific Expo., San Francisco, 1915, No. 3868; Mus. of Mod. Art, N. Y., 1932–3, No. 28 (repr. in cat.).
Lit.: N. Heermann, *Frank Duveneck,* 1918, 8 (repr.); D. C. Thomson, *The Connoisseur,* LXI (Sept., 1921), 4 (repr.); F. F. Sherman, *Art in America,* XVI (1928), 97, No. 11; E. M. Clark, *Ohio Art and Artists,* 1932, frontispiece, 87.

THOMAS EAKINS, American, 1844–1916
454. Addie (1900)
Oil on canvas, 24⅛ x 18¼ in.
Signed: T. E. 1900.
Lent by The Pennsylvania Museum of Art, Philadelphia, Pennsylvania.
Coll.: Mrs. Thos. Eakins, Phil.
Exh.: Mus. of Mod. Art, N. Y., 1930, No. 107 (repr. in cat.).
Lit.: L. Goodrich, *Thomas Eakins,* 1933, 191, No. 333 and Pl. 54.
The sitter is Miss Mary Adeline Williams, childhood friend of Thos. and Margaret Eakins, who lived with the family from 1900 on. Eakins painted another head of her in 1899 (coll. Mrs. Eakins).

THOMAS EAKINS, American, 1844–1916
*455. Music (1904) (Pl. LXXXIV)
Oil on canvas, 39⅛ x 49 in.
Signed: EAKINS, 1904.
Owned by The Art Institute of Chicago (Friends of American Art Collection).
Coll.: G. H. McFadden (1924).
Exh.: Penn. Acad. of Fine Arts, 1917–18 (repr. in cat.); Mus. of Mod. Art, N. Y., 1930.
Lit.: *The Arts,* V (1924), 332; D. C. Rich, *Bull.,* XXI (1927), 97 (repr.), 101–2; L. Goodrich, *Thomas Eakins,* 1933, 199, No. 402, and Pl. 62; *Guide,* 1932, 114 (repr.).
An oil sketch of the violinist is owned by the Penn. Mus. of Art, Phil.
The violinist is Hedda van der Beemt of the Phil. orchestra; the pianist is Samuel Myers.
In the background is a reproduction of Whistler's "Sarasate."

THOMAS EAKINS, American, 1844–1916
†456. Sketch for "The Pathetic Song"
Oil on panel, 11¼ x 8¼ in.
Lent by The Babcock Gallery, New York.
Coll.: D. W. Jordan, N. Y.
Lit.: L. Goodrich, *Thomas Eakins,* 1933, 174, No. 149.
A sketch for the painting in the Corcoran Gall., Washington, D. C.
The singer is Miss Harrison, sister of the painters, Alexander and Birge Harrison; the pianist is Susan H. MacDowell, later Mrs. Thos. Eakins.

GEORGE FULLER, American, 1822–1884
457. Psyche
Oil on composition board, 36 x 28 in.
Signed: G. FULLER.
Owned by The Art Institute of Chicago (Friends of American Art Collection).
Coll.: W. A. Tower, Boston.
Exh.: Met. Mus. of Art, N. Y., 1923, No. 17 (repr. in cat.); Macbeth Gall., N. Y., 1932.
Lit.: A. G. Fuller, *George Fuller,* 1886, opp. 82 (repr.), 92.
Engraved on wood by W. B. Closson.
Painted in 1884.

CHARLES W. HAWTHORNE, American, 1872–1930
458. Little Sylvia
Oil on panel, 40 x 40 in.
Signed: C. W. HAWTHORNE.
Owned by The Art Institute of Chicago (Friends of Amer. Art Collection).

ROBERT HENRI, American, 1865–1929
*459. Herself (Pl. LXXXVI)
Oil on canvas, 31¼ x 26 in.
Signed: ROBERT HENRI.
Owned by The Art Institute of Chicago (Walter H. Schulze Memorial).
Coll.: Macbeth Gall., N. Y.
Exh.: Met. Mus. of Art, N. Y., 1930.
Lit.: *Cat. of the Walter H. Schulze Gallery,* 1924, 16 (repr.); *Guide,* 1932, 127 (repr.).
Painted in 1913.
The companion "Himself" is also in the Institute collection.

WINSLOW HOMER, American, 1836–1910

*460. The Herring Net (1885) (Pl. LXXXIII)

Oil on canvas, 30 x 48 in.

Signed: homer '85.

Lent by Mrs. Martin A. Ryerson, Chicago.

Coll.: C. W. Gould, N. Y., No. 137; M. A. Ryerson, Chi.

Exh.: World's Columbian Expo. (Chi., 1893); Carnegie Inst., Pitts., 1908; Metropol. Mus., New York, 1911; Mus. of Mod. Art, N. Y., 1930, No. 9 (repr. in cat.).

Lit.: W. H. Downes, *Life and Works of Winslow Homer,* 1911, opp. 134 (repr.), 137, 231, 258; K. Cox, *Winslow Homer,* 1914, opp. 34 (repr.), 51; T. Bolton, *The Fine Arts,* XVIII (Febr., 1932), 52, 54; M. B. W., *Bulletin,* XVII (1923), 56 (repr.), 58.

Also known by the title "Grand Banks Fishermen."

WINSLOW HOMER, American, 1836–1910

461. The Lookout—"All's Well!" (1896)

Oil on canvas, 40⅛ x 30⅛ in.

Signed: homer, 1896.

Lent by The Museum of Fine Arts, Boston, Massachusetts.

Coll.: Thos. B. Clark (Sale, 1899).

Exh.: Union League Club, N. Y., 1898; Internatl. Expo., Paris, 1900, No. 154; Carnegie Inst., Pittsburgh, 1908; Royal Academy of Arts, Berlin, 1910.

Lit.: W. A. Coffin, *The Century Mag.,* LVIII (1899), 653, 654 (repr.); F. W. Morton, *Brush and Pencil,* X (1902), 49, 54 (repr.); C. Brinton, *Winslow Homer,* 1911, 19 (repr.); W. H. Downes, *Life and Works of Winslow Homer,* 1911, 220 (repr.); K. Cox, *Winslow Homer,* 1914, opp. 50 (repr.), 51; T. Bolton, *The Fine Arts,* XVIII (Feb., 1932), 55.

Etched by W. H. W. Bicknell.

WINSLOW HOMER, American, 1836–1910

462. On a Lee Shore (1900)

Oil on canvas, 39 x 39 in.

Signed: homer, 1900.

Lent by The Museum of Art, Rhode Island School of Design, Providence, Rhode Island.

Coll.: M. O'Brien and Son, Chi.; Dr. F. W. Gunsaulus, Chi.

Exh.: Carnegie Inst., Pitts., 1908; Mus. of Fine Arts, Boston, 1911; Mus. of Mod. Art, N. Y., 1930, No. 15 (repr. in cat.).

Lit.: F. W. Morton, *Brush and Pencil,* X (1902), 49 (repr.); W. H. Downes, *Life and Works of Winslow Homer,* 1911, 149, 208–9; *Bull. of the R. I. School of Design,* V (1917), 17 (repr.), 18; L. Goodrich, *The Arts,* VI (1924), 200 (repr.); T. Bolton, *The Fine Arts,* XVIII (Febr., 1932), 55.

WINSLOW HOMER, American, 1836–1910

463. Signal of Distress

Oil on canvas, 26½ x 40 in.

Signed: winslow homer, 1892–6.

Lent by Mr. Ralph Cudney, Chicago.

Coll.: E. T. Stotesbury, Phil.

Exh.: Int. Society of Sculptors, Painters, and Gravers. Lond., 1906; The Art Inst. of Chi., 1929; The Mus. of Mod. Art, N. Y., 1930, No. 16.

Lit.: W. H. Downes, *Life and Works of Winslow Homer,* 1911, 151–2, 156, 158–9, opp. 166 (repr.), 183; T. Bolton, *The Fine Arts,* XVIII (Febr., 1932), 52, 54.

Downes states it was painted in 1891. The inscription "1892–6" would indicate that Homer worked on it until 1896. Bolton follows Downes in giving it to 1891.

WINSLOW HOMER, American, 1836–1910

464. Watching the Breakers (1891)

Oil on canvas, 30¼ x 40⅜ in.

Signed: homer, 1891.

Owned by The Art Institute of Chicago (Friends of American Art Collection).

Coll.: M. A. Ryerson, Chi., 1911–13.

Exh.: Albright Art Gall., Buffalo, N. Y., 1929; Mus. of Mod. Art, N. Y., 1930.

Lit.: *Bull.,* VI (1913), 49 (repr.); E. M. Stuart, *Fine Arts Journal,* XXXV (Apr., 1917), 252; T. Bolton, *The Fine Arts,* XVIII (Febr., 1932), 54; *Guide,* 1932, 113 (repr).

Sometimes confused with a painting of the same title executed in 1896.

GEORGE INNESS, American, 1825–1894

465. Coast of Cornwall (1887)

Oil on canvas, 32 x 42 in.

Signed: g. inness, 1887.

Lent by Mr. and Mrs. Charles H. Worcester, Chicago.

Exh.: Albright Art Gall., Buffalo, N. Y., 1925.

GEORGE INNESS, American, 1825–1894

466. Moonlight on Passamaquoddy Bay (1893)

Oil on canvas, 30 x 45½ in.

Signed: g. inness, 1893.

Owned by The Art Institute of Chicago (Mr. and Mrs. Martin A. Ryerson Collection).

Coll.: Estate of the painter (Sale, 1895); M. A. Ryerson, Chi. (1895).

Exh.: Albright Art Gall., Buffalo, N. Y., 1925; Mus. of Mod. Art, N. Y., 1932, No. 58.

Lit.: Geo. Inness, Jr., *Life, Art and Letters of George Inness,* 1917, 263 (repr.).

GEORGE INNESS, American, 1825–1894

467. The Storm (1876)

Oil on canvas, 25⅜ x 38¼ in.

Signed: g. inness, 1876.

Owned by The Art Institute of Chicago (Edward B. Butler Collection).

Lit.: *Cat. of the Butler Coll.,* 1930, 32 (repr.); *Guide,* 1932, 110 (repr.).

J. GARI MELCHERS, American, 1860–1932

468. Mother and Child

Oil on canvas, 25 x 21⅜ in.

Signed: MELCHERS.

Owned by The Art Institute of Chicago (James Deering Collection).

Exh.: Paris Salon, 1906; 19. Amer. Ptg. & Sc., 1906, No. 218; Albright A. Gall., Buffalo, 1930; Memorial A. Gall., Rochester, N. Y., 1930; Dayton Art Inst., 1930.

J. GARI MELCHERS, American, 1860–1932

469. An Old Salt (Sketch)

Oil on canvas, 22 x 16 in.

Signed: G. MELCHERS.

Owned by The Art Institute of Chicago (James Deering Collection).

MAURICE PRENDERGAST, American, 1861–1924

470. Resting at St. Malo

Oil on canvas, 24 x 30 in.

Signed: PRENDERGAST.

Lent by The Columbus Gallery of Fine Arts (Howald Collection), Columbus, Ohio.

Painted c. 1918.

THEODORE ROBINSON, American, 1852–1896

471. Landscape

Oil on canvas, 23 x 40 in.

Lent by Mr. William S. Stimmel, Pittsburgh, Pennsylvania.

Coll.: G. Hearn, N. Y. (Sale, 1918, Pt. I, No. 111, repr. in cat.).

Lit.: *Cat. of the Geo. Hearn Coll.*, 1908, 174, No. 218.

ALBERT P. RYDER, American, 1847–1917

*472. Diana's Hunt (Pl. LXXXV)

Oil on canvas, 18⅛ x 14¹⁄₁₆ in.

Lent by Mr. Ralph Cudney, Chicago.

Coll.: C. M. Dewey.

Exh.: The Art Inst. of Chi., 1929.

Lit.: F. F. Sherman, *Albert Pinkham Ryder*, 1920, 68, No. 31; F. N. Price, *Ryder*, 1932, No. 32.

ALBERT P. RYDER, American, 1847–1917

473. Elegy in a Country Churchyard

Oil on canvas, 12³⁄₁₆ x 10⁷⁄₁₆ in.

Signed: RYDER.

Lent by Mr. Ralph Cudney, Chicago.

Exh.: The Art Inst. of Chi., 1929.

Lit.: F. F. Sherman, *Albert Pinkham Ryder*, 1920, opp. 56 (repr.), 68, No. 28; F. N. Price, *Ryder*, 1932, No. 36.

ALBERT P. RYDER, American, 1847–1917

474. Moonlight in Maine

Oil on canvas, 11 x 11¾ in.

Owned by The Art Institute of Chicago (Mr. and Mrs. Martin A. Ryerson Collection).

Coll.: Macbeth Gall., N. Y.; M. A. Ryerson, Chi. (1923).

Lit.: F. N. Price, *Ryder*, No. 107 (repr.).

ALBERT P. RYDER, American, 1847–1917

475. The Race Track or Death on a Pale Horse

Oil on canvas, 28¼ x 35¼ in.

Signed A. P. RYDER.

Lent by The Cleveland Museum of Art (The J. H. Wade Collection).

Coll.: Dr. A. T. Sanden; Ferargil Gall., N. Y.

Exh.: Met. Mus. of Art, N. Y., 1918–24; Cleveland Mus., 1928; The Mus. of Mod. Art, N. Y., 1930, No. 61 (repr. in cat.); Met. Mus. of Art, N. Y., Summer, 1932.

Lit.: F. F. Sherman, *Albert Pinkham Ryder*, 1920, opp. 38 (repr.) 46–8, No. 105; *The Arts*, V (1924), 173 (repr.); H. E. Schnakenberg, *The Arts*, VI (1924), 273 (repr.); W. M. Milliken, *Bull. Cleveland Mus. of Art*, XV (1928), 66, 67 (repr.); F. N. Price, *Internatl. Stu.*, LXXXI (July, 1928), 287; M. Mann, *Internatl. Studio*, XCVI (June, 1930), 70 (repr.); Price, *Ryder*, 1932, No. 27 (repr.).

JOHN S. SARGENT, American, 1856–1925

476. Mrs. Charles Gifford Dyer (1880)

Oil on canvas, 24½ x 17 in.

Inscribed: TO MY FRIEND MRS. DYER, JOHN S. SARGENT, VENICE, 1880.

Owned by The Art Institute of Chicago (Friends of American Art Collection).

Coll.: Ch. G. Dyer; M. A. Ryerson.

Exh.: Grand Cent. Gall., N. Y., 1924, No. 49; Milwaukee Art Inst., 1925; Mus. of Mod. Art, N. Y., 1932–3.

Lit.: *Bull.*, X (1916), 141 (repr.), 143; W. H. Downes, *John Singer Sargent*, 1925, opp. 24 (repr.), 124–5; E. Charteris, *Sargent*, 1927, 257.

May Anthony (1850–1914), wife of the American landscape painter Charles Gifford Dyer (1851–1912). An oil sketch is in the possession of Miss Stella Loring, Chi.

JOHN S. SARGENT, American, 1856–1925

477. Nude Study of an Egyptian Girl

Oil on canvas, 73 x 23 in.

Signed: JOHN S. SARGENT.

The Charles Deering Collection, Lent by Mrs. R. E. Danielson and Mrs. Chauncey McCormick.

Coll.: Ch. Deering, Chi.

Exh.: New English Art Club, Lond., 1891; World's Columbian Expo., Chi., 1893, No. 1043; Sargent Loan Exh., Boston, 1899; Panama-Pacific Expo., San Francisco, 1915, No. 3623 (repr. in cat. opp. 386); Mus. of Fine Arts, Boston, 1916; Corcoran Gall., Wash., 1916–17.

Lit.: V. Meynell, *The Work of John Singer Sargent*, 1903, no number (repr.); W. H. Downes, *John Singer Sargent*, 1925, 165–6; R. Cortissoz, *Scribner's Mag.*, LXXV (1924), 347 (repr.); E. Charteris, *Sargent*, 1927, 114, 284 (1890).

Painted in Egypt in 1891. The model was a native girl.

JOHN S. SARGENT, American, 1856–1925

478. Rehearsal of the Lamoureux Orchestra, Paris

Oil on canvas, 36½ x 39¾ in.

Signed: to g. henschel, j. s. sargent.

The Charles Deering Collection, Lent by Mr. and Mrs. Chauncey McCormick, Chicago.

Coll.: Geo. Henschel, Lond.; Ch. Deering, Chi.

Exh.: The Art Inst. of Chi., 1930–31.

Painted c. 1885–90 (?).

JOHN S. SARGENT, American, 1856–1925

*479. Robert Louis Stevenson (1885) (Pl. LXXXIV)

Oil on canvas, 20¼ x 24¼ in.

Signed: to r. l. stevenson, his friend, john s. sargent, 1885.

Lent by Mrs. Payne Whitney, New York.

Exh.: New English Art Club, Lond., 1887; Grand Cent. Gall., N. Y., 1924, No. 28; Met. Mus. of Art, 1925, No. 11 (repr. in cat.).

Lit.: W. H. Downes, *John Singer Sargent,* 1925, 141–2; *The Works of John Singer Sargent,* 1927, no number, (repr.).

Robert Louis Stevenson (1850–94), Scotch novelist, essayist, and poet.
Painted at Bournemouth, 1885. In the shadow is the seated figure of Mrs. Stevenson.

JOHN S. SARGENT, American, 1856–1925

480. Venetian Glass Workers

Oil on canvas, 22 x 33½ in.

Signed: john s. sargent.

Owned by The Art Institute of Chicago (Mr. and Mrs. Martin A. Ryerson Collection).

Coll.: M. A. Ryerson, Chi., 1912

Exh.: Mus. of Fine Arts, Boston, 1925, No. 15.

Lit.: W. H. Downes, *John Singer Sargent,* 1925, 144; E. Charteris, *Sargent,* 1927, 282.

Painted in 1881? Downes dates the picture 1886; Charteris, 1881.

ABBOTT H. THAYER, American, 1849–1921

481. Boy

Oil on canvas, 25 7/16 x 19¼ in.

Signed: a. thayer.

Owned by The Art Institute of Chicago (Friends of American Art Collection).

ABBOTT H. THAYER, American, 1849–1921

482. Study for an Angel

Oil on canvas, 54 x 38 in.

Lent by The Layton Art Gallery, Milwaukee, Wisconsin.

Coll.: J. Gellatly, N. Y.

Exh.: Macbeth Gall., N. Y., 1931.

Painted c. 1901.

JOHN H. TWACHTMAN, American, 1853–1902

483. From the Upper Terrace

Oil on canvas, 25 x 30 in.

Signed: j. h. twachtman (greenwich, conn.).

Owned by The Art Institute of Chicago (Friends of American Art Collection).

Exh.: Panama-Pacific Expo., San Francisco, 1915, No. 4070; Montclair (N. J.) Art Museum, 1933.

Painted c. 1890.

JOHN H. TWACHTMAN, American, 1853–1902

484. Gloucester

Oil on canvas, 25 x 30 in.

Signed: j. h. twachtman.

Owned by The Art Institute of Chicago (Walter H. Schulze Memorial).

Lit.: *Cat. of the Walter H. Schulze Gallery,* 1924, 17 (repr.); *Bull.,* XIX (1925), 8 (repr.), 9.

Painted c. 1898–9.

JOHN H. TWACHTMAN, American, 1853–1902

*485. Snow-Bound (Pl. LXXXIII)

Oil on canvas, 25½ x 30½ in.

Signed: j. h. twachtman.

Owned by The Art Institute of Chicago (Friends of American Art Collection).

Exh.: Milwaukee Art Inst., 1925.

Lit.: *Guide,* 1932, 119 (repr.).

JOHN H. TWACHTMAN, American, 1853–1902

486. The Waterfall

Oil on canvas, 28¾ x 21¼ in.

Signed: j. h. twachtman.

The Charles Deering Collection, Lent by Mr. and Mrs. R. E. Danielson, Boston.

J. ALDEN WEIR, American, 1852–1919

487. The Gray Bodice (1898)

Oil on canvas, 30 x 25 in.

Signed: j. alden weir, 1898.

Owned by The Art Institute of Chicago (Friends of American Art Collection).

Exh.: The Art Inst. of Chi., 1911, No. 383 (repr. in cat., 11); Met. Mus. of Art, N. Y., 1924; Milwaukee Art Inst., 1925.

Lit.: *Julian Alden Weir, an Appreciation,* (Century Assn.), 1921, 132, Pl. 8.

A portrait of Miss M. . . .

JAMES McNEILL WHISTLER, AMERICAN, 1834–1903

488. THE ARTIST IN THE STUDIO
Oil on panel, 24¾ x 18¾ in.
Signed with the Butterfly.
Owned by The Art Institute of Chicago (Friends of American Art Collection).

COLL.: D. Freshfield.

EXH.: Int. Society of Sculptors, Painters and Gravers, Lond., 1905, No. 13; Albright Art Gall., Buffalo, N. Y., 1919; Milwaukee Inst. of Art., 1925.

LIT.: E. L. Cary, *The Works of Whistler,* 1907, 212, No. 375; E. R. and J. Pennell, *Life of James McNeill Whistler,* 1908, I, 184–5 (repr.); A. E. Gallatin, *Art in America,* I (1913), 156, No. V and Fig. 11; L. M. Bryant, *Amer. picts. and their painters,* 1917, 95–6 (fig. 55); Gallatin, *Portraits of Whistler,* 1918, 27–8 (repr. after 32), No. 6; *Guide,* 1932, 112 (repr.).

Painted in 1874.
Another version said to be a sketch (but according to the Pennells, rejected by Whistler) is in the Municipal Art Gall., Dublin.
A study for a projected picture "In the Studio" which was to include Fantin, Albert Moore, Whistler, "Jo" on the sofa and "la Japonaise" walking about—all as Whistler himself wrote "that would shock the Academicians."

JAMES McNEILL WHISTLER, AMERICAN, 1834–1903

489. NOCTURNE IN BLACK AND GOLD: SOUTHAMPTON WATERS
Oil on canvas, 20 x 30 in.
Signed with the Butterfly.
Owned by The Art Institute of Chicago.

EXH.: Grosvenor Gall., Lond., 1884; Memorial Exh., Boston, 1904, No. 58; Int. Soc. of Sculptors, Painters and Gravers, Lond., 1905, No. 9; Memorial Exh., Paris, 1905, No. 67; Cincinnati Art Mus., 1910.

LIT.: *Bull.,* III (1910), 34; E. L. Cary, *The Works of Whistler,* 1907, 165, No. 58.

The complete title is "Nocturne, Black and Gold: Entrance to Southampton Waters." First exhibited at the Grosvenor Gall., 1884, but painted several years earlier.

JAMES McNEILL WHISTLER, AMERICAN, 1834–1903

*490. PORTRAIT OF THE ARTIST'S MOTHER, ARRANGEMENT IN GREY AND BLACK (Pl. LXXXII)
Oil on canvas, 56 x 64 in.
Signed with the Butterfly.
Lent by The Louvre Museum, Paris, through The Museum of Modern Art, New York.

EXH.: Royal Academy, Lond., 1872; Penn. Acad. of Fine Arts, Phil., 1881; Society of American Artists, N. Y., 1882; Salon, Paris, 1883; Dublin Sketching Club, 1884; Amsterdam, 1889; Inst. of Fine Arts, Glasgow, 1889; Purchased by The Luxembourg for $800, 1891; Int. Society of Sculptors, Painters and Gravers, Lond., 1905, No. 23 (repr. in cat. opp. 62); Mus. of Mod. Art, N. Y., 1932–3, No. 112 (repr. in cat.).

LIT.: T. R. Way and G. R. Dennis, *The Art of James McNeill Whistler,* 1903, 42 (repr.); E. L. Cary, *The Works of Whistler,* 1907, 73, opp. 76 (repr.), 187, No. 188; E. R. and J. Pennell, *Life of James McNeill Whistler,* 1908, I, 157, 168–170 (repr.); 297–99, II, 116–17; S. Hartmann, *The Whistler Book,* 1910, 144–6 (repr.); T. R. Way, *Memories of Whistler* (1912), 13, 29, 71, 85; T. Duret, *Whistler* (trans. by F. Rutter), 1917, 29, opp. 38 (repr.), 101; L. M. Bryant, *Amer. Picts. and their Painters,* 1917, 90–2 (fig. 50).

Painted c. 1871.
Anna Mathilda McNeill (d. 1881), daughter of Dr. Charles D. McNeill of Wilmington, N. C., second wife of G. W. Whistler. (On the portrait see a letter from Mrs. Whistler, published in *The Art Digest,* Jan. 1, 1933, 6, 30.)

CONTEMPORARY AMERICAN PAINTING

GALLERIES 52, 52*b*, 51, *G*52–*G*56

CHRISTIAN ABRAHAMSEN, AMERICAN, 1887–

491. PORTRAIT OF MR. J. (1926)
Oil on canvas, 24 x 20 in.
Signed: C. ABRAHAMSEN, 26 APRIL 27.
Lent by the Artist.

JEAN CRAWFORD ADAMS, AMERICAN, 1890–

†492. PINEHURST (1931)
Oil on canvas, 27 x 31 in.
Signed: JEAN C. ADAMS.
Lent by the Artist.

KATHERINE LANGHORNE ADAMS, AMERICAN CONTEMPORARY

493. TEN O'CLOCK BREAKFAST (c. 1922)
Oil on canvas, 25⅛ x 30⅛ in.
Signed: K. LANGHORNE ADAMS.
Lent by the Estate of Mrs. L. L. Coburn, Chicago.

WAYMAN ADAMS, AMERICAN, 1883–

494. JOSEPH PENNELL (PORTRAIT)
Oil on canvas, 52 x 43¼ in.
Signed: WAYMAN ADAMS.
Owned by The Art Institute of Chicago (Friends of American Art Collection).

IVAN L. ALBRIGHT, American, 1897–
†495. Heavy the Oar to Him who is Tired (1929–1930)
Oil on canvas, 53 x 34 in.
Signed: IVAN LE LORRAINE ALBRIGHT.
Lent by the Artist.

JOSEPH ALLWORTHY, American, 1897–
†496. Reflections (1932)
Oil on board, 32¾ x 25¾ in.
Signed: ALLWORTHY S. A. N. A.
Lent by the Artist.

ANTHONY ANGAROLA, American, 1893–1929
497. Main Traveled Road, Cagnes (1928)
Oil on canvas, 24¾ x 31½ in.
Signed: ANTHONY ANGAROLA.
Owned by The Art Institute of Chicago.

BORIS ANISFELD, American, 1879–
498. Early Snow (1926)
Oil on canvas, 40 x 45 in.
Signed: BORIS ANISFELD, N. Y. 1926.
Lent by Mr. R. W. Glasner, Chicago.

EDMUND ARCHER, American, 1904–
†499. Brick Carrier (1931)
Oil on canvas, 46 x 28 in.
Signed: EDMUND ARCHER, 1931.
Lent by the Artist.

EMIL ARMIN, American, 1883–
†500. The Open Bridge (1930)
Oil on canvas, 28 x 22 in.
Signed: EMIL ARMIN, SEPT. 1930.
Lent by the Artist.

FREDERIC CLAY BARTLETT, American, 1873–
†501. Fish (1930)
Oil on canvas, 31 x 39½ in.
Signed: FREDERIC CLAY BARTLETT, '30.
Lent by the Artist.

MACENA BARTON, American, 1901–
†502. Beatrice (1930)
Oil on canvas, 48 x 42 in.
Signed: MACENA BARTON, 1930.
Lent by the Artist.

GIFFORD BEAL, American, 1879–
503. The Spotlight (1915)
Oil on canvas, 34⅞ x 46¾ in.
Signed: GIFFORD BEAL, '15.
Owned by The Art Institute of Chicago (Mr. and Mrs. Martin A. Ryerson Collection).

FRANK WESTON BENSON, American, 1862–
504. A Rainy Day (1906)
Oil on canvas, 25 x 30 in.
Signed: F. W. BENSON, 1906.
Owned by The Art Institute of Chicago (Friends of American Art Collection).

TRESSA EMERSON BENSON, American, 1893–
†505. Girl's Head (1932)
Oil on canvas, 25⅝ x 21⅜ in.
Signed: TRESSA BENSON.
Lent by the Artist.

THOMAS H. BENTON, American, 1889–
†506. Cotton Pickers
Oil and tempera with a gesso surface on canvas, mounted, 30 x 40 in.
Signed: THOMAS H. BENTON.
Lent by the Artist.

THERESA F. BERNSTEIN, American contemporary
†507. View of Gloucester (1929)
Oil on canvas, 26 x 32 in.
Signed: T. BERNSTEIN.
Lent by the Artist.

LOUIS BETTS, American, 1873–
508. The Sea Shell (c. 1928)
Oil on canvas, 39½ x 29⅝ in.
Signed: LOUIS BETTS.
Owned by The Art Institute of Chicago (Friends of American Art Collection).

GEORGE BIDDLE, American, 1885–
†509. Folly Beach Pavilion (1931)
Oil on canvas, 39½ x 50 in.
Signed: BIDDLE, 1931.
Lent by Mr. F. K. M. Rehn, New York.

FRED BIESEL, American, 1894–
†510. Dunes Landscape (1922)
Oil on canvas, 24 x 36 in.
Signed: FRED BIESEL.
Lent by the Artist.

ISABEL BISHOP, American, 1902–
511. Girl Combing Her Hair (1932)
Oil on canvas, 20 x 17 in.
Signed: bishop, '32.
Lent by The Whitney Museum of American Art, New York.

ARNOLD BLANCH, American, 1896–
†512. The Bather (1931)
Oil on canvas, 30 x 42 in.
Signed: arnold blanch.
Lent by Mr. Frank K. M. Rehn, New York.

ERNEST L. BLUMENSCHEIN, American, 1874–
†513. Adobe Village, Winter (1929)
Oil on canvas, 34 x 50 in.
Signed: e. blumenschein, taos, 1929.
Lent by the Artist through The Grand Central Art Galleries, New York.

AARON BOHROD, American, 1907–
†514. Burlesque (1933)
Oil on canvas, 17 x 24 in.
Signed: aaron bohrod.
Lent by the Artist.

GUY PENE DU BOIS, American, 1884–
515. Four Arts Ball (1929)
Oil on canvas, 36 x 28¾ in.
Signed: guy pene du bois, '29.
Lent by Mr. John F. Kraushaar, New York.

ADOLPH BORIE, American, 1877–
516. Seated Nude (c. 1927)
Oil on canvas, 39 x 32 in.
Lent by The Whitney Museum of American Art, New York.

HENRY A. BOTKIN, 1896–
†517. Angelo Brothers (1932)
Oil on canvas, 25 x 21 in.
Signed: botkin.
Lent by The Downtown Gallery, New York.

LOUIS BOUCHE, American, 1896–
518. Stamford Harbor (1932)
Oil on canvas, 29 x 36 in.
Signed: louis bouche, 1932.
Lent by The Whitney Museum of American Art, New York.

ALEXANDER BROOK, American, 1898–
*519. The Children's Lunch (1928) (Pl. XC)
Oil on canvas, 35½ x 40¼ in.
Signed: a. brook, 1928.
Owned by The Art Institute of Chicago.

EDWARD BRUCE, American, 1879–
†520. Tuscan Farm
Oil on canvas, 19 x 32 in.
Signed: edward bruce.
Lent by the Artist through The Milch Galleries, New York.

GEORGE DE F. BRUSH, American, 1855–
520a. Family Group (1907)
Oil on canvas, 31 x 39 in.
Signed: george de forest brush, 1907.
Owned by The Art Institute of Chicago.

CLAUDE BUCK, American, 1890–
†521. Free Coffee (1926)
Oil on canvas, 19½ x 22¾ in.
Signed: claude buck 1926.
Lent by the Artist.

KARL ALBERT BUEHR, American Contemporary
†522. Girl by Stream (1912)
Oil on canvas, 30 x 36 in.
Signed: k.a.b.
Lent by the Artist.

CHARLES E. BURCHFIELD, American, 1893–
*523. Promenade (1929) (Pl. LXXXVII)
Water color on paper, 32 x 42 in.
Lent by Mr. A. Conger Goodyear, New York.

BRYSON BURROUGHS, American, 1869–
524. The Fishermen (1915)
Oil on canvas, 24 x 36 in.
Signed: bryson burroughs, 1915.
Owned by The Art Institute of Chicago (Friends of American Art Collection).

EDGAR SPIER CAMERON, American, 1862–
525. Cabaret Breton (1916)
Oil on canvas, 34½ x 40½ in.
Signed: e. cameron.
Owned by The Art Institute of Chicago (Friends of American Art Collection).

ARTHUR B. CARLES, American, 1882–
526. Arrangement
Oil on canvas, 46¼ x 39½ in.
Signed: carles.
Owned by The Art Institute of Chicago.

JOHN CARROLL, American, 1892–
†527. The Siamese Cat
Oil on canvas, 34 x 44 in.
Signed: JOHN CARROLL.
Lent by Mr. Frank Crowninshield, New York.

FRANCIS CHAPIN, American, 1899–
528. The Pink House (1932)
Oil on canvas, 30 x 25½ in.
Signed: FRANCIS CHAPIN.
Owned by The Art Institute of Chicago.

JAMES CHAPIN, American, 1887–
529. Negro Boxer (1928)
Oil on canvas, 48 x 41 in.
Signed: JAMES CHAPIN, '28.
Lent by Mr. M. H. Collins, Cedar Rapids, Iowa.

RUSSELL CHENEY, American, 1881–
†530. Kittery Point (1928)
Oil on canvas, 29 x 36 in.
Signed: RUSSELL CHENEY.
Lent by the Artist.

NICOLAI CIKOVSKY, American, 1894–
531. Pigeons (1931)
Oil on canvas, 30⅜ x 42 3/16 in.
Signed: N. CIKOVSKY.
Owned by The Art Institute of Chicago.

RALPH ELMER CLARKSON, American, 1861–
532. Nouvart Dzeron, a Daughter of Armenia (1912)
Oil on canvas, 80 x 40 in.
Signed: RALPH CLARKSON, 1912.
Owned by The Art Institute of Chicago (Friends of American Art Collection).

GLENN COLEMAN, American, 1887–1932
†533. The Park
Oil on canvas, 25 x 29½ in.
Signed: COLEMAN.
Lent by The Downtown Gallery, New York.

JOHN E. COSTIGAN, American, 1888–
534. Sheep at the Brook (1922)
Oil on canvas, 33½ x 39 in.
Signed: J. E. COSTIGAN, 1922.
Owned by The Art Institute of Chicago.

RICHARD M. CRISLER, American, 1908–
†535. Canyon Landscape (1931)
Oil on canvas, 36 x 42 in.
Signed: CRISLER.
Lent by the Artist.

JOHN STEUART CURRY, American, 1897–
*536. Baptism in Kansas (1928) (Pl. XC)
Oil on canvas, 40 x 50 in.
Signed: JOHN STEUART CURRY.
Lent by The Whitney Museum of American Art, New York.

GUSTAF DALSTROM, American, 1893–
†537. Snowbound (1930)
Oil on canvas, 25¾ x 29¾ in.
Signed: G. DALSTROM, '30.
Lent by the Artist.

RANDALL DAVEY, American, 1887–
†538. The Jockey
Oil on canvas, 70 x 48 in.
Signed: RANDALL DAVEY.
Lent by the Artist through The Grand Central Art Galleries, New York.

STEPHEN ETNIER, American, 1903–
†539. Near Baltimore (1931)
Oil on canvas, 30 x 25 in.
Signed: S. ETNIER.
Lent by the Artist through The Milch Galleries, New York.

JERRY FARNSWORTH, American, 1895–
†540. Consuela (1930)
Oil on canvas, 48 x 40 in.
Signed: JERRY FARNSWORTH.
Lent by the Artist.

NICOLAI FECHIN, American, 1881–
541. Lady in Pink (1912)
Oil on canvas, 45¾ x 35½ in.
Signed: N. FECHIN, 1912.
Lent by Mr. William S. Stimmel, Pittsburgh, Pennsylvania.

LAUREN FORD, American, 1891–
†542. Vision of the Innocents (1932)
Oil on canvas, 23 x 31 in.
Signed: LAUREN FORD.
Lent by the Artist.

RUTH VAN SICKLE FORD, American, 1898–
†543. New England (1930)
Oil on canvas, 30 x 32 in.
Signed: R. FORD.
Lent by the Artist.

FRANCES FOY, American, 1890–
†544. Betty (1930)
Oil on canvas, 26 x 30 in.
Signed: frances foy, 1930.
Lent by the Artist.

FREDERICK CARL FRIESEKE, American, 1874–
545. Torn Lingerie (1915)
Oil on canvas, 51¼ x 51¾ in.
Signed: f. c. frieseke, 1915.
Lent by The City Art Museum of St. Louis, St. Louis, Missouri.

MAURICE FROMKES, American, 1872–1931
†546. Angelita and Her Mother
Oil on canvas, 39 x 34 in.
Signed: m. fromkes.
Lent by The Estate of the Artist through The Milch Galleries, New York.

DANIEL GARBER, American, 1880–
547. Hills of Byram
Oil on canvas, 42 x 46½ in.
Signed: daniel garber.
Owned by The Art Institute of Chicago (Friends of American Art Collection).

WALTER GAY, American, 1856–
548. The Commode
Oil on canvas, 26 x 21½ in.
Signed: walter gay.
Owned by The Art Institute of Chicago (Friends of American Art Collection).

HOWARD GILES, American, 1876–
549. MacMahan's, Maine
Oil on canvas, 30 x 30 in.
Signed: h. giles.
Owned by The Art Institute of Chicago (Friends of American Art Collection).

WILLIAM J. GLACKENS, American, 1870–
*550. Chez Mouquin (1905) (Pl. XCI)
Oil on canvas, 48 x 39 in.
Signed: w. glackens, '05.
Owned by The Art Institute of Chicago (Friends of American Art Collection).

ANNE GOLDTHWAITE, American, contemporary
†551. Selma (1929)
Oil on canvas, 24 x 20 in.
Signed: anne goldthwaite.
Lent by The Downtown Gallery, New York.

HARRY GOTTLIEB, American contemporary
†552. Winter Landscape (1930)
Oil on canvas, 30 x 50 in.
Signed: h. gottlieb, '30.
Lent by Mr. Frank K. M. Rehn, New York.

JOHN R. GRABACH, American, 1890–
553. Washday in Spring
Oil on canvas, 30¾ x 29 in.
Signed: john r. grabach.
Owned by The Art Institute of Chicago (Friends of American Art Collection).

FREDERIC M. GRANT, American, 1883–
†554. Orchestration (1932)
Oil on canvas, 31 x 33 in.
Signed: frederic m. grant.
Lent by the Artist.

J. JEFFREY GRANT, American, 1883–
†555. Industry (1930)
Oil on canvas, 26 x 30 in.
Signed: j. jeffrey grant.
Lent by the Artist.

FRANCES CRANMER GREENMAN, American, 1890–
†556. Patty with Apples (1923)
Oil on canvas, 36 x 30 in.
Signed: frances cranmer greenman, 1923.
Lent by the Artist.

DAVENPORT GRIFFEN, American, 1894–
†557. Romany Gut, St. Thomas (1931)
Oil on canvas, 30 x 38 in.
Signed: d. griffen, 1931.
Lent by the Artist.

OLIVER DENNETT GROVER, American, 1861–1927
558. Mountain, Sea and Cloud (1911)
Oil on canvas, 24 x 30 in.
Signed: oliver dennett grover, 1911.
Owned by The Art Institute of Chicago (Friends of American Art Collection).

SAMUEL HALPERT, American, 1884–1930
559. After the Siesta (1925)
Oil on canvas, 38 x 49 in.
Signed: s. halpert, 1925.
Lent from a Private Collection.

MARSDEN HARTLEY, American, 1878–
560. The Window
Oil on canvas, 25½ x 36 in.
Lent by The Columbus Gallery of Fine Arts (Howald Collection).

CHILDE HASSAM, American, 1859–
561. New England Headlands (1899)
Oil on canvas, 27 x 26¾ in.
Signed: CHILDE HASSAM, 1899.
Owned by The Art Institute of Chicago (Walter H. Schulze Memorial Collection).

KNUTE HELDNER, American, 1884–
†562. The Cotton Pickers (1927)
Oil on canvas, 34 x 34 in.
Signed: KNUTE HELDNER.
Lent by the Artist.

W. VICTOR HIGGINS, American, 1884–
563. Spring Rains (c. 1924)
Oil on canvas, 40 x 43 in.
Signed: VICTOR HIGGINS.
Owned by The Art Institute of Chicago (Friends of American Art Collection).

HARRY LESLIE HOFFMAN, American, 1880(?)–
564. The Cotton Gin (1919)
Oil on canvas, 30 x 40 in.
Signed: H. L. HOFFMAN, '19.
Owned by The Art Institute of Chicago (Friends of American Art Collection).

EMIL HOLZHAUER, American, 1887–
†565. Cribbage Players (1928)
Oil on canvas, 30 x 40 in.
Signed: HOLZHAUER, 1928.
Lent by the Artist.

JAMES R. HOPKINS, American, 1878–
566. A Kentucky Mountaineer
Oil on canvas, 32 x 26 in.
Signed: JAMES R. HOPKINS.
Owned by The Art Institute of Chicago (Friends of American Art Collection).

CHARLES HOPKINSON, American, 1869–
567. The Artist's Daughter (Portrait) (c. 1915)
Oil on canvas, 30 x 25 in.
Signed: CHARLES HOPKINSON.
Lent by The Museum of Art, Rhode Island School of Design.

EDWARD HOPPER, American, 1882–
*568. Automat (1927) (Pl. LXXXIX)
Oil on canvas, 28 x 36½ in.
Signed: EDWARD HOPPER.
Lent by Mr. and Mrs. Lesley G. Sheafer, New York.

EARL HORTER, American Contemporary
569. Gloucester (1932)
Oil on canvas, 17 x 25½ in.
Signed: E. HORTER, '32.
Lent by The Whitney Museum of American Art, New York.

RUDOLPH F. INGERLE, American, 1879–
570. Swappin' Grounds (1928)
Oil on canvas, 52 x 58½ in.
Signed: R. F. INGERLE, '28.
Owned by The Art Institute of Chicago (Friends of American Art Collection).

JOHN CHRISTEN JOHANSEN, American, 1876–
571. Evening Hour
Oil on canvas, 29⅝ x 39¾ in.
Signed: J. C. JOHANSEN.
Owned by The Art Institute of Chicago (Friends of American Art Collection).

J. THEODORE JOHNSON, American, 1902–
572. The Black Mantilla (1928)
Oil on canvas, 30¾ x 37¼ in.
Signed: J. THEO. JOHNSON.
Owned by The Art Institute of Chicago.

MORRIS KANTOR, American, 1896–
573. Haunted House (1930)
Oil on canvas, 37⅛ x 33¼ in.
Signed: M. KANTOR, 1930.
Owned by The Art Institute of Chicago.

BERNARD KARFIOL, American, 1886–
*574. Hilda (Pl. LXXXVIII)
Oil on canvas, 35 x 45 in.
Signed: B. KARFIOL.
Lent by The Whitney Museum of American Art, New York.

CAMILLE ANDRENE KAUFFMANN, American, 1905–
†575. Ballet Girl (1933)
Oil on canvas, 19⅜ x 24 in.
Signed: ANDRENE.
Lent by the Artist.

HENRY G. KELLER, American, 1870–
†576. First Show at Two (1932)
Oil on canvas, 30 x 40 in.
Signed: H. G. KELLER.
Lent by the Artist.

LEON KELLY, American, 1901–
577. La Goulue (1927)
Oil on canvas, 25 x 21 in.
Signed: kelly.
Lent by La France Institute, Philadelphia, Pennsylvania.

ROCKWELL KENT, American, 1882–
578. Mount Equinox, Winter (1921)
Oil on canvas, 33¼ x 43½ in.
Signed: rockwell kent, vermont, 1921.
Owned by The Art Institute of Chicago.

ALICE RIDDLE KINDLER, American, 1892–
†579. Winter; St. Vincent (1929)
Oil on canvas, 23¾ x 28¾ in.
Signed: riddle.
Lent by the Artist.

GEORGINA KLITGAARD, American, 1893–
†580. Winter
Oil on canvas, 50 x 32 in.
Signed: g. klitgaard.
Lent by the Artist.

KARL KNATHS, American, 1891–
†581. Rooster (1927)
Oil on canvas, 26 x 22 in.
Signed: knaths.
Lent by The Downtown Gallery, New York.

WALTER KRAWIEC, American, 1889–
†582. The Big Top (1932)
Oil on canvas, 30¼ x 40 in.
Signed: w. krawiec.
Lent by the Artist.

LEON KROLL, American, 1884–
*583. Leo Ornstein at the Piano (1918) (Pl. LXXXIX)
Oil on canvas, 34 x 40 in.
Signed: kroll, 1918.
Owned by The Art Institute of Chicago (Friends of American Art Collection).

LOUIS KRONBERG, American, 1872–
584. Watching the Dancers
Oil on panel, 12½ x 15½ in.
Signed: louis kronberg.
Lent by Mr. and Mrs. Charles H. Worcester, Chicago.

MAX KUEHNE, American, 1880–
†585. Main Street, Gloucester (1928)
Oil on canvas, 20 x 24 in.
Signed: kuehne.
Lent by the Artist.

WALT KUHN, American, 1880–
586. Girl with Mirror (1928)
Oil on canvas, 24 x 20 in.
Signed: walt kuhn.
Lent by The Phillips Memorial Gallery, Washington, D. C.

YASUO KUNIYOSHI, American, 1893–
587. The Swimmer
Oil on canvas, 20 x 30 in.
Lent by The Columbus Gallery of Fine Arts, Columbus, Ohio (Howald Collection).

HARRY B. LACHMAN, American, 1886–
588. St. Nicolas du Chardonnet (1918)
Oil on canvas, 36 x 36 in.
Signed: harry b. lachman, '18.
Owned by The Art Institute of Chicago (Friends of American Art Collection).

SIDNEY LAUFMAN, American, 1891–
589. Landscape (1930)
Oil on canvas, 28½ x 39½ in.
Signed: sidney laufman.
Lent by The Downtown Gallery, New York.

ERNEST LAWSON, American, 1873–
590. Ice-Bound Falls (1919)
Oil on canvas, 39½ x 50 in.
Signed: e. lawson, 1919.
Owned by The Art Institute of Chicago (Friends of American Art Collection).

HAYLEY LEVER, American, 1876–
†591. Misty Morning, Nantucket
Oil on canvas, 24 x 36 in.
Signed: hayley lever.
Lent by the Artist through The Milch Galleries, New York.

BEATRICE S. LEVY, American, 1892–
†592. Maude (1931)
Oil on canvas, 28 x 34 in.
Signed: beatrice levy.
Lent by the Artist.

JONAS LIE, American, 1880–
593. Deep River
Oil on canvas, 34 x 36 in.
Signed: jonas lie.
Lent by The Whitney Museum of American Art, New York.

LUIGI LUCIONI, American, 1900–
†594. My Sister Alice (1928)
Oil on canvas, 52 x 40 in.
Signed: luigi lucioni.
Lent by the Artist.

GEORGE LUKS, American, 1867–
595. Portrait of Otis Skinner (c. 1919)
Oil on canvas, 52 x 44 in.
Signed: GEORGE LUKS.
Lent by The Phillips Memorial Gallery, Washington, D. C.

PEPPINO MANGRAVITE, American, 1896–
596. Family Portrait (1930)
Oil on canvas, 24 x 30 in.
Signed: MANGRAVITE, 1930.
Lent by The Corcoran Gallery of Art, Washington, D. C.

IRVING MANOIR, American, 1891–
†597. The Carrousel (1931)
Oil on canvas, 30 x 36 in.
Signed: IRVING MANOIR.
Lent by the Artist.

REGINALD MARSH, American, 1898–
†598. Tattoo and Haircut (1932)
Oil on canvas, 48 x 48 in.
Lent by Mr. Frank K. M. Rehn, New York.

VIRGINIA ARMITAGE McCALL, American, 1906–
†599. Spring (1931)
Oil on canvas, 25 x 30 in.
Lent by the Artist.

HENRY LEE McFEE, American, 1886–
†600. Interior with Still Life (1931)
Oil on canvas, 45 x 30 in.
Signed: MC FEE.
Lent by Mr. Frank K. M. Rehn, New York.

HERMAN MENZEL, American, 1904–
†601. The White Horse (1929)
Oil on canvas, 18 x 21 in.
Signed: HERMAN MENZEL, 1929.
Lent by the Artist.

WILLARD LEROY METCALF, American, 1858–1925
602. Icebound (1909)
Oil on canvas, 28 x 26½ in.
Signed: W. L. METCALF, 1909.
Owned by The Art Institute of Chicago (Walter H. Schulze Memorial).

Quadrangle Club (Univ. of Chi.), 1922.

Exh.: 23. Amer. Paintg. & Sculp., 1910, 154 (repr.); Toledo Mus. Inaugural, 1912, No. 64, opp. 27 (repr.); Lit.: E. Neuhaus, *Hist. and Ideals,* 274 (repr.).

HERBERT MEYER, American, 1882–
†603. East River (1932)
Oil on canvas, 30 x 40 in.
Signed: HERBERT MEYER.
Lent by The Macbeth Gallery, New York.

WILLIAM MEYEROWITZ, American, 1889-
†604. Staffordshire
Oil on canvas, 35 x 27 in.
Signed: WM. MEYEROWITZ.
Lent by the Artist.

KENNETH HAYES MILLER, American, 1876–
605. Interior (1922)
Oil on canvas, 34 x 28 in.
Signed: HAYES MILLER, '22.
Lent from The Mr. and Mrs. Preston Harrison Gallery, Los Angeles Museum, Los Angeles, California.

ROSS MOFFETT, American, 1888–
†606. Gull Hill (1929)
Oil on canvas, 48¼ x 60 in.
Signed: MOFFETT.
Lent by the Artist.

HERMON MORE, American Contemporary
†607. Landscape
Oil on canvas, 22¼ x 30¼ in.
Signed: HERMON MORE.
Lent by the Artist.

ARCHIBALD JOHN MOTLEY, Jr., American, 1891–
†608. Blues (1929)
Oil on canvas, 36 x 42 in.
Signed: A. J. MOTLEY JR., PARIS, 1929.
Lent by the Artist.

HERMANN DUDLEY MURPHY, American, 1867–
609. Charles H. Woodbury (1906)
Oil on canvas, 29½ x 24½ in.
Signed: 19 (M) '06.
Owned by The Art Institute of Chicago.

JEROME MYERS, American, 1867–
610. The End of the Street (1922)
Oil on canvas, 24½ x 29½ in.
Signed: JEROME MYERS, N. Y., 1922.
Owned by The Art Institute of Chicago.

JOHN WARNER NORTON, American, 1876–
611. Light and Shadow (c. 1924)
Oil on canvas, 35½ x 41½ in.
Signed: NORTON.
Owned by The Art Institute of Chicago (Friends of American Art Collection).

SAM OSTROWSKY, American, 1885–
612. Still Life with Fish and Melon (1932)
Oil on canvas, 19¾ x 25½ in.
Signed: sam ostrowsky.
Lent by Mr. David A. Smart, Chicago.

PAULINE PALMER, American Contemporary
613. Against the Light (1928)
Oil on canvas, 26 x 32 in.
Signed: pauline palmer.
Lent by Mrs. John E. Jenkins.

ROBERT PHILLIP, American, 1895–
†614. Night Club Hostess (1931)
Oil on canvas, 20 x 24 in.
Signed: phillip.
Lent by the Artist.

MARJORIE PHILLIPS, American, 1895–
†615. Breakfast Table (1931)
Oil on canvas, 25 x 32 in.
Signed: marjorie phillips.
Lent by the Artist.

WALDO PEIRCE, American Contemporary
†616. Bulls at Pamplona (1927)
Oil on canvas, 46 x 32 in.
Signed: w. peirce, '27.
Lent by the Artist.

JOSEPH POLLET, American, 1897–
†617. Parlor, Bedroom and Bath (c. 1929)
Oil on canvas, 50 x 40 in.
Lent by The Downtown Gallery, New York.

TUNIS PONSEN, American, 1891–
†618. Rock Quarry (c. 1932)
Oil on canvas, 19¾ x 23¾ in.
Signed: tunis ponsen.
Lent by the Chicago Galleries.

ABRAM POOLE, American, 1882–
619. Miss McFadden
Oil on canvas, 28¼ x 23 in.
Owned by The Art Institute of Chicago (Friends of American Art Collection).

HENRY VARNUM POOR, American, 1888–
†620. Nude at Table
Oil on canvas, 28½ x 21¼ in.
Signed: h. v. poor.
Lent by the Artist through The Montross Gallery, New York.

CONSTANTINE POUGIALIS, American, 1894–
†621. Water Carriers (1931)
Oil on canvas, 30 x 36 in.
Signed: c. pougialis.
Lent by the Artist.

GRACE RAVLIN, American, 1885–
622. Procession of Il Redentore, Venice (1914)
Oil on canvas, 25 x 23 in.
Signed: ravlin, v. '14.
Owned by the Art Institute of Chicago (Friends of American Art Collection).

EDWARD W. REDFIELD, American, 1869–
623. The Village in Winter
Oil on canvas, 40½ x 52¼ in.
Signed: e. w. redfield.
Lent by Mr. William S. Stimmel, Pittsburgh, Pennsylvania.

LOUIS RITMAN, American, 1889–
†624. La Toilette (1932)
Oil on canvas, 49 x 42 in.
Signed: l. ritman.
Lent by the Artist.

INCREASE ROBINSON, American, 1890–
†625. Spring Morning (1930)
Oil on canvas, 29 x 30½ in.
Signed: increase robinson.
Lent by the Artist.

LEON ROECKER, American Contemporary
†626. Wisconsin Farmyard (c. 1931)
Oil on canvas, 25 x 30 in.
Signed: h. l. roecker.
Lent by the Artist.

DORIS ROSENTHAL, American Contemporary
†627. Garret Studio (1928)
Oil on canvas, 20 x 22 in.
Signed: doris rosenthal, 1928.
Lent by the Artist.

W. VLADIMIR ROUSSEFF, American, 1890–
628. Figure with Still Life
Oil on canvas, 40 x 30 in.
Signed: Rousseff.
Lent by Mr. Le Roy J. Steffen.

EUGENE FRANCIS SAVAGE, American, 1883–
629. Arbor Day (1920)
Oil on canvas, 45 x 33½ in.
Signed: eugene francis savage, xx.
Owned by The Art Institute of Chicago (Friends of American Art Collection).

CARL SCHMITT, American, 1889–
630. A Picnic (1927)
Oil on canvas, 35 x 42 in.
Signed: carl schmitt, '27.
Lent by Mr. Arthur Judson, New York.

HENRY SCHNAKENBERG, American, 1892–
†631. Girl at Window (1928)
Oil on canvas, 36 x 30 in.
Signed: henry schnakenberg.
Lent by C. W. Kraushaar Art Galleries, New York.

FLORA I. SCHOFIELD, American, 1879–
†632. The Prayer (1930)
Oil on canvas, 32½ x 47½ in.
Signed: schofield, '30.
Lent by the Artist.

WILLIAM S. SCHWARTZ, American, 1896–
†633. Chicago River Harbor (1932)
Oil on canvas, 30 x 36 in.
Signed: william s. schwartz.
Lent by the Artist.

LEOPOLD SEYFFERT, American, 1887–
†634. A Basque (1932)
Oil on canvas, 46 x 36 in.
Signed: leopold seyffert, 1932.
Lent by the Artist.

CHARLES SHEELER, American, 1883–
635. Ford Factory (1930)
Oil on canvas, 24 x 31 in.
Signed: sheeler, 1930.
Lent from a Private Collection, New York.

MILLARD SHEETS, American, 1907–
636. Women of Cartagena (1930)
Oil on canvas, 40 x 50 in.
Signed: millard sheets.
Lent by Mrs. H. A. Everett, Los Angeles, California.

EVERETT SHINN, American, 1873–
637. London Hippodrome
Oil on canvas, 25½ x 34¼ in.
Signed: e. shinn.
Owned by The Art Institute of Chicago (Friends of American Art Collection).

GERRIT V. SINCLAIR, American, 1890–
†638. Pont Royal (1930)
Oil on canvas, 26 x 32 in.
Signed: g. sinclair, 1930, paris.
Lent by the Artist.

JOHN SLOAN, American, 1871–
639. Backyard, Greenwich Village (1914)
Oil on canvas, 26 x 32 in.
Signed: john sloan, '14.
Lent by C. W. Kraushaar Art Galleries, New York.

GEORGE MELVILLE SMITH, American, 1879–
†640. Interior (1931)
Oil on canvas, 24 x 33 in.
Signed: george melville smith.
Lent by the Artist.

JACOB GETLAR SMITH, American, 1898–
†641. The Peasant (1929)
Oil on canvas, 39½ x 32 in.
Signed: jacob getlar smith, '29.
Lent by the Artist.

JUDSON SMITH, American, 1880–
†642. A Deserted Mill (1931)
Oil on canvas, 48 x 60 in.
Signed: judson smith.
Lent by the Artist.

RAPHAEL SOYER, American, 1899–
†643. The Subway (c. 1930)
Oil on canvas, 27 x 28 in.
Signed: raphael soyer.
Lent by the Artist.

ELIZABETH SPARHAWK-JONES, American, 1885–
644. Shop Girls
Oil on canvas, 38 x 48 in.
Signed: elizabeth sparhawk-jones.
Owned by The Art Institute of Chicago (Friends of American Art Collection).

EUGENE SPEICHER, American, 1883–
*645. Babette (1931) (Pl. XCI)
Oil on canvas, 56 x 45 in.
Signed: eugene speicher.
Lent by The Department of Fine Arts, Carnegie Institute, Pittsburgh, Pennsylvania.

FRANCIS SPEIGHT, American, 1896–
†646. Late Afternoon (1931)
Oil on canvas, 30 x 22 in.
Lent by the Artist through The Milch Galleries, New York.

ROBERT SPENCER, American, 1879–1931
647. The Huckster Cart (1913)
Oil on canvas, 30 x 36 in.
Signed: robert spencer, 1913.
Owned by The Art Institute of Chicago (Friends of American Art Collection).

JOHN STEPHAN, American, 1906–
†648. East Division Street (1931)
Oil on canvas, 19 x 25 in.
Lent by the Artist.

MAURICE STERNE, American, 1877–
*649. Afternoon at Anticoli (1924) (Pl. XCII)
Oil on canvas, 45 x 32 in.
Signed: sterne, 1924.
Lent by The Phillips Memorial Gallery, Washington, D. C.

HENRY OSSAWA TANNER, American, 1859–
650. The Two Disciples at the Tomb
Oil on canvas, 50½ x 40½ in.
Signed: h. o. tanner.
Owned by The Art Institute of Chicago.

HELEN J. TAYLOR, American, 1903–
†651. Cat and Whatnot (1932)
Oil on canvas, 24 x 30 in.
Signed: helen j. taylor.
Lent by the Artist.

FREDERIC TELLANDER, American, 1878–
†652. Winter in the White Mountains (1930)
Oil on canvas, 40 x 56 in.
Signed: frederic tellander '30.
Lent by the Artist.

PAUL TREBILCOCK, American, 1902–
†653. Nude (1932)
Oil on canvas, 38 x 42 in.
Signed: paul trebilcock.
Lent by the Artist.

CARROLL TYSON, American, 1878–
†654. Maine (1931)
Oil on canvas, 30 x 36 in.
Signed: carroll tyson, 1931.
Lent by the Artist.

WALTER UFER, American, 1876–
655. Solemn Pledge, Taos Indians
Oil on canvas, 40½ x 36½ in.
Signed: w. ufer.
Owned by The Art Institute of Chicago (Friends of American Art Collection).

LAURA VAN PAPPELENDAM, American Contemporary
†656. Back of the Church (1931)
Oil on canvas, 27 x 33 in.
Signed: laura van pappelendam.
Lent by the Artist.

STUYVESANT VAN VEEN, American, 1910–
657. Below Queensboro Bridge, New York (1929)
Oil on canvas, 34 x 43 in.
Signed: stuyvesant van veen '29.
Lent by Mr. E. Felix Shaskan, Cedarhurst, Long Island.

DOROTHY VARIAN, American, 1895–
658. Interior with Nude and Stove (1932)
Oil on canvas, 24½ x 19½ in.
Signed: d. varian.
Lent from a Private Collection, New York.

FRANKLIN C. WATKINS, American, 1894–
659. Suicide in Costume (1931)
Oil on canvas, 36½ x 44½ in.
Signed: watkins.
Lent by Mr. Albert C. Lehman, Pittsburgh, Pennsylvania.

MAX WEBER, American, 1881–
660. Still Life with Loaf of Bread (1929)
Oil on canvas, 20 x 24 in.
Signed: max weber.
Lent from a Private Collection, New York.

HAROLD WESTON, American, 1894–
†661. Woman Smoking (1931)
Oil on canvas, 22 x 29 in.
Signed: weston.
Lent by the Artist.

WARREN WHEELOCK, American, 1880–
†662. The Arrival (1926)
Oil on canvas, 16 x 20 in.
Signed: wheelock.
Lent by the Artist.

GUY WIGGINS, American, 1883–
663. Lightly Falling Snow
Oil on canvas, 34 x 40 in.
Signed: guy wiggins.
Owned by The Art Institute of Chicago (Walter H. Schulze Memorial).

CHARLES A. WILIMOVSKY, American, 1885–
664. On the Way to the Pueblo, New Mexico (1930)
Oil on canvas, 24¼ x 29¼ in.
Signed: wilimovsky.
Lent by Mr. Frank G. Logan.

IRVING R. WILES, American, 1861–
†665. The Family
Oil on canvas, 42 x 54 in.
Signed: irving r. wiles.
Lent by the Artist through The Grand Central Art Galleries, New York.

GRANT WOOD, American, 1892–
*666. American Gothic (1930) (Pl. XCII)
Oil on composition board, 29⅞ x 25 in.
Signed: grant wood, 1930.
Owned by The Art Institute of Chicago (Friends of American Art Collection).

ROBERT STRONG WOODWARD, American, 1885–
†667. A Country Piazza (1930)
Oil on canvas, 25 x 30 in.
Signed: robert strong woodward.
Lent by The Macbeth Gallery, New York.

MARGUERITE ZORACH, American, 1888–
†668. Snow and Steam (1932)
Oil on canvas, 20 x 23¾ in.
Signed: marguerite zorach.
Lent by the Artist.

ZSISSLY, American, 1897–
†669. After the Meal (1932)
Oil on canvas, 27⅞ x 48 in.
Signed: zsissly, '32.
Lent by the Artist.

CONTEMPORARY FRENCH PAINTING

GALLERIES G57 and G60

ALBERT ANDRE, French, 1869–
670. The Catalans at Marseilles
Oil on canvas, 37 x 43 in.
Signed: albert andre.
Owned by The Art Institute of Chicago.

ALBERT ANDRE, French, 1869–
671. Sewing
Oil on canvas, 32 x 32 in.
Signed: albert andre.
Owned by The Art Institute of Chicago (Mr. and Mrs. Martin A. Ryerson Collection).

ALBERT ANDRE, French, 1869–
672. Square des Batignolles, Paris
Oil on canvas, 18½ x 25¾ in.
Signed: albert andre.
Owned by The Art Institute of Chicago (Mr. and Mrs. Martin A. Ryerson Collection).

PIERRE BONNARD, French, 1867–
†*673. Breakfast Room (Pl. LXIX)
Oil on canvas, 25 x 42 in.
Signed: bonnard.
Lent by Mr. Frank Crowninshield, New York.

PIERRE BONNARD, French, 1867–
*674. The Dining Room (1928) (Pl. LXIX)
Oil on canvas, 30 x 29½ in.
Signed: bonnard.
Lent by Mr. and Mrs. Walter S. Brewster, Chicago.

PIERRE BONNARD, French, 1867–
675. Early Spring (1910)
Oil on canvas, 34½ x 52 in.
Signed: bonnard, 1910.
Lent by The Phillips Memorial Gallery, Washington, D. C.

PIERRE BONNARD, French, 1867–
676. The Palm (1926)
Oil on canvas, 44 x 57½ in.
Signed: bonnard, '26.
Lent by The Phillips Memorial Gallery, Washington, D. C.

PIERRE BONNARD, French, 1867–
677. Vestibule (1928)
Oil on canvas, 39 x 23 in.
Signed: bonnard.
Lent by Mr. and Mrs. Charles H. Worcester, Chicago.

GEORGES CAPON, French, 1890–
678. The Cafe, Terrace—an Habitue (c. 1926)
Oil on canvas, 28½ x 36 in.
Signed: capon.
Lent by Mr. Oscar F. Mayer, Chicago.

MAURICE DENIS, French, 1870–
679. In the Forest (1903)
Oil on canvas, 24 x 20½ in.
Signed: mavd, 1903.
Owned by The Art Institute of Chicago.

ANDRE DERAIN, French, 1880–
*680. The Bagpipe Player (1910-11) (Pl. LXX)
Oil on canvas, 74 x 59 in.
Signed: a. derain.
Lent by Mr. and Mrs. James T. Soby, Hartford, Connecticut.

ANDRE DERAIN, French, 1880–
†681. Bridge at Ollieres (1930)
Oil on canvas, 29 x 36½ in.
Signed: a. derain.
Lent by The Marie Harriman Gallery, New York.

ANDRE DERAIN, French, 1880–
682. Forest at Martigues (c. 1908)
Oil on canvas, 32⅜ x 39¾ in.
Owned by The Art Institute of Chicago (Arthur Jerome Eddy Memorial).

ANDRE DERAIN, French, 1880–
683. The Fountain
Oil on panel, 10⅞ x 13¾ in.
Signed: derain.
Owned by The Art Institute of Chicago (Helen Birch Bartlett Memorial).

ANDRE DERAIN, French, 1880–
684. Grapes
Oil on canvas, 11½ x 18½ in.
Signed: a. derain.
Owned by The Art Institute of Chicago (Helen Birch Bartlett Memorial).

ANDRE DERAIN, French, 1880–
685. Landscape
Oil on canvas, 23⅛ x 28½ in.
Signed: a. derain.
Owned by The Art Institute of Chicago (Helen Birch Bartlett Memorial).

ANDRE DERAIN, French, 1880–
†686. Landscape in the Midi (1926)
Oil on canvas, 29½ x 37 in.
Signed: a. derain.
Lent by The Marie Harriman Gallery, New York.

ANDRE DERAIN, French, 1880–
687. Window on the Park (1912)
Oil on canvas, 35 x 51 in.
Signed: derain.
Lent by Mrs. Cornelius J. Sullivan, New York.

CHARLES DUFRESNE, French, 1876–
*688. Scene in Morocco (Pl. LXXII)
Oil on canvas, 43½ x 43½ in.
Signed: dufresne.
Lent by The Worcester Art Museum, Worcester, Massachusetts.

CHARLES DUFRESNE, French, 1876–
689. Still Life: Flowers
Oil on canvas, 25½ x 23¾ in.
Lent by Mr. Frederic Clay Bartlett, Chicago.

CHARLES DUFRESNE, French, 1876–
690. Still Life with Compote
Oil on canvas, 32 x 21½ in.
Signed: dufresne.
Owned by The Art Institute of Chicago (Joseph Winterbotham Collection).

RAOUL DUFY, French, 1877–
691. Villerville
Oil on canvas, 32 x 39½ in.
Signed: raoul dufy.
Owned by The Art Institute of Chicago (Joseph Winterbotham Collection).

E. OTHON FRIESZ, French, 1879–
*692. Figure Composition (Pl. LXXI)
Oil on canvas, 22 x 26½ in.
Signed: e. othon friesz.
Lent by The Detroit Institute of Arts.

E. OTHON FRIESZ, French, 1879–
693. Harbor of Toulon (c. 1922)
Oil on canvas, 24⅞ x 31¾ in.
Signed: e. othon friesz.
Owned by The Art Institute of Chicago (Joseph Winterbotham Collection).

EDOUARD GOERG, French, 1893–
694. The Epicure
Oil on canvas, 39⅜ x 32 in.
Signed: ed. goerg.
Owned by The Art Institute of Chicago (Joseph Winterbotham Collection).

EDOUARD GOERG, FRENCH, 1893–
695. TABLE D'HOTE (c. 1928).
Oil on canvas, 36 x 28½ in.
Signed: GOERG.
Lent by Mr. Carter H. Harrison, Chicago.

ANDRE LHOTE, FRENCH, 1885–
696. FRENCH LANDSCAPE (1930)
Oil on canvas, 28½ x 36 in.
Signed: A. LHOTE.
Lent by Mr. Oscar F. Mayer, Chicago.

ANDRE LHOTE, FRENCH, 1885–
697. WOMEN OF AVIGNON (c. 1923)
Oil on canvas, 43⅜ x 33 in.
Signed: A. LHOTE.
Owned by The Art Institute of Chicago (Helen Birch Bartlett Memorial).

JEAN MARCHAND, FRENCH, 1883–
698. THE GARDEN
Oil on canvas, 27¼ x 23 in.
Signed: J. MARCHAND.
Owned by The Art Institute of Chicago (Joseph Winterbotham Collection).

JEAN MARCHAND, FRENCH, 1883–
699. THE HILL
Oil on canvas, 20 x 25 in.
Signed: J. S. MARCHAND.
Owned by The Art Institute of Chicago (Mr. and Mrs. Martin A. Ryerson Collection).

ALBERT MARQUET, FRENCH, 1875–
700. ENVIRONS OF ALGIERS (c. 1914)
Oil on canvas, 12½ x 15⅝ in.
Signed: MARQUET.
Owned by The Art Institute of Chicago (Mr. and Mrs. Martin A. Ryerson Collection).

ALBERT MARQUET, FRENCH, 1875–
701. PONT ST. MICHEL, PARIS (c. 1910)
Oil on canvas, 12½ x 15⅝ in.
Signed: MARQUET.
Owned by The Art Institute of Chicago (Mr. and Mrs. Martin A. Ryerson Collection).

AMEDEO MODIGLIANI, ITALIAN, 1884–1920
702. DOUBLE PORTRAIT (JACQUES LIPCHITZ AND HIS WIFE)
Oil on canvas, 31½ x 21 in.
Signed: MODIGLIANI.
Owned by The Art Institute of Chicago (Helen Birch Bartlett Memorial).

LIT.: Cat. of the Birch Bartlett Memorial, 1929, 50 (repr.), 65.

AMEDEO MODIGLIANI, ITALIAN, 1884–1920
*703. GYPSY WOMAN AND CHILD (1919) (Pl. LXX)
Oil on canvas, 45½ x 28¾ in.
Signed: MODIGLIANI.
Lent from The Chester Dale Collection, New York.

COLL.: Paul Guillaume, Paris.

EXH.: "Loan Exh. from The Chester Dale Coll.," N. Y., 1928, No. 28; Fogg Art Mus., Cambridge, Mass., 1929, No. 64 (repr. in cat., Pl. XLVII); Gall. of Living Art, N. Y. University, 1929, No. 38; Demotte Gall., N. Y., 1931, No. 3.

LIT.: G. Scheiwiller, *Modigliani,* 1927, Pl. 13; M. Dale, *Before Manet to Modigliani,* 1929, Pl. 95; A. Pfannstiel, *Modigliani,* 1929, 54 (repr.); *The Arts,* XV (1929), 298 (repr.); M. Dale, *Modigliani,* 1931, frontispiece; Dale, *Formes,* No. XVIII (October, 1932), opp. 132; *Creative Art,* X (1932), opp. 93 (repr.).

JULES PASCIN, FRENCH SCHOOL, 1885–1930
704. CLAUDINE RESTING (c. 1926–7)
Oil on canvas, 31½ x 23 in.
Signed: PASCIN.
Lent by Mr. Carter H. Harrison, Chicago.

ODILON REDON, FRENCH, 1840–1916
707. BOUQUET OF FLOWERS
Oil on panel, 26½ x 21 in.
Signed: ODILON REDON.
Owned by The Art Institute of Chicago (Mr. and Mrs. L. L. Coburn Collection).

ANDRE D. DE SEGONZAC, FRENCH, 1885–
†710. BRIDGE AT JOINVILLE (Pl. LXXII)
Oil on canvas, 21 x 31½ in.
Signed: A. DUNOYER DE SEGONZAC.
Lent by C. W. Kraushaar Art Galleries, New York.

ANDRE D. DE SEGONZAC, FRENCH, 1885–
†711. LANDSCAPE—SPRING (1927)
Oil on canvas, 39½ x 32 in.
Signed: A. DUNOYER DE SEGONZAC.
Lent by Mr. Frank Crowninshield, New York.

ANDRE D. DE SEGONZAC, FRENCH, 1885–
712. A SUMMER GARDEN (c. 1924)
Oil on canvas, 18 x 43 in.
Signed: A. DUNOYER DE SEGONZAC.
Owned by The Art Institute of Chicago (Joseph Winterbotham Collection).

MAURICE UTRILLO, FRENCH, 1883–
713. RUE ST. VINCENT DE PAUL (1913)
Oil on canvas, 25 x 39¼ in.
Signed: MAURICE UTRILLO V., 20 JUIN, 1913.
Owned by The Art Institute of Chicago (Mr. and Mrs. Martin A. Ryerson Collection).

MAURICE UTRILLO, French, 1883–
714. Street in Paris (1914)
Oil on canvas, 25 x 31½ in.
Signed: maurice utrillo v., 1914.
Owned by The Art Institute of Chicago (Helen Birch Bartlett Memorial).

HENRI VERGE-SARRAT, French, 1880–
715. Jeanne d'Arc Street, Ile d'Yeu (c. 1925)
Oil on canvas, 28½ x 23½ in.
Signed: verge-sarrat.
Lent by Mr. Oscar F. Mayer, Chicago.

MAURICE DE VLAMINCK, French, 1876–
716. Road to the Village
Oil on canvas, 26 x 32 in.
Signed: vlaminck.
Lent by Mr. and Mrs. Frederic Clay Bartlett, Jr., Chicago.

MAURICE DE VLAMINCK, French, 1876–
717. Village (Rueil) (c. 1912)
Oil on canvas, 29 x 36¼ in.
Signed: vlaminck.
Owned by The Art Institute of Chicago (Arthur Jerome Eddy Memorial).

EDOUARD VUILLARD, French, 1868–
*718. Child in a Room (Pl. LXXI)
Oil on panel, 17⅛ x 23¾ in.
Signed: e. vuillard.
Owned by The Art Institute of Chicago (Mr. and Mrs. M. A. Ryerson Collection).

EDOUARD VUILLARD, French, 1868–
719. Interior
Oil on canvas, 17½ x 15 in.
Signed: e. vuillard.
Lent by Mr. and Mrs. Charles H. Worcester, Chicago.

CONTEMPORARY INTERNATIONAL PAINTING

GALLERY G58

HERMENGILDO ANGLADA CAMARASA, Spanish, 1873–
720. Cove of Puat
Oil on canvas, 43 x 43 in.
Signed: h. anglada camarasa.
Lent by Mr. Homer Saint-Gaudens, Pittsburgh, Pennsylvania.

HERMENGILDO ANGLADA CAMARASA, Spanish, 1873–
721. The Girl with the Green Eyes
Oil on canvas, 70 x 46 in.
The Charles Deering Collection. Lent by Mr. and Mrs. R. E. Danielson, Boston.

FELICE CARENA, Italian, 1880–
*722. The Class (1928) (Pl. LXXIII)
Oil on canvas, 67 x 116 in.
Signed: felice carena, 1928.
Lent by Mr. Albert C. Lehman, Pittsburgh, Pennsylvania.

ANTO CARTE, Belgian, 1886–
723. Motherhood (1927)
Oil on canvas, 31¼ x 39¼ in.
Signed: anto carte, 1927.
Lent by The Department of Fine Arts, Carnegie Institute, Pittsburgh.

FELICE CASORATI, Italian, 1886–
724. A Pupil
Oil on canvas, 48½ x 33½ in.
Signed: casorati, and inscribed on the back: "felice casorati, ritratto di un allievo."
Lent by The Museum of Fine Arts, Boston.

MARC CHAGALL, Russian, 1887–
*725. Portrait of a Rabbi (Pl. LXXIV)
Oil on canvas, 35 x 46 in.
Signed: marc chagall.
Lent by Mr. P. M. Sweeney, New York.

JACQUES CHAPIRO, Russian Contemporary
726. Landscape
Oil on canvas, 38½ x 38 in.
Signed: j. chapiro.
Lent by Mr. David A. Smart, Chicago.

FERRUCCIO FERRAZZI, Italian, 1891–
727. Horitia and Fabiola (1926)
Oil on canvas, 74 x 41 in.
Signed: ferrazzi, 1926.
Lent by Mr. William S. Stimmel, Pittsburgh, Pennsylvania.

ROBERT GENIN, Russian, 1884–

728. Thirst (1913)
Oil on canvas, 39½ x 31½ in.
Signed: R. GENIN, '13.
Owned by The Art Institute of Chicago (Arthur Jerome Eddy Memorial).

FERDINAND HODLER, Swiss, 1853–1918

729. The Grand Muveran
Oil on canvas, 27¾ x 37 in.
Signed: FR. HODLER.
Owned by the Art Institute of Chicago (Helen Birch Bartlett Memorial).

AUGUSTUS JOHN, English, 1879–

*730. Dr. Stresemann (Portrait) (c. 1924) (Pl. LXXIV)
Oil on canvas, 42½ x 31 in.
Signed: JOHN.
Lent by The Buffalo Fine Arts Academy (Albright Art Gallery), Buffalo, New York.

Dr. Gustav Stresemann (1878–1929), Germany's greatest postwar statesman, Foreign minister, leader of the People's Party and peace promoter.

JOAN JUNYER, Spanish, 1904–

731. Festival in Majorca (1926)
Oil on canvas, 39 x 48½ in.
Signed: J. JUNYER, '26.
Lent by Mr. Albert C. Lehman, Pittsburgh, Pennsylvania.

GEORGES KARS, Czechoslovakian, 1882–

732. Oriental Girl with a Jar (1930)
Oil on canvas, 39 x 31½ in.
Signed: KARS, '30.
Lent by Mr. Carter H. Harrison, Chicago.

PER KROHG, Norwegian, 1889–

733. The Ambassadress—a "Nouveau Riche" (1929)
Oil on canvas, 45 x 34 in.
Signed: PER KROHG.
Lent by Mr. Carter H. Harrison, Chicago.

ALFRED K. LAWRENCE, English, 1893–

734. Head of a Young Woman (1927)
Oil on canvas, 20 x 24 in.
Signed: A. K. LAWRENCE, 1927.
Lent by Mr. Albert C. Lehman, Pittsburgh, Pennsylvania.

BARNARD LINTOTT, English, 1875–

†735. Clown with Butterfly (1932)
Oil on canvas, 30 x 25 in.
Signed: LINTOTT.
Lent by the Artist.

JOHN NASH, English, 1893–

736. Meadle
Oil on canvas, 30 x 22 in.
Signed: JOHN NASH.
Lent by The Museum of Fine Arts, Boston.

DOD PROCTER, English Contemporary

737. Girl with Parrot
Oil on canvas, 52½ x 34 in.
Signed: DOD PROCTER.
Lent by Mr. William S. Stimmel, Pittsburgh, Pennsylvania.

DIEGO RIVERA, Mexican, 1886–

*738. The Rivals (1931) (Pl. LXXIII)
Oil on canvas, 60 x 48 in.
Signed: DIEGO RIVERA, 1931.
Lent from a Private Collection, New York.

GIOVANNI ROMAGNOLI, Italian, 1893–

739. After the Bath (1921)
Oil on canvas, 41½ x 37½ in.
Signed: GIOVANNI ROMAGNOLI, 1921.
Lent by Mr. Edgar J. Kaufmann, Pittsburgh, Pennsylvania.

JOSE GUTIERREZ SOLANA, Spanish, 1886–

740. The Tooth-Extractor
Oil on canvas, 17½ x 21¾ in.
Signed: J. SOLANA.
Lent by The Brooklyn Museum, Brooklyn, New York.

HAIM SOUTINE, Russian, 1884–

741. Small Town Square
Oil on canvas, 28 x 18¼ in.
Signed: SOUTINE.
Owned by The Art Institute of Chicago (Joseph Winterbotham Collection).

COSTIA TERECHKOVITCH, Russian, 1902–

742. Jalasone (1929)
Oil on canvas, 23½ x 31 in.
Signed: C. TERECHKOVITCH, '29.
Lent by Mr. David A. Smart, Chicago.

EUGENE ZAK, Polish, 1884–1926

743. The Shepherd
Oil on canvas, 46 x 32⅛ in.
Signed: EUG. ZAK.
Owned by The Art Institute of Chicago (Arthur Jerome Eddy Memorial).

Exh.: Internatl. Exhn. of Mod. Art, New York, 1913, No. 233; Chicago, 1913, No. 452; A. J. Eddy Coll., Art Institute, 1922, No. 67 (repr.).

Lit.: A. J. Eddy, *Cubists and Post-Impressionism*, 1919, 8 (repr.), 200–1; *Creative Art*, X (1932), 215 (repr. 115); *The Eddy Coll. of Mod. Paintings & Sculpture*, 1932, 77 (repr.); *Guide*, 1932, 77 (repr.).

CONTEMPORARY GERMAN PAINTING

GALLERY G59

MAX BECKMANN, German, 1884–
†744. Landscape with Factories (1922)
Oil on canvas, 24 x 36 in.
Signed: beckmann, F. '22.
Lent by J. B. Neumann, New York.

MAX BECKMANN, German, 1884–
745. The Old Actress (1926)
Oil on canvas, 39 x 27¼ in.
Signed: beckmann, F. '26.
Lent from a private collection.

HEINRICH CAMPENDONK, German, 1889–
746. Still Life with Cat (1926)
Oil on canvas, 29½ x 30½ in.
Signed: c., '26.
Lent by The Société Anonyme, New York.

HEINRICH CAMPENDONK, German, 1889–
*747. The White Tree (1925) (Pl. LXXV)
Oil on canvas, 31¼ x 35½ in.
Lent by Miss Katherine S. Dreier, New York.

OTTO DIX, German, 1891–
*748. Dr. Meyer-Hermann (1926) (Pl. LXXVI)
Oil on canvas, 58½ x 39 in.
Signed: o d, 1926.
Lent by The Museum of Modern Art, New York.

DIETZ EDZARD, German, 1893–
749. Girl Combing her Hair (c. 1930)
Oil on canvas, 24 x 19¾ in.
Signed: d. edzard.
Lent by Mr. Josef Stransky, New York, through The Worcester Art Museum, Worcester, Massachusetts.

REINHARD EWALD, German Contemporary
751. Landscape (1919)
Oil on composition board, 32¾ x 43¼ in.
Signed: reinhard ewald, '19.
Lent by Dr. Karl Lilienfeld through The College Art Association, New York.

ERICH HECKEL, German, 1883–
752. Boats
Oil on canvas, 30 x 39½ in.
Signed: e. heckel.
Lent by Dr. W. R. Valentiner, Detroit, Michigan.

KARL HOFER, German, 1878–
*753. Girl with Melons (Pl. LXXVI)
Oil on canvas, 54 x 40 in.
Signed: k h.
Lent by The Worcester Art Museum, Worcester, Massachusetts.

ALEXEI JAWLENSKY, German School, 1864–
754. Neapolitan Woman
Oil on composition board, 25½ x 18½ in.
Lent by Dr. Karl Lilienfeld through The College Art Association, New York.

PAUL KLEINSCHMIDT, German, 1883–
†755. The Manicure
Oil on canvas, 49¼ x 37½ in.
Signed: p. kl.
Lent by Mr. and Mrs. Erich Cohn, New York.

OSKAR KOKOSCHKA, Austrian, 1886–
756. Girl with Doll (1920)
Oil on canvas, 36 x 32 in.
Signed: o. k.
Lent by Dr. W. R. Valentiner, Detroit, Michigan.

FRANZ MARC, German, 1880–1916
757. The Bewitched Mill
Oil on canvas, 51⅜ x 35¾ in.
Signed: m.
Owned by The Art Institute of Chicago (Arthur Jerome Eddy Memorial).

Exh.: A. J. Eddy Coll., Art Institute of Chicago, 1922, No. 50; 1932, 20, No. 12, 23 (repr.).

Lit.: A. J. Eddy, *Cubists and Post-Impressionism,* 1919, 115; *Creative Art,* X (1932), 215 (repr.); *Guide,* 1932, 33 (repr.).

MORIZ MELZER, German, 1877–
758. Riders
Oil on canvas, 36 x 46 in.
Signed: melzer.
Lent by Dr. Karl Lilienfeld through The College Art Association, New York.

OTTO MUELLER, German, 1874–1930
759. Girls Bathing (1921)
Oil on canvas, 31 x 37 in.
Signed: o. m.
Lent by Dr. W. R. Valentiner, Detroit, Michigan.

GABRIELE MUENTER, German Contemporary

761. Still Life with Queen (1912)
Oil on canvas, 31 x 22⅛ in.
Signed: MUENTER, 1912.
Owned by The Art Institute of Chicago (Arthur Jerome Eddy Memorial).

MAX PECHSTEIN, German, 1881–

762. The Bridge (1913)
Oil on canvas, 39 x 39 in.
Lent by Dr. Karl Lilienfeld through The College Art Association, New York.

MAX PECHSTEIN, German, 1881–

763. The Indian (1910)
Oil on canvas, 35 x 35 in.
Signed: H M P, 1910.
Lent by Dr. Karl Lilienfeld through The College Art Association, New York.

KARL SCHMIDT-ROTTLUFF, German, 1884–

764. Evening on the Sea (1920)
Oil on canvas, 34 x 40 in.
Signed: S. ROTTLUFF.
Lent by Dr. W. R. Valentiner, Detroit, Michigan.

KARL STERRER, Austrian, 1855–

765. Girl with Ships (1925)
Signed: KARL STERRER, 1925.
Oil on canvas, 50½ x 35½ in.
Lent by The Department of Fine Arts, Carnegie Institute, Pittsburgh, Pennsylvania.

ABSTRACT PAINTING
International, Twentieth Century

GALLERY G61

ALBERT BLOCH, American, 1882–

766. Scene from a Pantomime
Oil on canvas, 40 x 53⅜ in.
Signed with monogram AB.
Owned by The Art Institute of Chicago (Arthur Jerome Eddy Memorial).

PETER BLUME, American, 1906–

767. Parade (1930)
Oil on canvas, 48¾ x 55¾ in.
Signed: PETER BLUME, 1930.
Lent from a Private Collection, New York.

GEORGES BRAQUE, French, 1883–

768. Still Life (1919)
Oil on canvas, 21½ x 37¾ in.
Signed: G. BRAQUE, '19.
Owned by The Art Institute of Chicago (Joseph Winterbotham Collection).

MASSIMO CAMPIGLI, Italian, 1895–

769. The Sewers (1927)
Oil on canvas, 16 x 13 in.
Signed: MASSIMO CAMPIGLI, 1927.
Lent by Mrs. Flora I. Schofield, Chicago.

GIORGIO DE CHIRICO, Italian, 1888–

†771. A Room in a Museum (1929)
Oil on canvas, 18¼ x 21½ in.
Signed: G. DE CHIRICO.
Lent by Chester H. Johnson Gallery, Chicago.

SALVADOR DALI, Spanish Contemporary

772. The Shades of Night Descending (1931)
Oil on canvas, 24 x 19¾ in.
Signed: SALVADOR DALI.
Lent by Mr. Joseph Winterbotham, Burlington, Vermont.

MARCEL DUCHAMP, French Contemporary

*773. Nude Descending the Stairs (1912) (Pl. LXXVIII)
Oil on canvas, 56 x 34½ in.
Signed: NU DESCENDANT UN ESCALIER—MARCEL DUCHAMP, '12.
Lent by Mr. and Mrs. Walter Conrad Arensberg, Hollywood, California.

ALBERT GLEIZES, French, 1881–

†774. Man on the Balcony (1912)
Oil on canvas, 75¼ x 44 in.
Signed: ALBERT GLEIZES, 1912.
Lent by Mr. and Mrs. Jerome O. Eddy, Skull Valley, Arizona.

JUAN GRIS, Spanish, 1887–1927

775. Abstraction (1913)
Oil on canvas, 36 x 23½ in.
Lent by Mrs. Flora I. Schofield, Chicago.

STEFAN HIRSCH, American, 1899–
†776. Three Donkeys (1932)
Tempera on canvas, 28¾ x 39 in.
Signed: stefan hirsch, 1932.
Lent by The Downtown Gallery, New York.

WASSILJ KANDINSKY, Russian, 1866–
*777. Improvisation No. 30 (Warlike Theme) (1913) (Pl. LXXV)
Oil on canvas, 43¼ x 43¾ in.
Signed: kandinsky, '13.
Owned by The Art Institute of Chicago (Arthur Jerome Eddy Memorial).

WASSILJ KANDINSKY, Russian, 1866–
778. Improvisation with Green Center (No. 176) (1912)
Oil on canvas, 43¼ x 47½ in.
Signed: kandinsky, 1912.
Owned by The Art Institute of Chicago (Arthur Jerome Eddy Memorial).

WASSILJ KANDINSKY, Russian, 1866–
779. Two Poplars (1912)
Oil on canvas, 31 x 39½ in.
Signed: kandinsky.
Owned by The Art Institute of Chicago (Arthur Jerome Eddy Memorial).

PAUL KLEE, German, 1879–
780. Maid of Saxony
Oil on tracing cloth, 7⅛ x 11¾ in.
Signed: klee, 1922.
Lent by Mrs. Galka Scheyer, Hollywood, California.

FERNAND LEGER, French, 1881–
781. Composition in Blue (1921–1927)
Oil on canvas, 51½ x 39⅜ in.
Signed: f. leger, 21–27.
Lent by Mr. and Mrs. Charles H. Worcester, Chicago.

JEAN LURÇAT, French, 1892–
782. Delphi (1928)
Oil on canvas, 35 x 45¾ in.
Signed: lurçat, '28.
Owned by The Art Institute of Chicago (Joseph Winterbotham Collection).

LOUIS C. MARCOUSSIS, Polish, 1883–
784. Abstraction
Oil on canvas, 25½ x 39½ in.
Signed: marcoussis.
Lent by La France Art Institute, Philadelphia, Pennsylvania.

JOAN MIRO, Spanish, 1900–
*785. Dog Barking at the Moon (1926) (Pl. LXXVII)
Oil on canvas, 28¾ x 36¼ in.
Signed: miro, 1926.
Lent by Mr. Albert Eugene Gallatin, New York.

FRANCIS PICABIA, Spanish, 1878–
†786. Dance at the Spring (1912)
Oil on canvas, 45¾ x 45½ in.
Signed: picabia 1912 and inscribed: danse a la source.
Lent by Mr. and Mrs. Jerome O. Eddy, Skull Valley, Arizona.

PABLO PICASSO, Spanish, 1881–
*787. Seated Woman (1927) (Pl. LXXVIII)
Oil on canvas, 52 x 39 in.
Signed: picasso, '27.
Lent by Mr. and Mrs. James T. Soby, Hartford, Connecticut.

THEODORE J. ROSZAK, American, 1907–
†788. Composition Alastor (1932)
Oil on canvas, 32 x 48 in.
Signed: tjr.
Lent by the Artist.

GEORGES ROUAULT, French, 1871–
†789. Clowns (1920–25) (Pl. LXXVII)
Oil on canvas, 28¾ x 41¾ in.
Signed: rouault.
Lent by Pierre Matisse Gallery, New York.

PIERRE ROY, French, 1880–
790. Danger on the Stairs (1928)
Oil on canvas, 35¼ x 23⅛ in.
Signed: p. roy.
Lent from a Private Collection, New York.

SAUL SCHARY, American, 1904–
†791. Telephone Conversation (1932)
Oil on canvas, 20 x 30 in.
Signed: schary, '32.
Lent by The John Becker Gallery, New York.

JEAN SOUVERBIE, French, 1891–
792. Three Figures (1927)
Oil on canvas, 39 x 32 in.
Signed: souverbie, '27.
Lent by La France Art Institute, Philadelphia, Pennsylvania.

AMADEO DE SOUZA-CARDOSO, Portuguese, 1887–1918

793. The Leap of the Rabbit (1911)
Oil on canvas, 19⅝ x 24⅛ in.
Signed: A. DE SOUZA-CARDOSO, 1911.
Owned by The Art Institute of Chicago (Arthur Jerome Eddy Memorial).

Exh.: Internatl. Expo. of Mod. Art, Art Institute of Chi., 1913, No. 386; A. J. Eddy Coll., Art Inst. of Chi., 1922, No. 17 (repr.); 1931–2, 22, No. 15, 27 (repr.).

Lit.: A. J. Eddy, *Cubists and Post-Impressionism,* 1914, opp. 84 (repr.).

LEOPOLD SURVAGE, Russian, 1879–

†794. Woman at the Window (1926)
Oil on canvas, 32 x 29½ in.
Signed: SURVAGE, '26.
Lent by Chester H. Johnson Gallery, Chicago.

PAUL TCHELITCHEW, Russian, 1898–

†795. Still Life (1930)
Oil on canvas, 39 x 25 in.
Signed: P. TCHELITCHEW, 1930.
Lent by Demotte, Inc., New York.

Drawings, Water Colors and Pastels

EUROPEAN

Sixteenth, Seventeenth, Eighteenth and Nineteenth Centuries

ANGELI (AGNOLO DEL MORO), VERONESE, 1512–15..
796. GROUP OF FIGURES
Wash drawing on blue grey paper, 11 x 6⅞ in.
Owned by The Art Institute of Chicago (Charles Deering Collection).

ANONYMOUS, ITALIAN, FIFTEENTH CENTURY
797. HORSES' AND RAMS' HEADS
Pen (sepia) drawing on tan paper, 7½ x 5¾ in.
Owned by the Art Institute of Chicago (Mrs. E. Crane Chadbourne Collection).

CARLO CALIARI, VENETIAN, 1570–1596
798. ADORATION OF THE MAGI
Pen and wash on grey paper, 8½ x 12⅜ in.
Marked: No. 1,130.
Owned by The Art Institute of Chicago (Gurley Memorial).

LUCA CAMBIASO, GENOESE, 1527–1585
799. ALLEGORY OF HISTORY
Pen and wash on white paper, 11¾ x 10 in.
Owned by The Art Institute of Chicago (Gurley Memorial).

LUCA CAMBIASO, GENOESE, 1527–1585
800. MARRIAGE OF SAINT CATHERINE
Pen and wash on white paper, 16 x 10⅞ in.
Marked: NUM. 9 LUCA CAMBIASI.
Owned by The Art Institute of Chicago (Gurley Memorial).

ANNIBALE CARRACCI, ITALIAN, 1560–1609
801. FINDING OF MOSES
Pen on white paper, 7½ x 10½ in.
Owned by The Art Institute of Chicago (Gurley Memorial).

FRANÇOIS CLOUET, FRENCH, c. 1500–1572
802. COURT LADY
Pencil and crayon on paper, 11 x 9 in.
Owned by The Art Institute of Chicago (R. Allerton Collection).

JOHN SINGLETON COPLEY, AMERICAN, 1737–1815
803. TWO SOLDIERS
Pencil on bluish paper, 11 x 13¼ in.
Signed: J. S. COPLEY.
Owned by The Art Institute of Chicago (R. Allerton Collection).

LORENZO DI CREDI SCHOOL, FLORENTINE, SIXTEENTH CENTURY
804. TWO FULL LENGTH FIGURES
Pencil partly inked on pink-washed paper, 9³⁄₁₆ x 7¹⁄₁₆ in.
Marked: LORENZO DI CRE—
Owned by The Art Institute of Chicago (Gurley Memorial).

ARENT DE GELDER, DUTCH, 1645–1727
805. DEGRADATION OF HAMAN
Pen and wash drawing on paper, 7¹⁄₁₆ x 6⁷⁄₁₆ in.
Owned by The Art Institute of Chicago (C. Deering Collection).

HENDRIK GOLTZIUS (?), DUTCH, 1558–1616
806. VENUS AND CUPID
Drawing on white paper, 7⁷⁄₁₆ x 5⁵⁄₁₆ in.
Marked: HEINRICH.
Owned by The Art Institute of Chicago (C. Deering Collection).

GUERCINO (GIOVANNI FRANCESCO BARBIERI), BOLOGNESE, 1591–1666
807. RAPE OF DEIANIRA
Sepia pen and wash drawing, 14⅜ x 11 in.
Owned by The Art Institute of Chicago.

GUERCINO (GIOVANNI FRANCESCO BARBIERI), BOLOGNESE, 1591–1666
808. TWO YOUNG WOMEN IN CONVERSATION
Pen and ink on white paper, 8¾ x 8¹⁄₁₆ in.
Owned by The Art Institute of Chicago (C. Deering Collection).

SAMUEL VAN HOOGSTRATEN, Dutch, 1627–1678

809. Jacob and Esau
Brush and wash on paper, 3 9/16 x 6 in.
Owned by The Art Institute of Chicago (C. Deering Collection).

ITALIAN SCHOOL, Sixteenth Century

810. Landscape
Pen and wash on paper, 10¾ x 10 in.
Owned by The Art Institute of Chicago (Gurley Memorial).

PHILIPS DE KONINGH, Dutch, 1619–1688

811. Christ and the Woman Taken in Adultery
Pen and wash, 5⅜ x 7 7/16 in.
Inscription: vrouwzin. in ovelspree (?).
Owned by The Art Institute of Chicago.

CHRISTOPH MAURER, German, c. 1595–16. .

812. Spring (March) (for calendar)
Pen and wash drawing on white paper, 8⅜ x 7⅜ in.
Signed: frühling—c. maurer.
Owned by The Art Institute of Chicago (Gurley Memorial).

REMBRANDT, Dutch, 1606–1669

813. Joseph's Coat (c. 1660)
Pen on white paper, 4¾ x 7 5/16 in.
Owned by The Art Institute of Chicago (C. Deering Collection).

REMBRANDT, Dutch, 1606–1669

814. Peasant Blowing Hot and Cold (1634/5)
Pen and wash, 7⅛ x 6½ in.
Owned by The Art Institute of Chicago (C. Deering Collection).

HUBERT ROBERT, French, 1733–1808

815. Landscape with Ruins
Sanguine drawing on pale grey paper, 14⅜ x 11 in.
Owned by The Art Institute of Chicago (C. Deering Collection).

THOMAS ROWLANDSON, English, 1756–1827

816. Concerto Spirituale
Pen drawing with water color, 7⅞ x 6½ in.
Stamped: t. rowlandson; inscribed: messrs. boch and abel.
Owned by The Art Institute of Chicago (O. S. Swan Memorial).

THOMAS ROWLANDSON, English, 1756–1827

817. Landscape with Wayside Cross and Cottages
Water color on wash ground, 6¼ x 8 15/16 in.
Owned by The Art Institute of Chicago.

THOMAS ROWLANDSON, English, 1756–1827

818. Outside the Salutation Inn, Greenwich
Water color on cream paper, 13 x 19 7/16 in.
Lent by Clarence Buckingham Collection.

THOMAS ROWLANDSON, English, 1756–1827

819. Dr. Syntax
Pen drawing with water color, 9½ x 14¾ in.
Stamped: t. rowlandson.
Owned by The Art Institute of Chicago (O. S. Swan Memorial).

THOMAS ROWLANDSON, English, 1756–1827

820. Village Fair; Harlequin and Quack (1800)
Water color on creamy paper, 8 3/16 x 11 1/16 in.
Signed: rowlandson, 1800.
Owned by The Art Institute of Chicago (R. Allerton Collection).

GIANBATTISTA TIEPOLO, Venetian, 1696–1770

821. Two Penitent Monks or Two Hermits in Meditation
Pen and bistre wash drawing, 16½ x 11½ in.
Owned by The Art Institute of Chicago.

GIANDOMENICO TIEPOLO, Venetian, 1727–1804

822. Scene from the Creation I
Pen and wash on white paper, 11 x 7¾ in.
Signed: dome tiepolo f.
Owned by The Art Institute of Chicago.

GIANDOMENICO TIEPOLO, Venetian, 1727–1804

823. Scene from the Creation II
Pen and wash on white paper, 10 15/16 x 7 12/16 in.
Signed: dom. tiepolo.
Owned by The Art Institute of Chicago.

PAOLO VERONESE (?), VENETIAN, 1528–1588
824. DESCENT FROM THE CROSS
Pen, ink on blue paper, 10 9/16 x 8 in.
Marked: NO. 810—PAOLO.
Owned by The Art Institute of Chicago (Gurley Collection).

FRANCIS WHEATLEY, ENGLISH, 1747–1801
825. THE LADY AND THE QUEEN WASP
Wash, pen, water color, 14 3/16 x 10 11/16 in.
Owned by The Art Institute of Chicago.

DAVID WILKIE, SCOTCH, 1785–1841
826. FIGURES NEAR A HOUSE
Pencil and water color, w. wash, cream paper, 5¾ x 8¼ in.
Owned by The Art Institute of Chicago.

PHILIPS WOUWERMAN, DUTCH, 1619–1688
827. LANDSCAPE: THE INN
Pen, pencil, brush, 8½ x 11¾ in.
Owned by The Art Institute of Chicago (Gurley Memorial).

EUROPEAN AND AMERICAN
Nineteenth and Twentieth Centuries

CHARLES BARGUE, FRENCH, d. 1883
828. ARAB MERCHANT SEATED
Pencil, 11⅛ x 7⅛ in.
Owned by The Art Institute of Chicago (C. Deering Collection).

ANTOINE LOUIS BARYE, FRENCH, 1796–1875
829. FAMILY OF LIONS
Water color, 5 7/16 x 9½ in.
Signed: BARYE.
Owned by The Art Institute of Chicago (P. Palmer Collection).

ANTOINE LOUIS BARYE, FRENCH, 1796–1875
830. LEOPARD
Water color, 9⅞ x 13 3/16 in.
Signed: BARYE.
Owned by The Art Institute of Chicago (P. Palmer Collection).

AUBREY BEARDSLEY, ENGLISH, 1872–1898
831. HOW A DEVIL IN WOMAN'S LIKENESS WOULD HAVE TEMPTED SIR BROS (1892)
(Two illustrations from 'Morte d'Arthur,' vol. II, p. 768/9)
Two black and white drawings on café-au-lait paper, 10⅛ x 7⅜ in.
Owned by The Art Institute of Chicago (James Deering Collection).

AUBREY BEARDSLEY, ENGLISH, 1872–1898
832. THE LITANY OF MARY MAGDALEN (1892)
Pencil drawing on white paper arched at top, 9 x 6⅝ in.
Title in pencil, lettered.
Owned by The Art Institute of Chicago (C. Deering Collection).

AUBREY BEARDSLEY, ENGLISH, 1872–1898
833. VIRGILIUS, THE SORCERER
Pen drawing (black and white), 9 x 5½ in.
Owned by The Art Institute of Chicago (R. Allerton Collection).

GEORGE W. BELLOWS, AMERICAN, 1882–1925
834. HEAVY LIES THE HEAD THAT WEARS A BRAIN
Black crayon on white paper, 15¾ x 15¼ in.
Signed: GEO. BELLOWS.
Owned by The Art Institute of Chicago.

GEORGE W. BELLOWS, AMERICAN, 1882–1925
835. MOTHER AND CHILD
Pencil on brown paper, 11¼ x 8½ in.
Signed: GEO. BELLOWS.
Owned by The Art Institute of Chicago (Friends of American Art Collection).

GEORGE W. BELLOWS, AMERICAN, 1882–1925
836. MY MOTHER (STUDY OF DRAPERIES FOR) (1920)
Pencil on creamy paper, 16⅝ x 11½ in.
Signed: G. BELLOWS.
Owned by The Art Institute of Chicago (Friends of American Art Collection).
(See No. 432.)

GEORGE W. BELLOWS, AMERICAN, 1882–1925
837. STUDY FOR PORTRAIT OF EMMA
Black crayon on white paper, 10⅛ x 8⅞ in.
Signed: GEO. BELLOWS.
Owned by The Art Institute of Chicago (J. B. Fair Collection).

GEORGE W. BELLOWS, American, 1882–1925

838. Study of Head and Arms; Recumbent
Crayon on white paper, 7½ x 11½ in.
Signed: geo. bellows.
Owned by The Art Institute of Chicago (Friends of American Art Collection).

GEORGE W. BELLOWS, American, 1882–1925

839. Three Women Visiting
Pencil and crayon on white paper, 11⅝ x 13½ in.
Signed: geo. bellows.
Owned by The Art Institute of Chicago (Friends of American Art Collection).

GEORGE W. BELLOWS, American, 1882–1925

840. Two Figures (1920)
Pencil on white paper, 11⅜ x 7⅞ in.
Signed: geo. bellows.
Owned by The Art Institute of Chicago.

JOSEPH BERNARD, French, 1866–1931

841. Mother and Child, Dancing (Nudes)
Wash on medium dark tan paper, 10¼ x 13½ in.
Signed: j. bernard.
Owned by The Art Institute of Chicago (R. Allerton Collection).

JOSEPH BERNARD, French, 1866–1931

842. Pan and Syrinx
Wash on pink-brown paper, 12⅞ x 10⅛ in.
Signed: j. bernard.
Owned by The Art Institute of Chicago (R. Allerton Collection).

E. ANTOINE BOURDELLE, French, 1861–1929

843. Antiquity: Centaur with a Genius
Water color, wash, brush and crayon, 15⅜ x 19⅝ in.
Signed: antoine bourdelle—temps antiques: centaure avec un genie, 2e etude. a l. beneditte, cordialement: antoine bourdelle.
Owned by The Art Institute of Chicago (R. Allerton Collection).

HERCULES B. BRABAZON, English, 1821–1906

844. Ightham Mote, Kent
Water color on white paper, 9½ x 13½ in.
Signed: h b b (monogram).
Owned by The Art Institute of Chicago (O. S. Swan Memorial).

PAUL CEZANNE, French, 1839–1906

845. Jas de Bouffan
Water color on white paper, 20½ x 16½ in.
Lent by Mrs. Martin A. Ryerson, Chicago.

CHARLES CONDER, English, 1868–1909

846. Street in Seville
Gouache and oil, 13⅞ x 10 in.
Signed: conder-seville.
Owned by The Art Institute of Chicago (Chadbourne Collection).

CHARLES CONDER, English, 1868–1909

847. Women in a Loge
Water color and gouache, 9⅛ x 8½ in.
Owned by The Art Institute of Chicago (Chadbourne Collection).

CAMILLE COROT, French, 1795–1875

848. Landscape with a Dome
Charcoal on light colored tan paper, 11½ x 8¼ in.
Owned by The Art Institute of Chicago.

DAVID COX, Scotch, 1783–1859

849. The Windmill
Sepia wash, 6 x 9¾ in.
Signed: david.
Owned by The Art Institute of Chicago.

HONORE DAUMIER, French, 1808–1879

850. Les Badauds (Gaping Idlers)
Crayon on white paper, 11½ x 8⅜ in.
Signed: h. d. (monogram).
Owned by The Art Institute of Chicago (C. Deering Collection).

HONORE DAUMIER, French, 1808–1879

851. Figure Recoiling
Crayon drawing on white paper, 6⅞ x 7⅞ in.
Owned by The Art Institute of Chicago (R. Allerton Collection).

HONORE DAUMIER, French, 1808–1879

852. Head (Man with Top-Hat)
Pen drawing on grey paper, 6⅛ x 4½ in.
Owned by The Art Institute of Chicago (R. Allerton Collection).

HONORE DAUMIER, French, 1808–1879

853. Man with Top Hat (Profile Portrait)
Pen, ink, wash on white paper, 5¾ x 5 in.
Signed: h.d.
Owned by The Art Institute of Chicago (R. Allerton Collection).

ARTHUR B. DAVIES, AMERICAN, 1862–1928
854. ARCHER (SAGITTARIUS)
Chalk on pinkish brown paper, 12¼ x 8¼ in.
Signed: ARTHUR B. DAVIES.
Owned by The Art Institute of Chicago (Friends of American Art Collection).

ARTHUR B. DAVIES, AMERICAN, 1862–1928
855. AUTUMN (TWO FIGURES)
Drawing with water color on brown paper, 8½ x 12¾ in.
Signed: ARTHUR B. DAVIES.
Lent by R. Allerton.

ARTHUR B. DAVIES, AMERICAN, 1862–1928
856. NUDE, STANDING; LEFT KNEE UP
White chalk on buff paper, 16⅛ x 11⅛ in.
Signed: ARTHUR B. DAVIES.
Owned by The Art Institute of Chicago (Friends of American Art Collection).

ARTHUR B. DAVIES, AMERICAN, 1862–1928
857. RECLINING NUDE
Crayon on pink paper, 9 x 11 in.
Owned by The Art Institute of Chicago.

ARTHUR B. DAVIES, AMERICAN, 1862–1928
858. RECUMBENT NUDE
Charcoal and pastel on grey paper, 10 x 17¼ in.
Owned by The Art Institute of Chicago (Friends of American Art Collection).

ARTHUR B. DAVIES, AMERICAN, 1862–1928
859. STANDING NUDE
Chalk on brown paper, 12 x 7 in.
Signed: ARTHUR B. DAVIES.
Owned by The Art Institute of Chicago (R. Allerton Collection).

EDGAR DEGAS, FRENCH, 1834–1917
860. DANCER AT THE BAR
Three crayons on white paper, 12 x 9 in.
Signed: DEGAS.
Owned by The Art Institute of Chicago (Mr. and Mrs. M. A. Ryerson Collection).

EDGAR DEGAS, FRENCH, 1834–1917
861. DANCER AT THE BAR (LES POINTES)
Charcoal on dark cream paper, 11⅜ x 9 in.
Signed: DEGAS.
Owned by The Art Institute of Chicago (R. Allerton Collection).

EDGAR DEGAS, FRENCH, 1834–1917
862. DANCER CURTSYING
Crayon and chalk on grey-blue paper, 17½ x 11½ in.
Signed: DEGAS.
Owned by The Art Institute of Chicago (Mr. and Mrs. M. A. Ryerson Collection).

EDGAR DEGAS, FRENCH, 1834–1917
863. SPENT DANCER (DANSEUSE LANGUISSANTE)
Charcoal on buff paper, 19¼ x 16¾ in.
Signed: DEGAS (in red).
Owned by The Art Institute of Chicago (R. Allerton Collection).

EUGENE DELACROIX, FRENCH, 1798–1863
864. LION FACES AND PAWS
Pencil and light sepia on creamy paper, 7⅜ x 4⅝ in.
Signed: E.D. (monogram).
Owned by The Art Institute of Chicago (R. Allerton Collection).

EUGENE DELACROIX, FRENCH, 1798–1863
865. NUDE: BACK (STUDY AFTER VERONESE'S "UNFAITHFULNESS")
Pencil on buff paper, 3¼ x 6³⁄₁₆ in.
Signed: E.D. (monogram).
Owned by The Art Institute of Chicago (J. H. Wrenn Memorial).

HENRI FANTIN-LATOUR, FRENCH, 1836–1904
866. INGRES (PORTRAIT) (1865)
Charcoal on white paper, 6⅜ x 4¼ in.
Signed: FANTIN, 28 9BRE 1865.
Owned by The Art Institute of Chicago (Chadbourne Collection).

JEAN-LOUIS FORAIN, FRENCH, 1852–1931
867. DANCER AND MAN (DANSEUSE ET HOMME)
Pen, pencil, colored washes, 15⅞ x 13¾ in.
Owned by The Art Institute of Chicago (R. Allerton Collection).

JEAN-LOUIS FORAIN, FRENCH, 1852–1931
868. THE HAT SHOP
Charcoal, touches India ink, 12⅛ x 19⅝ in.
Signed: FORAIN.
Owned by The Art Institute of Chicago (R. Allerton Collection).

JEAN-LOUIS FORAIN, FRENCH, 1852–1931
869. THE REPORTER
Charcoal, 15 x 18¼ in.
Signed: FORAIN.
Owned by The Art Institute of Chicago.

JEAN-LOUIS FORAIN, French, 1852–1931
870. Trickster Lawyers (Hommes d'Affaires) (1924)
Black chalk, Chinese white, sepia-bistre wash, 12 15/16 x 17 7/8 in.
Signed: FORAIN.
Owned by The Art Institute of Chicago (O. S. Swan Memorial).

H. GAUDIER-BRZESKA, Russian, 1892–1915
871. Figures of Men and Women
Pen drawings, 8 1/2 x 13 5/8 in.
Signed: H. GAUDIER, 10.
Owned by The Art Institute of Chicago (R. Allerton Collection).

PAUL GAUGUIN, French, 1848–1903
872. Peacock and Natives, Tahiti
Pen and crayon drawing on paper, 9 1/8 x 15 1/8 in.
Owned by The Art Institute of Chicago (Chadbourne Collection).

PAUL GAUGUIN, French, 1848–1903
873. Tahitian Child
Water color on light brown paper, 13 x 9 in.
Owned by The Art Institute of Chicago (Chadbourne Collection).

PAUL GAUGUIN, French, 1848–1903
874. Tahitian Drinking from Waterfall
Water color on cream paper, 12 1/2 x 8 1/2 in.
Signed: G.O.
Owned by The Art Institute of Chicago (Chadbourne Collection).

PAUL GAUGUIN, French, 1848–1903
875. Tahiti Man (front face and profile)
Charcoal on buff paper, 12 3/4 x 11 in.
Owned by The Art Institute of Chicago (Chadbourne Collection).
Lit.: R. Rey, *Gauguin* (Engl. transl.), 1924, Pl. 19.

PAUL GAUGUIN, French, 1848–1903
876. Two Tahiti Women in Landscape
Water color, 12 1/2 x 9 1/8 in.
Owned by The Art Institute of Chicago (Chadbourne Collection).

PAUL GAUGUIN, French, 1848–1903
877. Polynesians (Group of)
Charcoal, 9 3/8 x 8 1/2 in.
Owned by The Art Institute of Chicago (R. Allerton Collection).

GAVARNI (HIPPOLYTE GUILLAUME SULPICE CHEVALIER), French, 1804–1866
878. Scene in Hyde Park (1842)
Pen and water color, 7 3/8 x 7 1/2 in.
Inscribed: PARIS, 1842.
Owned by The Art Institute of Chicago (C. Deering Collection).

GAVARNI (HIPPOLYTE GUILLAUME SULPICE CHEVALIER), French, 1804–1866
879. Woman in Spanish Costume
Charcoal, sanguine, Chinese white on grey paper, 11 1/4 x 8 in. (arched).
Signed: GAVARNI.
Owned by The Art Institute of Chicago (C. Deering Collection).

VINCENT VAN GOGH, Dutch, 1853–1890
880. Cypresses
Pen, pencil, wash, buff paper, 24 1/4 x 18 1/8 in.
Owned by The Art Institute of Chicago (R. Allerton Collection).

VINCENT VAN GOGH, Dutch, 1853–1890
881. Pastoral (Harvesting)
Pen drawing on buff paper, 7 5/8 x 11 3/4 in.
Signed: VINCENT.
Owned by The Art Institute of Chicago (Friends of American Art Collection).

CONSTANTIN GUYS, French, 1805–1892
882. After the Ballet
Pen and wash, white paper, 3 15/16 x 3 15/16 in.
Owned by The Art Institute of Chicago (R. Allerton Collection).

CONSTANTIN GUYS, French, 1805–1892
883. Lady with Muff
Wash drawing (sepia and green grey) on paper, 9 x 6 1/4 in.
Owned by The Art Institute of Chicago (O. S. Swan Memorial).

CONSTANTIN GUYS, French, 1805–1892
884. One of the Ladies of the Harem
Water color, pen, sepia on white paper, 13 3/4 x 9 13/16 in.
Marked: UNE DES DAMES DU HAREM.
Owned by The Art Institute of Chicago (O. S. Swan Memorial).

CONSTANTIN GUYS, French, 1805–1892
885. Reception
Water color and wash on paper, 6 7/8 x 7 5/8 in.
Owned by The Art Institute of Chicago (O. S. Swan Memorial).

CONSTANTIN GUYS, French, 1805–1892
886. One Woman Standing, Another Sitting
Wash drawing with color, 12¾ x 8¾ in.
Owned by The Art Institute of Chicago (O. S. Swan Memorial).

CONSTANTIN GUYS, French, 1805–1892
887. Woman
Wash drawing, bistre, sepia on paper, 13 9/16 x 9¾ in.
Owned by The Art Institute of Chicago (O. S. Swan Memorial).

FERDINAND HODLER, Swiss, 1853–1918
888. Call to Arms (Sketch for Iena Murals) (1908)
Pen, dry brush color on tracing-cloth, 10 x 16¾ in.
Signed: ferd. hodler.
Owned by The Art Institute of Chicago (R. Allerton Collection).

FERDINAND HODLER, Swiss, 1853–1918
889. The Mower
Pen and pencil on white paper, 12¾ x 12⅛ in.
Owned by The Art Institute of Chicago (R. Allerton Collection).

WINSLOW HOMER, American, 1836–1910
890. Adirondacks Guide (1892)
Water color, 12⅝ x 21 in.
Signed: h. '92.
Owned by The Art Institute of Chicago (Mr. and Mrs. M. A. Ryerson Collection).
Lit.: T. Bolton, *The Fine Arts*, XVIII, (Apr., 1932), 52.

WINSLOW HOMER, American, 1836–1910
891. After the Tornado, Bahamas (1892)
Water color, 14½ x 21 in.
Signed: homer.
Owned by The Art Institute of Chicago (Mr. and Mrs. M. A. Ryerson Collection).
Lit.: Mus. of Modern Art (New York): *Homer, Eakins, Ryder Catalogue*, 1930, No. 49; T. Bolton, *The Fine Arts*, XVIII (Apr., 1932), 54.

WINSLOW HOMER, American, 1836–1910
892. Breaking Storm, Maine Coast
Water color, 14¾ x 21 in.
Owned by The Art Institute of Chicago (Mr. and Mrs. M. A. Ryerson Collection).

WINSLOW HOMER, American, 1836–1910
893. Camp Fire, Adirondacks
Water color, 14⅞ x 21 in.
Signed: homer; sketch.
Owned by The Art Institute of Chicago (Mr. and Mrs. M. A. Ryerson Collection).

WINSLOW HOMER, American, 1836–1910
894. End of the Day, Adirondacks (1890)
Water color, 13⅝ x 19½ in.
Signed: homer, '90.
Owned by The Art Institute of Chicago (Mr. and Mrs. M. A. Ryerson Collection).

WINSLOW HOMER, American, 1836–1910
895. The Gulfstream (1889)
Water color, 11 x 19½ in.
Signed: w. h.—1889.
Owned by The Art Institute of Chicago (Mr. and Mrs. M. A. Ryerson Collection).

WINSLOW HOMER, American, 1836–1910
896. The Lone Boat, No. Woods Club (1892)
Water color, 14¾ x 21 in.
Signed: winslow homer, 1892.
Owned by The Art Institute of Chicago (Mr. and Mrs. M. A. Ryerson Collection).

WINSLOW HOMER, American, 1836–1910
897. Man in Boat, Maine Coast
Water color, 9 x 13½ in.
Signed: sketch w. h.
Owned by The Art Institute of Chicago (Mr. and Mrs. M. A. Ryerson Collection).

WINSLOW HOMER, American, 1836–1910
898. Marblehead
Water color, 8½ x 13 in.
Signed: homer.
Owned by The Art Institute of Chicago (Mr. and Mrs. M. A. Ryerson Collection).

WINSLOW HOMER, American, 1836–1910
899. North Woods Club, Adirondacks (1892)
Water color, 14¼ x 21⅛ in.
Signed: winslow homer, 1892, northwoods club, n. y.
Owned by The Art Institute of Chicago (Mr. and Mrs. M. A. Ryerson Collection).

WINSLOW HOMER, American, 1836–1910
900. The Outlook, Maine Coast (1894)
Water color, 13½ x 19½ in.
Signed: homer, '94.
Owned by The Art Institute of Chicago (Mr. and Mrs. M. A. Ryerson Collection).

WINSLOW HOMER, American, 1836–1910
901. Prout's Neck, Breakers (1883)
Water color, 14⅝ x 21 in.
Signed: winslow homer, 1883.
Owned by The Art Institute of Chicago (Mr. and Mrs. M. A. Ryerson Collection).

WINSLOW HOMER, American, 1836–1910
902. Prout's Neck, Breaking Wave (1887)
Water color, 15 x 21⅛ in.
Signed: homer, '87.
Owned by The Art Institute of Chicago (Mr. and Mrs. M. A. Ryerson Collection).

WINSLOW HOMER, American, 1836–1910
903. Prout's Neck, Evening
Water color, 13½ x 20½ in.
Signed: w. h.
Owned by The Art Institute of Chicago (Mr. and Mrs. M. A. Ryerson Collection).

WINSLOW HOMER, American, 1836–1910
904. The Rapids, Hudson River (1894)
Water color, 14⅞ x 21 in.
Signed: hudson river, june 1894, w. h.
Owned by The Art Institute of Chicago (Mr. and Mrs. M. A. Ryerson Collection).

WINSLOW HOMER, American, 1836–1910
905. Stowing Sail, Bahamas (1903)
Water color, 13½ x 21½ in.
Signed: sketch from nature, dec. 22, 1903. homer.
Owned by The Art Institute of Chicago (Mr. and Mrs. M. A. Ryerson Collection).

WINSLOW HOMER, American, 1836–1910
906. Sunshine and Shadow, Prout's Neck (1894)
Water color, 14¾ x 21 in.
Signed: winslow homer, 1894.
Owned by The Art Institute of Chicago (Mr. and Mrs. M. A. Ryerson Collection).

WINSLOW HOMER, American, 1836–1910
907. Tynemouth Priory, England (1881)
Water color, 10 x 19½ in.
Signed: winslow homer, 1881. tinemouth priory (winslow homer) engld.
Owned by The Art Institute of Chicago (Mr. and Mrs. M. A. Ryerson Collection).

WINSLOW HOMER, American, 1836–1910
908. The Watcher, Tynemouth (1882)
Water color, 8 x 14½ in.
Signed: homer, '82.
Owned by The Art Institute of Chicago (Mr. and Mrs. M. A. Ryerson Collection).

JEAN DOMINIQUE INGRES, French, 1780-1867
909. Life Drawings: A Face and a Figure with a Staff
Pencil, 10½ x 7 in.
Owned by The Art Institute of Chicago (R. Allerton Collection).

JEAN DOMINIQUE INGRES, French, 1780-1867
910. Monsieur Tardieu (Portrait)
Pencil on white paper, 9⅝ x 7¼ in.
Signed: ingres—a madame tardieu.
Lent by Mrs. Charles Netcher, Chicago.

JAMES DICKSON INNES, English, 1887-1914
911. Coast at Cerberre
Water color, 13¼ x 20⅝ in.
Owned by The Art Institute of Chicago (R. Allerton Collection).

JOHAN BARTHOLD JONGKIND—Dutch, 1819–1891
912. Le Cafe
Pen, water color, wash, pencil, 8¾ x 8¾ in.
Signed: jongkind.
Owned by The Art Institute of Chicago (Friends of American Art Collection).

JOHN LA FARGE, American, 1835–1910
913. Battle Window (Sketch for)
Water color on yellowish paper, 7⅜ x 3¾ in.
Owned by The Art Institute of Chicago.

DERWENT LEES, Australian, died 1931
914. The Blue Hills
Water color, 9 x 14 in.
Signed: lees.
Owned by The Art Institute of Chicago (R. Allerton Collection).

ALPHONSE LEGROS, French, 1837–1911
915. G. F. Watts (Portrait)
Sanguine on pink paper, 11¼ x 7¾ in.
Signed: a. legros.
Owned by The Art Institute of Chicago (C. Deering Collection).

AUGUSTE LEPERE, French, 1849–1918
916. La Plaine; St. Jean de Monts
Charcoal, 5⅝ x 8⅛ in.
Signed: a. lepere.
Lent by Mr. Daniel V. Casey.

AUGUSTE LEPERE, French, 1849–1918

917. Spring—Crevecoeur
Wash drawing with pencil and gouache, 8½ x 13⅜ in.
Signed: A. LEPERE.
Lent by Mr. Daniel V. Casey, Chicago.

EDOUARD MANET, French, 1832–1883

918. Mlle. Lemonnier (Portrait)
Crayon outline on creamy tan paper, 7⅛ x 5½ in.
Signed: E. M. (monogram).
Owned by The Art Institute of Chicago (R. Allerton Collection).

EDOUARD MANET, French, 1832–1883

919. Study of Snails
Water color on white paper, 7⅛ x 4½ in.
Owned by The Art Institute of Chicago (R. Allerton Collection).

MAXIME MAUFRA, French, 1862–1918

920. Yport: Beached Boats
Water color and crayon on light buff paper, 19½ x 12 in.
Signed: MAUFRA—YPORT.
Owned by The Art Institute of Chicago (Mr. and Mrs. M. A. Ryerson Collection).

AMBROSE McEVOY, English, 1879–1927

921. Lady Davina Lytton
Water color, black chalk on paper, 19 x 11 in.
Signed: M'EVOY.
Owned by The Art Institute of Chicago (O. S. Swan Memorial).

FRANÇOIS MILLET, French, 1814–1875

922. Grande Bergere (Study for)
Charcoal, 13 x 7½ in.
Signed: JFM (stamped).
Owned by The Art Institute of Chicago (Friends of American Art Collection).

FRANÇOIS MILLET, French, 1814–1875

923. Wool Carder (Study for Etching)
Charcoal on grey paper, 10 x 6⅞ in.
Signed: JFM (stamped).
Owned by The Art Institute of Chicago (P. Palmer Collection).

BERTHE MORISOT, French, 1841–1895

924. Woman and Child on a Balcony
Water color on white paper, 7½ x 6 in.
Signed: B. M. (stamped).
Owned by The Art Institute of Chicago (Charles Netcher II Memorial).

WILLIAM ORPEN, English, 1878–1931

925. Nude: Athlete and Male Torso
Charcoal, crayon on cream paper, 23¾ x 16½ in.
Signed: ORPEN.
Owned by The Art Institute of Chicago (R. Allerton Collection).

WILLIAM ORPEN, English, 1878–1931

926. Sisters (Nudes on Sea Shore)
Water color and pencil on white paper, 29⅞ x 20⅜ in.
Signed: ORPEN.
Owned by The Art Institute of Chicago (O. S. Swan Memorial).

WILLIAM ORPEN, English, 1878–1931

927. Woman with a Fan (1899)
Sepia drawing, 8½ x 5¼ in.
Signed: W. ORPEN '99.
Owned by The Art Institute of Chicago (R. Allerton Collection).

CAMILLE PISSARRO, French, 1831–1903

928. Marketscene: Pontoise
Pen and sepia wash with some gouache, 6⅞ x 5 in.
Signed: C. PISSARRO.
Owned by The Art Institute of Chicago (R. Allerton Collection).

PIERRE CECILE PUVIS DE CHAVANNES, French, 1824–1898

929. Head of Woman
Pencil, 10 x 7⅜ in.
Stamped: PDC.
Owned by The Art Institute of Chicago (Robert Allerton Collection).

PIERRE CECILE PUVIS DE CHAVANNES, French, 1824–1898

930. The Fisherman's Family (1887)
Sanguine, 12 x 9⅝ in. (on pinkish tan paper).
Inscribed: A ROGER MARX, TEMOIGNAGE D'UNE VIVE SYMPATHIE, P. PUVIS DE CHAVANNES.
Owned by The Art Institute of Chicago (Robert Allerton Collection).
A study for No. 267.

AUGUSTE RAFFET, French, 1804–1860

931. M. Terrasson (1849)
Wash and water color, 11 15/16 x 7⅛ in.
Signed: BRUXELLES, LE 12 JANVIER 1849, S. TERRASSON (STP. VENTE RAFFET).
Owned by The Art Institute of Chicago.

ODILON REDON, French, 1840–1916
932. La Loge
Oil stick on dark cream paper, 17½ x 25⅜ in.
Signed: odilon redon.
Owned by The Art Institute of Chicago.

AUGUSTE RODIN, French, 1840–1917
933. Model Reclining
Line drawing (pencil) and pink wash, 9½ x 12 in.
Signed: rodin.
Owned by The Art Institute of Chicago (R. Allerton Collection).

AUGUSTE RODIN, French, 1840–1917
934. Nude, Seated, Arms Overhead
Pencil drawing, pink wash, 12⅜ x 9⅜ in.
Signed: a. rodin.
Owned by The Art Institute of Chicago (R. Allerton Collection).

AUGUSTE RODIN, French, 1840–1917
935. Nude in a Whirl
Outline drawing (pencil) with pink wash, 9⅝ x 12⅛ in.
Signed: a. rodin (middle lower margin).
Owned by The Art Institute of Chicago.

FELICIEN ROPS, Belgian, 1833–1898
936. Invitation to a Concert
Pen drawing on écru paper, 3¹³⁄₁₆ x 3½ in.
Inscription: (Couplets).
Owned by the Art Institute of Chicago.

FELICIEN ROPS, Belgian, 1833–1898
937. Wounded Zouave
Pencil, pen, wash, 12¼ x 9⅛ in.
Signed: felicien.
Owned by The Art Institute of Chicago (C. Deering Collection).

JOHN S. SARGENT, American, 1856–1925
938. Hands Bound (Figure in Circle)
Charcoal on white paper, 18¼ x 24⅜ in.
Signed: john s. sargent.
Owned by The Art Institute of Chicago (Friends of American Art).

JOHN S. SARGENT, American, 1856–1925
939. Seated Male Figure
Charcoal on white paper, 18¼ x 24⅜ in.
Signed: john s. sargent.
Owned by The Art Institute of Chicago (Friends of American Art).

JOHN S. SARGENT, American, 1856–1925
940. Seated Male Nude
Charcoal on white paper, 18½ x 21⅜ in.
Signed: john s. sargent.
Owned by The Art Institute of Chicago (R. Allerton Collection).

JOHN S. SARGENT, American, 1856–1925
941. Nude: Male (Study): Knees raised, Fore-arm flexed
Charcoal on white paper, 18¼ x 21⅜ in.
Signed: john s. sargent.
Owned by The Art Institute of Chicago (Friends of American Art).

JOHN S. SARGENT, American, 1856–1925
942. Study of Feet and Legs
Charcoal on white paper, 18¼ x 24½ in.
Signed: john s. sargent (upside down).
Owned by The Art Institute of Chicago (Friends of American Art Collection).

JOHN S. SARGENT, American, 1856–1925
943. Woodsheds; Tyrol
Water color on white paper, 15¼ x 20⅝ in.
Signed: john s. sargent—tirol.
Owned by The Art Institute of Chicago (O. S. Swan Memorial).

JOHN S. SARGENT, American, 1856–1925
944. Workmen, Carrara
Water color, 15½ x 20½ in.
Signed: john s. sargent—carrara.
Owned by The Art Institute of Chicago (O. S. Swan Memorial).

GEORGES SEURAT, French, 1859–1891
946. La Frileuse
Charcoal on paper, 12 x 8⅞ in.
Owned by The Art Institute of Chicago (R. Allerton Collection).

THEOPHILE A. STEINLEN, French, 1859–1923
947. Laundress
Charcoal on tan paper, 24 x 18 in.
Signed: steinlen.
Owned by The Art Institute of Chicago (R. Allerton Collection).

HENRI DE TOULOUSE-LAUTREC, French, 1864–1901
948. Mlle. Polaire
Line and sepia brush and charcoal on buff paper, 28¼ x 15½ in.
Signed with monogram in circle.
Owned by The Art Institute of Chicago.

ALBERT WEISGERBER, German, 1878–1915
949. Flagellation
Pen drawing on white paper, 6¼ x 7⅞ in.
Owned by The Art Institute of Chicago (R. Allerton Collection).

JAMES A. McNEILL WHISTLER, American, 1834–1903
950. Draped Model
Crayon on dark brown paper, 12⅞ x 9⅜ in.
Signed with butterfly monogram.
Owned by The Art Institute of Chicago (C. Deering Collection).

JAMES A. McNEILL WHISTLER, American, 1834–1903
951. Nude
Crayon on dark brown paper, 11 x 7⅛ in.
Signed with butterfly monogram.
Owned by The Art Institute of Chicago (C. Deering Collection).

EUROPEAN AND AMERICAN
Twentieth Century

RIFKA ANGEL, American, 1899–
952. Nursery Rhyme No. 1 (1932)
Water color, 8 x 6⅛ in.
Signed: rifka angel.
Lent by Mr. Arthur Heun, Chicago.

GIFFORD BEAL, American, 1879–
953. Fishing Boats, Rockport (1922)
Brush drawing on dark cream paper, 12¼ x 17⅞ in.
Signed: gifford beal, '22.
Owned by The Art Institute of Chicago.

GIFFORD BEAL, American, 1879–
954. New York Harbor (1924)
Water color on white paper, 14 x 21½ in.
Signed: gifford beal, 24.
Owned by The Art Institute of Chicago (O. S. Swan Memorial).

MAX BEERBOHM, English, 1872–
957. Resolved . . . (1909)
Pencil and wash on grey paper, 15¾ x 11 in.
Signed: max, 1909.
Owned by The Art Institute of Chicago (Chadbourne Collection).

MAX BEERBOHM, English, 1872–
958. Sir William Eden Revisiting Paris (1907)
Ink, pencil and wash, 12¾ x 8⅜ in.
Signed: max, '07.
Owned by The Art Institute of Chicago (Chadbourne Collection).

ALBERT BESNARD, French, 1849–
959. Woman at her Toilette
Crayon on white paper, 12⅜ x 9⅝ in.
Signed: a. besnard.
Owned by The Art Institute of Chicago (R. Allerton Collection).

MUIRHEAD BONE, English, 1876–
960. The Fort, Freshwater Bay
Water color and pencil on white paper, 8⅝ x 11⅛ in.
Signed: muirhead bone.
Owned by The Art Institute of Chicago.

MUIRHEAD BONE, English, 1876–
961. Loen, Norway
Water color, crayon & wash on white paper, 8⅛ x 11⅛ in.
Signed: muirhead bone.
Lent by Mr. Daniel V. Casey, Chicago.

MUIRHEAD BONE, English, 1876–
962. Trafalgar Square, London (1922)
Pen and ink on white paper, 10 x 12⅛ in.
Signed: muirhead bone, 1922.
Owned by The Art Institute of Chicago (Charles Netcher II Memorial).

GEORGE ELMER BROWNE, American, 1871–
963. Tetuan, Morocco
Water color on white paper, 11¼ x 15⅜ in.
Signed: geo. elmer browne.
Owned by The Art Institute of Chicago.

HEINRICH CAMPENDONK, German, 1889–

964. From Brittany
Water color on white paper, 22¼ x 18⅞ in.
Owned by The Art Institute of Chicago.

FRANCIS CHAPIN, American, 1899–

965. Sheltered Harbor, Roscoff (1928)
Water color on white paper, 19¾ x 14¾ in.
Owned by The Art Institute of Chicago.

JOHN E. COSTIGAN, American, 1888–

966. Sheep at the Gate (1923)
Water color on white paper, 12¼ x 18½ in.
Signed: J. E. COSTIGAN.
Owned by The Art Institute of Chicago.

HERMINE DAVID, French, 1886–

967. Hilly Landscape
Water color and crayon, 8⅝ x 12⅞ in.
Signed: HERMINE-DAVID.
Owned by The Art Institute of Chicago.

HERMINE DAVID, French, 1886–

968. Landscape
Water color and dry brush on white paper, 6½ x 8⅞ in.
Signed: HERMINE DAVID.
Owned by The Art Institute of Chicago.

ADOLF DEHN, American, 1895–

969. Noon Hour (1927)
Pen drawing with brush, 13½ x 20⅜ in.
Signed: ADOLF DEHN, 1927.
Lent by the Artist.

CHARLES DEMUTH, American, 1883–

970. Flowers (1920)
Water color on white paper, 13¾ x 11¾ in.
Signed: C. DEMUTH, 1920.
Owned by The Art Institute of Chicago (Helen Birch Bartlett Memorial).

ANDRE DERAIN, French, 1880–

971. Landscape (skyline)
Water color on white paper, 12½ x 18½ in.
Signed: A. DERAIN.
Owned by The Art Institute of Chicago (R. Allerton Collection).

ANDRE DERAIN, French, 1880–

972. Nude Leaning on Invisible Support
Pen outline drawing on white paper, 16½ x 10 in.
Signed: A. DERAIN.
Owned by The Art Institute of Chicago (R. Allerton Collection).

CHARLES DESPIAU, French, 1874–

973. Nude (arms between legs)
Sanguine on white paper, 13⅜ x 8⅞ in.
Signed: C. DESPIAU.
Owned by The Art Institute of Chicago (R. Allerton Collection).

OTTO DIX, German, 1891–

†974. Resting Woman (1928)
Water color on white paper, 12¼ x 21½ in.
Signed: DIX, '28.
Lent by Mr. J. B. Neumann, New York.

PAUL DOUGHERTY, American, 1877–

975. Trees
Charcoal on white paper, 9½ x 14½ in.
Signed: PAUL DOUGHERTY.
Owned by The Art Institute of Chicago (Friends of American Art Collection).

CHARLES DUFRESNE, French, 1876–

976. Grande Gouache
Gouache, 15⅛ x 18⅛ in.
Signed: DUFRESNE.
Owned by The Art Institute of Chicago (R. Allerton Collection).

CHARLES DUFRESNE, French, 1876–

977. Woman in an Interior
Water color and pastel, 9⅝ x 9⅜ in.
Signed: DUFRESNE.
Owned by The Art Institute of Chicago.

RAOUL DUFY, French, 1877–

978. The Blue Train
Water color and gouache, 19¾ x 25½ in.
Signed: RAOUL DUFY.
Lent by Mr. and Mrs. John U. Nef, Chicago.

GEORGE WILLIAM EGGERS, American, 1883–

979. John the Baptist (Sketch for) (1920)
Water color drawing on white paper, 11¾ x 8⅛ in.
Signed: EGGERS, 1920.
Owned by The Art Institute of Chicago.

GEORGE WILLIAM EGGERS, American, 1883–

980. Nude; with Arms Upraised (1917)
Sanguine on cream paper, 11¼ x 7½ in.
Signed: EGGERS, 1917.
Owned by The Art Institute of Chicago (Friends of American Art Collection).

GEORGE PEARSE ENNIS, American, 1884–
981. Home Port (1921)
Water color on white paper, 15½ x 19¾ in.
Signed: ENNIS.
Owned by The Art Institute of Chicago.

ALFEO FAGGI, American, 1885–
981A. Male Nude Bending Over
Sanguine on white paper, 14⅞ x 9⅜ in.
Signed: A. FAGGI (twice).
Owned by The Art Institute of Chicago.

SERGE FERAT, Russian, 1881–
982. Green Circus Riders (Ecuyers Verts)
Water color (pointillé) on white paper with wash, 21 x 15¾ in.
Signed: S. FERAT.
Owned by The Art Institute of Chicago (R. Allerton Collection).

W. RUSSELL FLINT, English, 1880–
983. Golden Sands, Bamburgh (1921)
Water color on white paper, 19¾ x 26½ in.
Signed: W. RUSSELL FLINT.
Owned by The Art Institute of Chicago.

W. RUSSELL FLINT, English, 1880–
984. Wet Sands, Bamburgh (1920)
Water color on white paper, 19¾ x 26⅜ in.
Signed: W. RUSSELL FLINT.
Owned by The Art Institute of Chicago.

ELMER A. FORSBERG, American, 1883–
985. Nude Torso from Back (1921)
Brown crayon on bluish paper, 8⁹⁄₁₆ x 11 in.
Signed: ELMER A. FORSBERG, 1921.
Owned by The Art Institute of Chicago.

KARL FREE, American, 1903–
†986. Souvenir of Brussels (1929)
Water color on white paper, 16½ x 13 in.
Signed: KARL FREE, '29—BRUXELLES.
Lent by the Artist.

FREDERICK CARL FRIESEKE, American, 1874–
987. Frances at the Piano (1929)
Water color on white paper, 11½ x 10⅞ in.
Signed: F. C. FRIESEKE, 1929.
Owned by The Art Institute of Chicago (O. S. Swan Memorial).

EDMUND GIESBERT, American, 1893–
†988. Baby (1927)
Charcoal drawing on white paper, 16½ x 13 in.
Signed: GIESBERT (another signature concealed by mat).
Lent by the Artist.

HOWARD GILES, American, 1876–
989. Shore-Line
Water color on white paper, 11½ x 15¼ in.
Owned by The Art Institute of Chicago.

ERIC GILL, English, 1882–
990. From Gordian (1923)
Pencil on white paper, 8⅞ x 6⅝ in.
Signed: FROM GORDIAN 2.12.23, E. G.
Owned by The Art Institute of Chicago (R. Allerton Collection).

RALPH W. GRAHAM, American, 1901–
†991. North Ave. Vista (1931)
Water color with gilt touches on white paper, 23³⁄₁₆ x 15¹⁵⁄₁₆ in.
Lent by the Artist.

GEORGE GROSZ, German, 1893–
992. Street in Paris (1928)
Water color on white paper, 23½ x 18 in.
Owned by The Art Institute of Chicago.

W. EMERTON HEITLAND, American, 1893–
993. Harbor, Puerto Plata (1924)
Water color on white paper, 19 x 22⅛ in.
Signed: HEITLAND.
Owned by The Art Institute of Chicago (O. S. Swan Memorial).

W. EMERTON HEITLAND, American, 1893–
994. Old Cemetery, Santo Domingo (1924)
Water color on white paper, 19 x 22 in.
Signed: HEITLAND.
Owned by The Art Institute of Chicago (O. S. Swan Memorial).

W. EMERTON HEITLAND, American, 1893–
995. Shanty, Tampa (1922)
Water color on white paper, 16¾ x 18½ in.
Signed: HEITLAND, 1922.
Owned by The Art Institute of Chicago.

WILLIAM P. HENDERSON, AMERICAN, 1877–
996. CURTAIN CALL
Pastel on dark grey paper, 8¾ x 5 in.
Owned by The Art Institute of Chicago.

WILLIAM P. HENDERSON, AMERICAN, 1877–
997. HARVEST DANCE
Pastel, chalk, wash, 9 x 11⅞ in.
Owned by The Art Institute of Chicago (Friends of American Art Collection).

WILLIAM P. HENDERSON, AMERICAN, 1877–
998. UTE DANCE AT TESUQUE
Pastel, chalk and wash, 9¼ x 12⅜ in.
Owned by The Art Institute of Chicago (Friends of American Art Collection).

HARRY HERING, AMERICAN, 1887–
†999. OVERLOOK (1930)
Water color, 20 x 28⅞ in.
Signed: HARRY HERING, '30 (twice).
Lent by the Artist.

EMIL HOLZHAUER, AMERICAN, 1887–
1000. PATRICIA (PORTRAIT) (1927)
Water color on white paper, 21⅝ x 14⅝ in.
Signed: HOLZHAUER, 1927.
Owned by The Art Institute of Chicago.

CHARLES HOPKINSON, AMERICAN, 1869–
1001. LUNG'ARNO THROUGH HOTEL WINDOW
Water color on white paper, 14¼ x 19⅞ in.
Signed: C. H. (monogram).
Owned by The Art Institute of Chicago.

EDWARD HOPPER, AMERICAN, 1882–
1002. GLOUCESTER MANSIONS (1923)
Water color and pencil on white paper, 13½ x 19½ in.
Signed: EDWARD HOPPER, GLOUCESTER, 1923.
Owned by The Art Institute of Chicago (O. S. Swan Memorial).

EDWARD HOPPER, AMERICAN, 1882–
1003. MODEL READING (1925)
Water color on white paper, 13⁹⁄₁₆ x 19⁹⁄₁₆ in.
Signed: EDWARD HOPPER, SANTA FE, 1925.
Owned by The Art Institute of Chicago (O. S. Swan Memorial).

EDWARD HOPPER, AMERICAN, 1882–
1004. LA PIERREUSE
Water color on white paper, 11⁵⁄₁₆ x 6⁷⁄₁₆ in.
Signed: EDWARD HOPPER.
Owned by The Art Institute of Chicago (O. S. Swan Memorial).

EDWARD HOPPER, AMERICAN, 1882–
1005. LE TERRASSIER (STREET MENDER)
Water color on paper, 11⁵⁄₁₆ x 6⁷⁄₁₆ in.
Signed: EDWARD HOPPER.
Owned by The Art Institute of Chicago (O. S. Swan Memorial).

EARL C. HORTER, AMERICAN CONTEMPORARY
1006. NUDE RECLINING
Water color on white paper, 11½ x 12½ in.
Signed: E. HORTER.
Owned by The Art Institute of Chicago.

FELICIE W. HOWELL, AMERICAN, 1897–
1007. THE CHEF (1926)
Water color on white paper, 9½ x 7½ in.
Signed: FELICIE WALDO HOWELL, 1926.
Owned by The Art Institute of Chicago.

NORMAN JACOBSEN, AMERICAN, 1884–
1008. BALINESE WINDING YARN WITH HER FEET
Crayon on grey-mottled paper, 9½ x 13⅜ in.
Signed: JACOBSEN.
Owned by The Art Institute of Chicago (R. Allerton Collection).

JOSEPH W. JICHA, AMERICAN, 1901–
1009. BAHAMA COAL VENDER (1928)
Water color on white paper, 14½ x 19¾ in.
Signed: JOSEPH W. JICHA, NASSAU.
Owned by The Art Institute of Chicago.

AUGUSTUS E. JOHN, ENGLISH, 1879–
1010. DAY (STUDY OF FEMALE FIGURE)
Crayon, 21½ x 17 in.
Signed: JOHN.
Owned by The Art Institute of Chicago.

AUGUSTUS E. JOHN, ENGLISH, 1879–
1011. AMBROSE M'EVOY, PROFILE TO LEFT (PORTRAIT)
Sanguine on grey paper, 7½ x 6⅝ in.
Signed: JOHN.
Owned by The Art Institute of Chicago (R. Allerton Collection).

AUGUSTUS E. JOHN, English, 1879–
1012. Samson and Delilah (?)
Sepia wash drawing, 8¾ x 9¼ in.
Owned by The Art Institute of Chicago (R. Allerton Collection).

AUGUSTUS E. JOHN, English, 1879–
1013. Two Women and a Child in a Landscape
Pencil drawing, 13¾ x 17¼ in.
Signed: JOHN.
Owned by The Art Institute of Chicago (Chadbourne Collection).

LLOYD R. JONES, American, 1890–
1014. The Artist (1929)
Water color on white paper, 12½ x 18⅛ in.
Signed: LLOYD R. JONES.
Owned by The Art Institute of Chicago.

HENRY G. KELLER, American, 1870–
1015. Winter Landscape (1929)
Water color on white paper, 19½ x 14½ in.
Signed: KELLER (and with monogram).
Owned by The Art Institute of Chicago.

ROCKWELL KENT, American, 1882–
1016. Running Water
Pen drawing on white paper, c. 9 x 7 in.
Signed: ROCKWELL KENT—ALASKA.
Owned by The Art Institute of Chicago (R. Allerton Collection).

ROCKWELL KENT, American, 1882–
1017. Self-Portrait (1923)
Pen drawing on white paper, 9 x 5⅞ in.
Signed: ROCKWELL KENT—PORTRAIT OF ME, IMPROVED, 1923.
Owned by The Art Institute of Chicago (R. Allerton Collection).

LAURA KNIGHT, English, 1877–
1018. Before the Act
Water color and black chalk, 14⅞ x 19¾ in.
Signed: LAURA KNIGHT.
Owned by The Art Institute of Chicago (O. S. Swan Memorial).

GEORG KOLBE, German, 1877–
1019. Nude Bending Over Sideways (to left)
Pen and ink wash on white paper, 15¾ x 13 in.
Signed: G. K. (monogram).
Owned by The Art Institute of Chicago (R. Allerton Collection).

GEORG KOLBE, German, 1877–
1020. Nude Jumping (Front)
Ink and wash on white paper, 18¾ x 12 in.
Signed: G. K. (monogram).
Owned by The Art Institute of Chicago (R. Allerton Collection).

LEON KROLL, American, 1884–
1021. Les Andelys
Pencil on white paper, 12¼ x 19⅛ in.
Signed: LEON KROLL.
Owned by The Art Institute of Chicago (R. Allerton Collection).

MARIE LAURENCIN, French, 1885–
1022. Two Women with Vine Decoration
Water color and pencil on white paper, 9¾ x 12¼ in.
Signed: M. LAURENCIN.
Owned by The Art Institute of Chicago (R. Allerton Collection).

MARIE LAURENCIN, French, 1885–
1023. Woman with Blue Kerchief
Wash on creamy paper, blue crayon scarf, 9⅜ x 6¼ in.
Signed: M. L. (monogram).
Owned by The Art Institute of Chicago (R. Allerton Collection).

GEORGE LUKS, American, 1867–
1024. Landscape
Water color on white paper, 13½ x 19$^{11}/_{16}$ in.
Signed: GEORGE LUKS.
Owned by The Art Institute of Chicago (O. S. Swan Memorial).

JAMES McBEY, English, 1883–
1025. View of Walcheren (1923)
Wash, water color, pen on white paper, 10⅝ x 17⅛ in.
Signed: MC BEY, VEERE, 3 SEPTEMBER 1923.
Lent by Mr. Daniel V. Casey.

DAVID JOHN McCOSH, American, 1903–
†1026. Shoppers Resting (1933)
Water color on white paper, 14$^{5}/_{16}$ x 23 in.
Signed: D. J. MC COSH, 33.
Lent by the Artist.

JEAN MacLANE, American, 1878–
1027. Along the Beach, England (1925)
Water color on white paper, 12¾ x 17⅜ in.
Signed: JEAN MAC LANE, 1925.
Owned by The Art Institute of Chicago.

ARISTIDE MAILLOL, French, 1861–
1028. Recumbent Nude (Falling)
Pencil on dark cream paper, 7⅛ x 9½ in.
Signed: m (monogram in cartouche).
Owned by The Art Institute of Chicago (R. Allerton Collection).

JOHN MARIN, American, 1875–
1029. The Little Tree; Maine (1914)
Water color on white paper, 13⅞ x 16⅛ in.
Signed: marin, '14.
Owned by The Art Institute of Chicago.

ALBERT MARQUET, French, 1875–
1030. Ghardaja; Arab Mother and Child
Line drawing (pen) on tan paper, 5¾ x 4 in.
Signed: marquet.
Owned by The Art Institute of Chicago.

ALBERT MARQUET, French, 1875–
1031. The Wharf, Audierne (1928)
Water color on white paper, 8½ x 11 in.
Signed: marquet, audierne, 1928.
Owned by The Art Institute of Chicago (O. S. Swan Memorial).

HENRI MATISSE, French, 1869–
1032. Girl with Cat
Pencil on white paper, 10¾ x 8¼ in.
Signed: henri matisse.
Owned by The Art Institute of Chicago (Chadbourne Collection).

HENRI MATISSE, French, 1869–
1033. Woman Nursing Knee—A Foot (1909)
Brush drawing on white paper, 11½ x 9⅛ in.
Signed: henri-matisse aout 1909.
Owned by The Art Institute of Chicago (Chadbourne Collection).

HENRI MATISSE, French, 1869–
1034. Study for White Plumes
Brush drawing on white paper, 11 x 14 in.
Signed: henri matisse.
Owned by The Art Institute of Chicago.
Compare No. 397.

HENRI MATISSE, French, 1869–
1035. Woman with Shawl
Pencil on white paper, 15 x 10⅞ in.
Signed: henri-matisse.
Owned by The Art Institute of Chicago (R. Allerton Collection).

IVAN MESTROVIC, Jugoslav, 1883–
1036. Dancing Figure
Charcoal on brown packing paper, 18¾ x 14¾ in.
Signature in Cyrillic letters.
Owned by The Art Institute of Chicago (R. Allerton Collection).

AMEDEO MODIGLIANI, Italian, 1884–1920
1037. Anatolia (Head)
Pencil line drawing, slightly inked in, 12⅛ x 8⅞ in.
Signed: anatolia—modigliani (in respective corners).
Owned by The Art Institute of Chicago (R. Allerton Collection).

JEROME MYERS, American, 1867–
1038. Group: Figures on Walk
Pencil on white paper, 8 x 8½ in.
Signed: jerome myers.
Owned by The Art Institute of Chicago (Friends of American Art Collection).

JEROME MYERS, American, 1867–
1039. Women and Children on Park Benches
Pencil on white paper, 8¼ x 10¾ in.
Signed: jerome myers.
Owned by The Art Institute of Chicago (Friends of American Art Collection).

PAUL NASH, English, 1889–
1040. Conservatory Window (1925)
Water color (with pencil), 22¼ x 15 in.
Signed: paul nash, 1925.
Owned by The Art Institute of Chicago (R. Allerton Collection).

JOHN NASH, English, 1893–
1041. Edge of the Plain (1919)
Water color, 10⅛ x 14⅛ in.
Signed: john nash, 1919.
Owned by The Art Institute of Chicago (R. Allerton Collection).

JOHN NASH, English, 1893–
1042. A Sapperton Village (1920)
Pencil and wash, 12¼ x 15 in.
Signed: john nash, 1920.
Owned by The Art Institute of Chicago (R. Allerton Collection).

JOHN W. NORTON, American, 1876–
1043. Sails and Nets, Honfleur (1925)
Water color on white paper, 9 5/16 x 14 5/16 in.
Signed: J. W. NORTON, 1925.
Owned by The Art Institute of Chicago.

PABLO PICASSO, Spanish, 1881–
1044. Girl and Boy
Pen drawing on yellow tan paper, 9 5/8 x 12 5/8 in.
Signed: PICASSO.
Owned by The Art Institute of Chicago (R. Allerton Collection).

PABLO PICASSO, Spanish, 1881–
1045. Male Nude, Right Arm Overhead, etc.
Pencil on light tan paper, 12 x 7 5/8 in.
Owned by The Art Institute of Chicago (R. Allerton Collection).

PABLO PICASSO, Spanish, 1881–
1046. Musical Instruments (cubist) (1916)
Water color on white paper, 5 3/4 x 4 5/8 in.
Signed: PICASSO.
Owned by The Art Institute of Chicago (R. Allerton Collection).

PABLO PICASSO, Spanish, 1881–
1047. Peasants from Andorra
Pen drawing on cream paper (line), 22 5/8 x 13 7/8 in.
Owned by The Art Institute of Chicago (R. Allerton Collection).

PABLO PICASSO, Spanish, 1881–
1048. Rider (Cavalier)
Pencil outline on tan paper, 18 1/8 x 11 1/2 in.
Signed: PICASSO.
Lent by Mr. Shreve Badger, Chicago.

PABLO PICASSO, Spanish, 1881–
1049. Woman Seated
Gouache and sepia on grey ground, 10 5/8 x 9 5/16 in.
Signed: PICASSO.
Lent by Mr. and Mrs. John U. Nef, Chicago.

FREDERICK V. POOLE, American Contemporary
1050. Boy in an Interior (Bennet) (1913–4)
Water color, 8 5/8 x 8 in.
Signed: F. V. POOLE.
Lent by the Estate of Mrs. Lewis L. Coburn.

JANE POUPELET, French, 1878–1932
1051. Cat
Charcoal on light tan paper, 8 1/8 x 9 7/8 in.
Signed: J. POUPELET.
Owned by The Art Institute of Chicago (R. Allerton Collection).

JANE POUPELET, French, 1878–1932
1052. Horse
Sepia, brush drawing on light tan paper, 9 2/8 x 12 1/8 in.
Signed: J. POUPELET.
Owned by The Art Institute of Chicago (R. Allerton Collection).

JANE POUPELET, French, 1878–1932
1053. Nude Sitting (Back View)
Brush outlines on light brown paper, 10 1/2 x 8 1/2 in.
Signed: J. POUPELET.
Owned by The Art Institute of Chicago (R. Allerton Collection).

MAURICE PRENDERGAST, American, 1856–1924
1054. Yachting
Water color, 18 1/8 x 20 4/8 in.
Signed: PRENDERGAST.
Owned by The Art Institute of Chicago.

PEDRO (PABLO) PRUNA, Spanish, 1904–
1055. Three Women, Enghien (1926)
Water color on white paper, 9 4/8 x 11 6/8 in.
Signed: PRUNA 1926 ENGHIEN.
Owned by The Art Institute of Chicago (R. Allerton Collection).

JAMES PRYDE, English, 1866–
1056. Ancient Monument
Wash drawing; water color touches, 6 x 5 in.
Signed: PRYDE.
Owned by The Art Institute of Chicago (R. Allerton Collection).

JAMES PRYDE, English, 1866–
1057. Courtyard
Wash drawing and gouache, 15 3/8 x 12 in.
Owned by The Art Institute of Chicago (R. Allerton Collection).

JAMES PRYDE, English, 1866–
1058. Use of the Globe (Sketch For)
Gouache on wash ground on white paper, 4 3/8 x 3 2/8 in.
Signed: PRYDE.
Owned by The Art Institute of Chicago (R. Allerton Collection).

JEAN FRANÇOIS RAFFAELLI, French, 1850–1924

1059. Rodin in his Studio
Water color drawing
Signed: J. F. RAFFAELLI.
Owned by The Art Institute of Chicago (O. S. Swan Memorial).

CHARLES RICKETTS, English, 1866–1931

1060. Centaur and Ruins
Pen drawing (line), $9\frac{6}{8}$ x $6\frac{4}{8}$ in.
Signed: CR (monogram).
Owned by The Art Institute of Chicago (R. Allerton Collection).

CHARLES RICKETTS, English, 1866–1931

1061. Teacher of Wisdom
Line drawing, ink on white paper, $9\frac{4}{8}$ x $6\frac{4}{8}$ in.
Signed: C.R.
Owned by The Art Institute of Chicago (R. Allerton Collection).

AIDEN L. RIPLEY, American, 1896–

1062. Swedish Peasant Girls
Water color on white paper, 16 x $19\frac{6}{8}$ in.
Signed: A. L. RIPLEY, 1927.
Owned by The Art Institute of Chicago.

WILLIAM ROTHENSTEIN, English, 1872–

1063. Arnold Bennett (Portrait) (1920)
Sanguine on pink paper, $13\frac{7}{8}$ x 10 in.
Signed: W. ROTHENSTEIN, 1920.
Owned by The Art Institute of Chicago (R. Allerton Collection).

WILLIAM ROTHENSTEIN, English, 1872–

1064. Women Fighting; East End
Pencil, ink, colored washes, $19\frac{2}{8}$ x $13\frac{1}{8}$ in.
Owned by The Art Institute of Chicago (R. Allerton Collection).

GEORGES ROUAULT, French, 1871–

1065. Maria Lani, Actress (1928)
Water color—dry brush on white paper, $16\frac{7}{8}$ x $12\frac{5}{16}$ in.
Signed: G. ROUAULT, 1928.
Owned by The Art Institute of Chicago.

ALBERT D. RUTHERSTON, English, 1881–

1066. Pierrot (costume)
Water color and pen drawing, $11\frac{2}{8}$ x 6 in.
Signed: ALBERT R. '09; FOR MRS. CHADBOURNE, ALB. R. '10.
Owned by The Art Institute of Chicago (Chadbourne Collection).

ALBERT D. RUTHERSTON, English, 1881–

1067. Girl on Cliff (1909)
Pen and water color (sketch in color), $7\frac{6}{8}$ x $6\frac{2}{8}$ in.
Signed: ALBERT R. '09.
Owned by The Art Institute of Chicago (Chadbourne Collection).

GEORGES H. SABBAGH, French, 1888–

1068. Still Life; Bottle, Bowl and Books
Water color on cream paper, $15\frac{1}{16}$ x $10\frac{1}{32}$ in.
Signed: G. H. SABBAGH, 1920.
Owned by The Art Institute of Chicago (Mr. and Mrs. M. A. Ryerson Collection).

HELEN SAWYER, American, 1900–

†1069. Jeweler's Wife
Dry brush with black on water color paper, $7\frac{4}{8}$ x 9 in.
Signed: JEWELER'S WIFE—HELEN SAWYER.
Lent by the Artist.

HENRY E. SCHNAKENBERG, American, 1892–

1070. Ronda—El Espiritu Santo
Water color on white paper, $13\frac{6}{8}$ x $19\frac{4}{8}$ in.
Signed: H. E. SCHNAKENBERG.
Owned by The Art Institute of Chicago (O. S. Swan Memorial).

RANDOLPH SCHWABE, English, 1885–

1071. Shepheard's, London
Wash drawing on white paper, $12\frac{6}{8}$ x 10 in.
Signed: R. SCHWABE.
Owned by The Art Institute of Chicago (R. Allerton Collection).

CARL SCHWALBACH, German, 1885–

1072. Girls Listening (1926)
Water color on paper, $15\frac{3}{8}$ x $11\frac{7}{8}$ in.
Signed: SCHWALBACH.
Owned by The Art Institute of Chicago.

ANDRE D. DE SEGONZAC, French, 1885–

1073. Recumbent Nude
Pen outline drawing on white paper, 9 x $17\frac{4}{8}$ in.
Signed: A. DUNOYER DE SEGONZAC.
Owned by The Art Institute of Chicago.

CHARLES SHEELER, American, 1883–

1074. Section of a Torso
Pencil on white paper, $4\frac{3}{8}$ x 6 in.
Owned by The Art Institute of Chicago (Friends of American Art Coll.).

CHARLES SHEELER, American, 1883–
1075. New York (1920)
Pencil on light cream paper, 19⅞ x 13 in.
Signed: sheeler, 1920.
Owned by The Art Institute of Chicago (Friends of American Art Collection).

PAUL SIGNAC, French, 1863–
1076. Groix (1923)
Water color on dark cream paper, 7⅝ x 11⅝ in.
Signed: p. signac, groix, 1923.
Owned by The Art Institute of Chicago.

PAUL SIGNAC, French, 1863–
1076A. Port Louis, Lomalo (1911)
Water color on deep cream paper.
Signed: p. signac, port-louis-lomalo, 1911.
Owned by The Art Institute of Chicago (Mr. and Mrs. M. A. Ryerson Collection).

FRANK SNAPP, American Contemporary
1077. A Reflection (1921)
Water color on white paper, 23⅝ x 15⅜ in.
Owned by The Art Institute of Chicago.

WILLIAM SOMMER, American, 1867–
1078. Boy (Portrait) (1930)
Water color on white paper, 14$^{15}/_{16}$ x 10⅘ in.
Signed: william sommer, 1930.
Owned by the Art Institute of Chicago.

MAURICE STERNE, American, 1877–
1079. Dancer
Pen drawing on tan paper, 10⅝ x 7⅞ in.
Signed: sterne.
Owned by The Art Institute of Chicago (R. Allerton Collection).

JOHN STORRS, American, 1885–
1080. Sleeper
Silverpoint drawing, 13 x 10⅛ in.
Signed: storrs, 30. 10. 28 II.
Owned by The Art Institute of Chicago (Mr. and Mrs. C. H. Worcester Collection).

MAURICE UTRILLO, French, 1883–
1081. Rue Ordener, Paris (1922)
Water color on white paper, 10$^{11}/_{16}$ x 14$^{13}/_{16}$ in.
Signed: maurice utrillo, v., 1922; rue ordener paris, 18eme.
Owned by The Art Institute of Chicago (O. S. Swan Memorial).

SUZANNE VALADON, French, 1867–
1082. Rising in the Morning (Le Lever) (1920)
Chalk, charcoal, crayon, 18⅞ x 14⅛ in.
Signed: suzanne valadon, 1920.
Owned by The Art Institute of Chicago (R. Allerton Collection).

MATHIEU VERDILHAN, French, 1876–1929
1083. Two Women Visiting
Black crayon and wash, 9 x 12⅛ in.
Signed: verdilhan-mathieu.
Owned by The Art Institute of Chicago.

HENRI VERGE-SARRAT, Belgian, 1880–
1084. Toulon (1925)
Water color and pen on white paper, 9$^{9}/_{16}$ x 12⅝ in.
Signed: verge-sarrat, 1925.
Owned by The Art Institute of Chicago (R. Allerton Collection).

MAURICE DE VLAMINCK, French, 1876–
1085. A Country Road
Black and white drawing on white paper, 11 x 14⅝ in.
Signed: vlaminck.
Owned by The Art Institute of Chicago (Mr. and Mrs. M. A. Ryerson Collection).

MAURICE DE VLAMINCK, French, 1876–
1086. Three Trees
Water color on white paper, 13$^{11}/_{16}$ x 17$^{7}/_{16}$ in.
Signed: vlaminck.
Owned by The Art Institute of Chicago (Mr. and Mrs. Martin A. Ryerson Collection).

MARTHA WALTER, American Contemporary
1087. Florian's Venice, No. 2 (1923)
Water color on paper, 9½ x 11 in.
Signed: martha walter.
Owned by The Art Institute of Chicago (O. S. Swan Memorial).

MAX WEBER, American, 1881–
1088. Attitudes (1930)
Water color, pen, ink, gouache on tan paper, 4 x 7¼ in.
Signed: max weber, 1930.
Owned by The Art Institute of Chicago (R. Allerton Collection).

HERMAN A. WEBSTER, American, 1878–
1089. Rue de la Boucherie, Limoges
Colored crayon on white paper, 11⅘ x 15⅖ in.
Signed: H. A. WEBSTER.
Owned by The Art Institute of Chicago (J. B. Fair Collection).

JOHN WHORF, American, 1903–
1090. Bather (1928)
Water color on white paper, 14¾ x 19⅞ in.
Signed: JOHN WHORF, 7.
Owned by The Art Institute of Chicago.

JOHN WHORF, American, 1903–
1091. Sea Apples
Water color on white paper, 15⅛ x 21 in.
Signed: JOHN WHORF.
Owned by The Art Institute of Chicago (O. S. Swan Memorial).

JOHN SCOTT WILLIAMS, American, 1877–
1092. Pool in Sherman Glen
Water color on white paper, 13 x 14⅝ in.
Signed: JOHN SCOTT WILLIAMS.
Owned by The Art Institute of Chicago.

CALEB WINHOLTZ, American Contemporary
1093. Little Italy
Water color, 14 x 10⅛ in.
Signed: WINHOLTZ.
Lent by the Artist.

WILLIAM ZORACH, American, 1887–
1094. The Cove (1927)
Water color on white paper, 14⅞ x 21⅞ in.
Signed: WILLIAM ZORACH, 1927.
Owned by The Art Institute of Chicago.

Sculpture

EUROPEAN AND AMERICAN

Nineteenth and Twentieth Centuries

MALVIN M. ALBRIGHT, American, 1897–
†1095. St. Francis
Plaster, 25 in. high; base, 24 x 14 in.
Signed: MALVIN MARR ALBRIGHT.
Lent by the Artist.

LIBERO ANDREOTTI, Italian, 1875–1933
1096. Madonna and Child (1928)
Carrara marble, 33½ in. high; base, 13½ x 12 in.
Signed: L. ANDREOTTI.
Lent by The Minneapolis Institute of Arts.

LILI AUER, German, 1904–
†1097. Mother and Child (1930)
Plaster, 20¼ in. high; base, 8 x 4½ in.
Signed: LILI AUER.
Lent by the Artist.

MAURICE BARDIN, American Contemporary
1098. Rabbit (1930)
Wood, 5¼ in. high; base, 11 x 4¼ in.
Owned by The Art Institute of Chicago.

ERNST BARLACH, German, 1870–
*1099. Head from the War Monument, Guestrow Cathedral (1927) (Pl. XCV)
Bronze, 18 in. high; base, 7⅞ x 7⅞ in.
Lent by Mr. Edward M. M. Warburg, New York.

GEORGE GREY BARNARD, American, 1863–
1100. I Feel Two Natures Struggling within Me (1893)
Plaster, copy of marble original in the Metropolitan Museum, New York. 8 ft. 10½ in. high; base, 7 ft. x 44½ in.
Owned by The Art Institute of Chicago.

RUDOLF BELLING, German, 1886–
†1103. Portrait of Max Schmeling
Bronze, 25 in. high; base, 9½ in. diam.
Lent by The Weyhe Gallery, New York.

RUDOLF BELLING, German, 1886–
1104. Portrait of Von Sternberg (1930)
Bronze (silvered), 20⅜ in. high; base, 8 x 7 in.
Signed: RUDOLF BELLING, 1930.
Lent by Mr. Josef von Sternberg, Hollywood, California.

HENRY BOUCHARD, French, 1875–
1105. Claus Sluter, Sculptor (1911)
Plaster, 7 ft. 6 in. high; base, 31½ x 31 in.
Signed: BOUCHARD 1911.
Owned by The Art Institute of Chicago.

HENRY BOUCHARD, French, 1875–
1106. Olivetan (Translator of the Bible)
Plaster, 6 ft. 1 in. high; base, 57½ x 5½ in.
Signed: H. BOUCHARD.
Owned by The Art Institute of Chicago.

HENRY BOUCHARD, French, 1875–
1107. Resignation
Plaster reproduction of war memorial to the soldiers of St. Gilles (1914–1918)
7 ft. 7 in. high; base, 30 x 23 in.
Owned by The Art Institute of Chicago.

E. ANTOINE BOURDELLE, French, 1861–1929
1108. Heracles, Archer (1909)
Bronze, 14¾ in. high (without bow); base, 24 x 10¼ in.
Signed: ANTOINE BOURDELLE.
Owned by The Art Institute of Chicago.
Exh.: The Art Institute of Chicago, 1922, No. 15.
Lit.: *L'Art et les Artistes*, N. S., VI (1923), 219 (repr.); A. Ronnebeck, *The Arts*, VIII (1925), 213; L. Gillet, *The Art Gallery Magazine* (Nov. 1925), Bourdelle Number, No. 11 (repr.); D. S. MacColl, *Art Work*, V (1929), 240 (repr.), 241–2; F. Payant, *Design*, XXXII (1931), 185 (repr.); *La Revue d'Art*, XXIX (1928), 237 (repr.), 246.

E. ANTOINE BOURDELLE, French, 1861–1929
†1109. Sappho with the Lyre (1907–8)
Bronze, 27¼ in. high; base, 17¼ x 11 in.
Signed: SAPHO—ANTOINE BOURDELLE.
Lent by The Rosenbach Company, New York.
Exh.: International Exhibition of Art, Venice, 1928, No. 81.

LIT.: *Art News,* XXVIII (Nov. 30, 1929), 3, 5 (repr.); L. Gillet, *The Art Gallery Magazine,* (Nov., 1925), No. 7 (repr.); *The Arts,* VIII (1925), 189 (repr.); *L'Art et les Artistes,* N. S., VII (1923), 214 (repr.); *La Revue d'Art,* XXIX (1928), 239 (repr.); *Creative Art,* III (1928), 419 (repr.).

E. ANTOINE BOURDELLE, FRENCH, 1861–1929

†1110. SKETCH FOR VICTORY FOR MONUMENT OF GENERAL ALVEAR, BUENOS AIRES (1914)
Bronze, 14¼ in. high; base, 4 x 3⅞ in.
Signed: LA VICTOIRE—BOURDELLE—MONTAUBAN —1914 15.
Lent by The Rosenbach Company, New York.

EXH.: International Exhibition of Art, Venice, 1928, No. 83.

LIT.: M. Pays, *L'Art et les Artistes,* N. S., VII (1923), 228–229, 232 (cf. repr.).

E. ANTOINE BOURDELLE, FRENCH, 1861–1929

1111. VIRGIN OF ALSACE (1921)
Marble, 24½ in. high; base, 7 x 5½ in.
Signed: ANTOINE BOURDELLE 1921.
Owned by The Art Institute of Chicago.

EXH.: The Art Institute of Chicago, 1922, No. 23.

LIT.: *L'Art et les Artistes,* N. S., VII (1923), 232, 237 (repr.); *Art in America,* XII (1924), 285 (repr.), 290; P. Gsell, *La Renaissance,* VII (1924), 376, 377 (repr.); H. A. Read, *The Arts,* VIII (1925), 190, 200; L. Gillet, *The Art Gallery Mag.* (Nov. 1925), No. 20 (repr.); H. A. Bull, *Internatl. Stu.,* XCIV (1929), 69, 70 (repr.); *Apollo,* XI (1930), 105 (repr.).

CONSTANTIN BRANCUSI, ROUMANIAN, 1876–

1112. TORSO (1912)
Marble, 12⅝ in. high; base, 6½ x 4 in.
Signed: C. BRANCUSI, 1912, PARIS.
Lent by Mr. Chester H. Johnson, Chicago.

JOHN DAVID BRCIN, AMERICAN, 1899–

†1113. FANTASY (1905)
Bronze, 42 in. high; base, 16 x 12 in.
Signed: J. D. BRCIN.
Lent by the Artist.

A. STIRLING CALDER, AMERICAN, 1870–

†1114. FRAGMENT (c. 1915)
Bronze, 17½ in. high; base, 9 x 5 in.
Signed: CALDER.
Lent by Marie Sterner, New York.

HAROLD CASH, AMERICAN, 1895–

†1116. HEAD OF A NEGRO (1928)
Bronze, 11¼ in. high; base (marble), 5½ x 4 in.
Signed: H. CASH NO. 3.
Lent by Ferargil, Inc., New York.

OLGA CHASSAING, AMERICAN, 1897–

†1117. PORTRAIT OF EDOUARD CHASSAING (1933)
Plaster, 20 in. high; base, 11 x 9½ x 6¾ in. high.
Signed: O. CHASSAING.
Lent by the Artist.

OLGA CHASSAING, AMERICAN, 1897–

1118. SHEPHERD BOY (1929)
Plaster, 24½ in. high; base, 7¼ x 7¼ in.
Signed: OLGA CHASSAING.
Owned by The Art Institute of Chicago.

JO DAVIDSON, AMERICAN, 1883–

1119. PORTRAIT OF JOHN D. ROCKEFELLER (1925)
Marble, 20 in. high; base, 20 x 10½ in.
Signed: JO DAVIDSON, KIJKUIT, 1925.
Lent by Mr. John D. Rockefeller, Tarrytown, N. Y.

ERNESTO DE FIORI, GERMAN, 1884–

†1120. BUST OF JACK DEMPSEY (c. 1925)
Terra cotta, 19¼ in. high; base, 5¼ x 5 in.
Lent by The Weyhe Gallery, New York.

EDGAR DEGAS, FRENCH, 1834–1917

1121. ARABESQUE
Bronze, 15½ in. high; base, 8 x 5 in.
Signed: DEGAS.
Owned by The Art Institute of Chicago.

COLL.: George F. Porter, Chicago.

LIT.: *Art et Décoration,* XXXVI (1919), 113 (repr.), 117; *The Arts,* VIII (1925), 263 (repr.).

CHARLES DESPIAU, FRENCH, 1874–

†1122. MADAME POMARET (1932)
Bronze, 13 in. high; base, 6⅝ x 6⅝ x 8 in. high.
Signed: C. DESPIAU.
Lent by The Brummer Gallery, Inc., New York.

CHARLES DESPIAU, FRENCH, 1874–

†1123. MME. WAROQUIER (1927)
Bronze, 15 in. high; base, 6 x 6 in.
Signed: C. DESPIAU 5/6.
Lent by Mr. Frank Crowninshield, New York.

CHARLES DESPIAU, FRENCH, 1874–

†1124. RECLINING NUDE (1922)
Bronze, 6¼ in. high; base, 10¾ x 4 in.
Signed: C. DESPIAU.
Lent by Mr. Frank Crowninshield, New York.

HUNT DIEDERICH, AMERICAN, 1884–

†1125. SPANISH GENTLEMAN (c. 1924)
Bronze, 17¾ in. high; base, 11¾ x 5 in.
Signed: H. DIEDERICH.
Lent by Ferargil, Inc., New York.

JOHN DONOGHUE, American, 1853–1903

1126. Young Sophocles, Leading the Victory Chorus (c. 1884)
Bronze, 6 ft. 11½ in. high; base, 30 x 22¼ in.
Signed: DONOGHUE, SC.
Owned by The Art Institute of Chicago.

Lit.: J. C. McCord, *Brush and Pencil,* XII (1903), 368, 370 (repr.); C. de Kay, *The Art Review,* I (1887), 1–3 (repr.); C. Stratton, *Art and Archaeology,* V (1917), 261–263, 260 (repr.).

JACOB EPSTEIN, American, 1880–

†1127. Mlle. Gabrielle Soene (1920)
Bronze, 22½ in. high; base, 15 x 9 in.
Lent by Scott and Fowles, New York.

JACOB EPSTEIN, American, 1880–

1128. Mask of Meum (1918)
Bronze, 12¼ in. high (with base); base, 10 x10 in.
Owned by The Art Institute of Chicago.

JACOB EPSTEIN, American, 1880–

*1129. Meum I (c. 1916) (Pl. XCIV)
Bronze, 21¾ in. high; base, 17½ x 12½ in.
Lent by The Buffalo Fine Arts Academy.

JACOB EPSTEIN, American, 1880–

†1130. Mother and Child (1913)
Marble, 17½ in. high; base, 17 x 4 in.
Lent by The Findlay Galleries, Inc., Chicago.

JACOB EPSTEIN, American, 1880–

1131. Selina (1922)
Bronze, 22¾ in. high; base, 16¼ x 10 in.
Lent by The Brooklyn Museum.

CHRISTIAN ERIKSSON, Swedish, 1858–

1132. Laplander
Bronze, 12 in. high; base (marble), 4½ x 4 x 4 in. high.
Signed: CHR. ERIKSSON.
Owned by The Art Institute of Chicago.

ALFEO FAGGI, American, 1885–

1133. Yone Noguchi (Bust) (c. 1921)
Bronze, 18¼ in. high; base, 4¾ x 4¼ in.
Signed: FAGGI.
Owned by The Art Institute of Chicago.

PABLO GARGALLO, Spanish, 1881–

1135. Head of a Picador (1928)
Bronze, 16 in. high; base (wood), 4¾ x 4½ in.
Signed: P. GARGALLO, 1928.
Lent by La France Art Institute, Philadelphia.

ARNOLD GEISSBUHLER, American Contemporary

†1136. Alabaster Head No. 2 (1929)
Alabaster, 11¾ in. high; base, 5 x 4½ in.
Signed: A. G.
Lent by Ferargil, Inc., New York.

CHARLES GRAFLY, American, 1862–1929

1137. Study for Head of War (Meade Memorial) (1921)
Bronze, 16 in. high; base, 6½ x 5¼ x 6 in. high.
Signed: GRAFLY 1921.
Owned by The Art Institute of Chicago.

Exh.: The Art Institute of Chicago, 1924, No. 256 and repr.

Lit.: *The Arts,* V (1924), 168 (repr.); *Bull.,* XVIII (1924), 104 (repr.), 105.

CHARLES GRAFLY, American, 1862–1929

1138. Frank Duveneck (Bust) (1915)
Bronze, 27 in. high; base, 14 x 11½ in.
Signed: CHARLES GRAFLY.
Owned by The Art Institute of Chicago.

Exh.: The Art Institute of Chicago, 1921, No. 239 and repr.

Lit.: *Internatl. Stu.,* LIX (1916), 187 (repr.); L. Taft, *Modern Tendencies in Sculpture,* 1917, 134, fig. 390; *Monumental News,* XXXIV (1922), 98 (repr.).

DOROTHEA S. GREENBAUM, American, 1893–

†1139. Sleeping Girl (1928)
Bronze, 8½ in. high; base, 9½ x 6¼ in.
Lent by The Weyhe Gallery, New York.

CARL HALLSTHAMMAR, American, 1897–

1140. The Old Ragpicker (1924)
Wood, 11¼ in. high; base, 4⅝ x 4⅛ in.
Owned by The Art Institute of Chicago.

CARL HALLSTHAMMAR, American, 1897–

1141. The Singing Brothers (1926)
Wood, 14¾ in. high; base, 15 x 6 in.
Signed: C. A. H. 1926.
Owned by The Art Institute of Chicago.

ELISABETH HASELTINE, American, 1894–

†1142. Baby Pegasus (1930)
Bronze, 10 in. high; base 10 x 4 in.
Signed: ELISABETH HASELTINE.
Lent by the Artist.

FREDERICK C. HIBBARD, American, 1881–

†1143. The Defense (1917)
Plaster, 12 in. high; base, 4 x 4 in.
Lent by the Artist.

CECIL HOWARD, American, 1888–
1144. Leaning Figure
Bronze, 31 in. high; base, 14¼ x 7 in.
Signed: HOWARD.
Lent by The Whitney Museum of American Art, New York.

ALFONSO IANNELLI, American, 1888–
†1145. Youth (1917)
Glazed terra cotta, 29¾ in. high; base, 7½ in. diam.
Lent by the Artist.

IVAR JOHNSSON, Swedish, 1885–
1146. Dancer
Bronze, 18½ in. high; base, 3½ x 3½ in.
Signed: IVAR JOHNSSON.
Lent by Mr. Tage Palm, Chicago.

IVAR JOHNSSON, Swedish, 1885–
1147. Head of David
Bronze, 16½ in. high; base, 5½ x 5½ in.
Signed: IVAR JOHNSSON.
Lent by Mr. Tage Palm, Chicago.

SYLVIA SHAW JUDSON, American, 1897–
†1148. Little Gardener (1929)
Plaster, 4 ft. 2 in. high; base 13 x 12 in.
Signed: S. S. J.
Lent by the Artist.

GEORG KOLBE, German, 1877–
*1149. Adagio (1923) (Pl. XCIII)
Bronze, 32½ in. high; base, 6½ x 5½ in.
Signed: G. K. II.
Lent by Mr. and Mrs. Charles H. Worcester, Chicago.

GEORG KOLBE, German, 1877–
1150. Praying Boy
Bronze, 18½ in. high; base, 6½ x 5½ in.
Signed: G. K. I.
Owned by The Art Institute of Chicago.

GEORG KOLBE, German, 1877–
†1151. Sorrow (1921)
Bronze, 16 in. high; base, 10 x 7½ in.
Signed: G. K.
Lent by The Weyhe Gallery, New York.

J. MARIO KORBEL, American, 1882–
1152. The Night (1921)
Bronze, 14 in. high; base, 31½ x 13¼ x 5 in. high.
Signed: MARIO KORBEL, 1921 NO. 2.
Owned by The Art Institute of Chicago.

GASTON LACHAISE, American, 1882–
†1153. Portrait of John Marin (1928)
Bronze, 14¼ in. high; base, 4½ x 4½ in.
Signed: G. LACHAISE.
Lent by The Weyhe Gallery, New York.

FRANCES KENT LAMONT, American Contemporary
†1154. Mother and Child (1922)
Bronze, 11 in. high; base, 5 x 3½ in.
Lent by Mr. Frank K. M. Rehn, New York.

ROBERT LAURENT, American, 1890–
†1155. Mimi (1928)
Bronze, 13⅝ in. high; base, 8 x 6 x 3 in. high.
Signed: LAURENT.
Lent by The Downtown Gallery, New York.

WILHELM LEHMBRUCK, German, 1881–1919
†1156. Head of "Pariser" Torso
Composition stone, 17 in. high; base, 17 x 8 in.
Signed: LEHMBRUCK.
Lent by The Downtown Gallery, New York.

WILHELM LEHMBRUCK, German, 1881–1919
1157. Head of a Young Woman
Composition stone, 21 in. high; base, 20 x 11⅛ in.
Signed: W. LEHMBRUCK.
Lent by The Buffalo Fine Arts Academy.
Coll.: A. C. Goodyear, N. Y.
Exh.: Mus. of Mod. Art, N. Y., 1930, No. 2 (Cat. Pl. 2).
Lit.: *The Arts,* XVI (1930), 606 (repr.); *Academy Notes,* Albright Art Gallery, XXI No. 1 (1930), 14 (repr.); XXII No. 1 (1931), 22 (repr.); *Die Kunst für Alle,* XXXV (1920), 150 (repr.).

WILHELM LEHMBRUCK, German, 1881–1919
*1158. Standing Female Figure (1910) (Pl. XCIII)
Bronze, 76 in. high; base, 21 x 20 in.
Signed: LEHMBRUCK.
Lent by The Museum of Modern Art, New York.
Coll.: S. C. Clark, N. Y.
Exh.: Mus. of Mod. Art, N. Y., 1930, No. 1.
Lit.: F. Watson, *The Arts,* XVI (1930), 567 (repr.), 568; *Art News,* XXVIII (Mar. 29, 1930), 6 (repr.); E. M. Benson, *Parnassus,* V, No. 3 (1933), 8.

WILHELM LEHMBRUCK, German, 1881–1919
1159. Standing Woman (1911)
Composition stone, 21½ in. high; base, 6½ x 5½ in.
Signed: W. LEHMBRUCK.
Owned by The Art Institute of Chicago.
Lit.: A. Hoff, *Wilhelm Lehmbruck,* 1933, 7 (repr.) (bronze).

FREDERICK MAC MONNIES, American, 1863–

1160. Nathan Hale (1890)
Bronze, 28½ in. high; base, 7¾ x 5¾ in.
Signed: F. MAC MONNIES, 1890.
Lent by Mr. Robert Allerton, Chicago.

ARISTIDE MAILLOL, French, 1861–

1161. Leda
Bronze, 11 in. high; base, 3¼ x 3 in.
Signed: M in circle.
Lent by Mr. Gifford Beal, New York.

ARISTIDE MAILLOL, French, 1861–

†1162. Seated Nude (1931)
Marble, 12½ in. high; base, 11 x 5 in.
Signed: MAILLOL.
Lent by The Pierre Matisse Gallery, New York.

PAUL MANSHIP, American, 1885–

1163. Albert J. Beveridge (Bust) (1928)
Bronze, 14 in. high; base, 6½ in. diam., 3½ in. high.
Signed: PAUL MANSHIP, 1928.
Owned by The Art Institute of Chicago.

PAUL MANSHIP, American, 1885–

1164. Dancer and Gazelles (1916)
Bronze, 31 in. high; base, 33¼ x 10 in.
Signed: PAUL MANSHIP, 1916.
Owned by The Art Institute of Chicago.

PAUL MANSHIP, American, 1885–

1165. Indian and Pronghorn Antelope (1914)
Bronze, Indian 13 in. high; base, 10¼ x 8¼ in; Antelope, 12¼ in. high; base, 10¼ x 8¼ in.
Signed: PAUL MANSHIP, 1914.
Owned by The Art Institute of Chicago.

HENRI MATISSE, French, 1869–

1166. Birth of Venus (1931)
Bronze, 13½ in. high; base, 8 x 7¾ in.
Signed: H. M.
Lent by Miss Etta Cone, Baltimore, Maryland.

HENRI MATISSE, French, 1869–

1167. Kneeling Nude
Bronze, 10½ in. high; base, 9¼ x 5¼ in.
Signed: H. M.
Lent by Miss Etta Cone, Baltimore, Maryland.

HENRI MATISSE, French, 1869–

1168. Seated Nude
Bronze, 9 in. high; base, 7¾ x 6 in.
Signed: H. M.
Lent by Miss Etta Cone, Baltimore, Maryland.

HENRI MATISSE, French, 1869–

1169. Seated Nude
Bronze, 13¾ in. high; base, 7 x 5¼ in.
Signed: H. M.
Lent by Miss Etta Cone, Baltimore, Maryland.

IVAN MESTROVIC, Jugoslav, 1883–

1170. Marko Marulic, Croatian Poet (1924)
Plaster, 9 ft. high; base, 39 x 34 in.
Owned by The Art Institute of Chicago.

IVAN MESTROVIC, Jugoslav, 1883–

1171. My Mother (1908)
Marble, 37½ in. high; base, 22½ x 18½ in.
Signed: MESTROVIC.
Owned by The Art Institute of Chicago.

IVAN MESTROVIC, Jugoslav, 1883–

1172. Study for Moses (1916)
Plaster, 23 in. high; base, 12 x 9½ in.
Owned by The Art Institute of Chicago.

CONSTANTIN MEUNIER, Belgian, 1831–1905

1173. The Hammerman (1884)
Bronze, 76½ in. high; base, 38 x 28 in.
Signed: C. MEUNIER.
Owned by The Art Institute of Chicago.

Exh.: Brussels, 1885; Paris, 1886; Albright Art Gallery, Buffalo, 1914.

Lit.: C. Brinton, *Special Exhibition Catalogue* (1914), No. 6; *Art and Progress,* V (1914), 119 (repr.); *Internatl. Stu.,* LI (1914), CLIII (repr.); L. Taft, *Modern Tendencies in Sculpture,* 1917, 81, fig. 265.

EDGAR MILLER, American, 1899–

†1174. Head (1930)
Terra cotta, 13 in. high; base (oval), 6½ x 5½ in.
Lent by the Artist.

CARL MILLES, Swedish, 1875–

1175. Angel of God (for a Swedenborg Memorial, London) (c. 1925)
Bronze, 27 in. high; base, 4¾ x 4¾ in.
Inscr.: EST—FACERE.
Lent by Mr. Chester H. Johnson, Chicago.

CARL MILLES, Swedish, 1875–

1176. Fountain of Tritons (1931), Copy of Fountain at Lidingoe, Sweden
Bronze, largest figure 70 in. high; base, 25 x 20 in.
Signed: CARL MILLES.
Owned by The Art Institute of Chicago.

Note: This fountain is installed in Alexander McKinlock Memorial Court.

REUBEN NAKIAN, American, 1897–
†1177. The Calf (c. 1929)
Marble, 15 in. high; base, 11½ x 9½ in.
Lent by The Downtown Gallery, New York.

KAI NIELSEN, Danish, 1882–1924
1178. Eve and the Apple (1918)
Bronze, 63 in. high; base, 15 in. diam.
Signed: KAI NIELSEN.
Lent by The Brooklyn Museum.
Coll.: A. Lewisohn, N. Y.
Exh.: Danish National Exh., Brooklyn Mus., 1927.
Lit.: A. Torrey, *Brooklyn Museum Quarterly*, XV (1928), 1, 2 (repr.); S. Casson, *XXth Century Sculptors*, 1930, Pl. 33.

VIOLA NORMAN, American, 1889–
†1179. Portrait of a Colored Boy (1932)
Bronze, 16 in. high; base (Belgian marble), 6 x 6 in.
Signed: VIOLA NORMAN.
Lent by the Artist.

CHANA ORLOFF, Russian, 1888–
1180. Guitarist (1924)
Bronze, 14½ in. high; base, 7 x 5 in.
Signed: CHANA ORLOFF, 1924.
Lent by Mrs. Flora I. Schofield, Chicago.

CHANA ORLOFF, Russian, 1888–
1181. My Son (1923)
Bronze, 36 in. high; base, 12 x 8 in.
Signed: CHANA ORLOFF, 1923.
Lent by Mrs. Flora I. Schofield, Chicago.

CHANA ORLOFF, Russian, 1888–
1182. Woman with Basket (1926)
Bronze, 24½ in. high; base, 7½ x 2¾ in.
Signed: CHANA ORLOFF, 1926.
Owned by The Art Institute of Chicago.

MAEBLE C. PERRY, American, 1900–
1183. Jeff (1932)
Bronze, 9¼ in. high; base, 5½ x 2¼ in.
Signed: MAEBLE C. PERRY.
Owned by The Art Institute of Chicago.

GLYN PHILPOT, English, 1884–
1184. Mask of a Faun
Bronze, 9½ in. high; base, 6 x 6 x 12 in. high.
Lent by Mr. Robert Allerton, Chicago.

PABLO PICASSO, Spanish, 1881–
†1185. Harlequin (1904)
Bronze, 16½ in. high; base, 14½ x 8½ in.
Lent by The Weyhe Gallery, New York.

PABLO PICASSO, Spanish, 1881–
†1186. Head No. 1
Bronze, 14 in. high; base, 9 x 8 in.
Signed: PICASSO.
Lent by The Weyhe Gallery, New York.

ALBIN POLASEK, American, 1879–
1187. Charles W. Hawthorne (1917)
Bronze, 22 in. high; base, 11¾ x 8½ in.
Signed: ALBIN POLASEK.
Owned by The Art Institute of Chicago.

ALBIN POLASEK, American, 1879–
1188. The Sower (1912)
Bronze, 84 in. high; base, 44 x 26 in.
Signed: ALBIN POLASEK.
Owned by The Art Institute of Chicago.

ALBIN POLASEK, American, 1879–
1189. Unfettered (1924)
Bronze, 56 in. high; base, 11¾ x 11¼ in.
Signed: ALBIN POLASEK, 1924.
Owned by The Art Institute of Chicago.

JANE POUPELET, French, 1878–1932
1190. The Bather
Bronze, 19½ in. high; base, 6½ x 5 in.
Owned by The Art Institute of Chicago.
Coll.: George F. Porter, Chicago.
Lit.: *The Studio*, XCI (1926), 285 (repr.); *The Art Digest*, II (Mar. 15, 1928), 8 (repr.).

JANE POUPELET, French, 1878–1932
1191. Group of Small Bronzes: Cat, Rabbit, Goat, Goose, Cock
Owned by The Art Institute of Chicago.

JANE POUPELET, French, 1878–1932
1192. Peasant and Cow
Bronze: Peasant, 10 in. high; base, 8⅞ x 4¼ in.; Cow, 9¼ in. high; base, 15 x 4⅞ in.
Owned by The Art Institute of Chicago.
Coll.: George F. Porter, Chicago.
Lit.: *The Arts*, V (1924), 37 (repr.); *Bulletin*, XXI (1927), 64, 67 (repr.).

JANE POUPELET, French, 1878–1932
1193. Woman at her Toilet
Bronze, 15½ in. high; base, 24 x 10¼ x 2½ in. high.
Owned by The Art Institute of Chicago.
Coll.: George F. Porter, Chicago.
Exh.: Salon, Paris, 1909.
Lit.: *Art et Décoration*, XXXIV (1913), 55 (repr.); *L'Art et les Artistes*, N.S., XIV (1926), 79 (repr.); *The Studio*, XCI (1926), 284 (repr.).

AUGUSTE RODIN, French, 1840–1917

1194. Adam (1881)

Bronze, 6 ft. 6 in. high; base, 30 x 29 in.

Signed: RODIN.

Owned by The Art Institute of Chicago (Robert Allerton Collection).

Lit.: *Fine Arts Journal,* XXXII (1915), 15 (repr.), 160 (side view), 163; *Internatl. Stu.,* LXVIII (1919), LI (repr.); C. N. Smiley, *Art and Archaeology,* III (1916), 110 (repr.), 111; *Bull.,* XVIII (1924), 69 (repr.), 70, 71.

AUGUSTE RODIN, French, 1840–1917

1195. Bronze Head, First Study of Burgher of Calais (1884–1888)

Bronze, 11¼ in. high; base, 6¾ x 5⅝ x 3¾ in. high.

Signed: A. RODIN.

Owned by The Art Institute of Chicago.

Coll.: Robert Allerton, Chicago.

Exh.: The Art Institute of Chicago, 1923, No. 8 and repr.

Lit.: *Bull.,* XVIII (1924), 70 (repr.), 71.

AUGUSTE RODIN, French, 1840–1917

1196. Brother and Sister (1890)

Bronze, 14 in. high; base, 6¾ x 5 in.

Signed: A. RODIN.

Owned by The Art Institute of Chicago.

Exh.: The Art Institute of Chicago, 1923, No. 9.

Lit.: *Bull.,* XVIII (1924), 72, 82 (repr.).

AUGUSTE RODIN, French, 1840–1917

1197. A Burgher of Calais (from a Bronze Monument in Calais) (1884–1888)

Plaster copy, 6 ft. 9½ in. high; base, 26 x 20 in.

Signed: A. RODIN.

Owned by The Art Institute of Chicago.

Exh.: World's Columbian Exposition, Chicago, 1893, France, No. 43.

Lit.: C. Mauclair, *Rodin,* 1905, 33–39, 36 (ensemble), 38 (repr.); K. Cox, *Architectural Record,* XVIII, No. 5 (1905), 333, 336 (repr.); D. S. MacColl, *Nineteenth Century Art,* 1902, 104; T. Child, *Art and Criticism,* 1892, 265–266; *Bull.,* XVIII (1924), 71.

AUGUSTE RODIN, French, 1840–1917

1198. Caryatid (1891)

Bronze, 17 in. high; base, 10¾ x 10½ in.

Signed: RODIN.

Owned by The Art Institute of Chicago.

Coll.: Robert Allerton, Chicago.

Lit.: F. Lawton, *The Life and Work of Auguste Rodin,* 1907, 126–7 (repr. faces 128); *Bull.,* XVIII (1924), 72 (repr.), 73.

AUGUSTE RODIN, French, 1840–1917

1199. Eve After the Fall (1881)

Marble, 29 in. high; base, 11 x 8¼ in.

Signed: A. RODIN.

Owned by The Art Institute of Chicago.

Coll.: Martin A. Ryerson, Chicago.

Lit.: F. Lawton, *The Life and Work of Auguste Rodin,* 1907, 109 (repr.); C. L. Borgmeyer, *Fine Arts Journal,* XXXII (1915), 156 (side view), 159 (repr. front view), 163; C. N. Smiley, *Art and Archaeology,* III (1916), 111 (repr.); *Bull.,* XVIII (1924), 71 (repr.).

AUGUSTE RODIN, French, 1840–1917

1200. The Man with the Broken Nose (1864)

Bronze, 12⅛ in. high; base, 5½ x 4½ x 4 in. high.

Signed: RODIN.

Owned by The Art Institute of Chicago (Arthur Jerome Eddy Memorial).

Coll.: Arthur Jerome Eddy, Chicago.

Exh.: Exhibition of the Eddy Collection, The Art Institute of Chicago, 1922, No. 58; 1931, No. 22.

Lit.: F. Lawton, *The Life and Work of Auguste Rodin,* 1907, 24–26 (repr.); *Gazette des Beaux Arts,* Per. 4, XIV (1918), 11 (repr.), 14–5.

AUGUSTE RODIN, French, 1840–1917

1201. Sorrow (1892)

Bronze, 8¾ in. high; base, 5¾ in. diam. x 4¼ in. high.

Signed: A. RODIN.

Owned by The Art Institute of Chicago.

Coll.: Robert Allerton, Chicago.

Lit.: *Worcester Art Museum Bulletin,* XIV (1923), 36, 37 (repr.); *Art News,* XXII (Oct. 20, 1923), 10 (repr.).

CHARLES C. RUMSEY, American, 1879–1922

*1202. Pagan Kin (1921) (Pl. XCV)

Plaster, 32 in. high; base, 57 x 31 in.

Signed: C. C. RUMSEY, 1921.

Lent by Mrs. Charles Cary Rumsey, New York.

Exh.: Brooklyn Museum, 1930, No. 437; Mus. of Modern Art, N. Y., 1932, No. 140, Pl. 140.

Lit.: *Whitney Museum Catalogue,* 1931 (bronze), No. 219 (repr.).

AUGUSTUS ST. GAUDENS, American, 1848–1907

1203. Amor: Caritas (1887)

Plaster, 8 ft. 9 in. high; base, 42½ x 9 in.

Signed: AUGUSTUS ST. GAUDENS MDCCCLXX(XVII).

Owned by The Art Institute of Chicago.

Lit.: R. Cortissoz, *Augustus St. Gaudens,* 1907, frontispiece; C. L. Hind, *Augustus St. Gaudens,* 1908, XXXIX (Pl. XVII); T. Williams, *Internatl. Stu.,* XXXIII (1908), CXXXIII, CXXXVIII; *The Art World,* I (1917), 302, frontispiece.

AUGUSTUS ST. GAUDENS, American, 1848–1907

1204. The Puritan (Deacon Samuel Chapin) (1887)
Plaster copy of original in Springfield, Massachusetts, 8 ft. 7½ in. high; base, 64 x 41½ in.
Owned by The Art Institute of Chicago.

Lit.: R. Cortissoz, *Augustus St. Gaudens,* 1907, 34–40 (repr.); C. L. Hind, *Augustus St. Gaudens,* 1908, Pls. XXVIII, XL (Pl. XVIII); T. Williams, *Internatl. Stu.,* XXXIII (1908), cxxix, cxxxii–cxxxiii (repr.); H. Bell, *Gazette des Beaux Arts,* Per. 5, I (1920), 370, 373 (repr.).

MARGARETT SARGENT, American, 1892–

1205. George Luks (1918)
Bronze, 15 in. high; base, 12 x 7¼ in.
Signed: m. sargent 1918.
Owned by The Art Institute of Chicago.

RICHARD SCHEIBE, German, 1879–

1206. Entry of Christ into Jerusalem
Bronze, 22⅞ in. high; base, 14¼ x 12¾ in.
Signed: r s.
Lent by Mr. and Mrs. Charles H. Worcester, Chicago.

JANET SCUDDER, American, 1875–

1207. Fountain (1911)
Bronze, 41 in. high; base, 28 in. diam.
Signed: janet scudder, 1911.
Owned by The Art Institute of Chicago.

EMORY P. SEIDEL, American, 1881–

†1208. Youth (1926)
Bronze, 19 in. high; base, 12½ x 3¾ in.
Signed: e. p. seidel, 1926.
Lent by the Artist.

RUTH SHERWOOD, American, 1890–

†1209. St. Francis (1922)
Plaster, 42 in. high; base, 22 x 10 in.
Signed: ruth sherwood.
Lent by the Artist.

EUGENIE T. SHONNARD, American, 1886–

†1209A. Religious Spirit of a Brittany Peasant
Wood, 24 in. high; base, 10 x 18½ in.
Signed: e. t. shonnard
Lent by the Artist.

RENEE SINTENIS, German, 1888–

1210. Running Colt (1929)
Bronze, 6¼ in. high; base, 7¾ x 2 in.
Owned by The Art Institute of Chicago.

RENEE SINTENIS, German, 1888–

†1211. Self-Portrait (1926)
Terra cotta, 17¼ in. high; base, 5¼ x 5¼ in.
Lent by The Weyhe Gallery, New York.

ALEXANDER STOLLER, American Contemporary

†1212. Mask No. 2 (1929)
Bronze, 12 in. high; base, 5 x 5 in.
Signed: s.2.
Lent by Ferargil, Inc., New York.

JOHN STORRS, American, 1885–

†1213. Standing Figure (1928)
Bronze, 49 in. high; base, 9 x 8½ in.
Signed: john storrs, chantecille, 1928.
Lent by The Downtown Gallery, New York.

JOHN STORRS, American, 1885–

1214. Winged Horse
Bronze, 13¾ in. high; base, 8¾ x 2½ in.
Owned by The Art Institute of Chicago.

LORADO TAFT, American, 1860–

1215. The Solitude of the Soul (1914)
Marble, 7 ft. 7 in. high; base, 51 x 41½ in.
Signed: lorado taft, sc., 1914.
Owned by The Art Institute of Chicago.

WILLIAM HAMO THORNYCROFT, English, 1850–1925

1216. Teucer (1881)
Bronze, 6 ft. 8 in. high; base, 27 in. diam.
Signed: hamo thornycroft—rome—1881.
Owned by The Art Institute of Chicago.

Lit.: W. Meynell, *Modern School of Art,* n. d., I, 58 (repr.), 59; "Sagittarius," *The Architects' Journal,* LXIII (1926), 134, 135 (repr.).

BESSIE POTTER VONNOH, American, 1872–

1217. Baby's Head (1901)
Bronze, 9¾ in. high; base, 7¼ x 6 in.
Signed: bessie potter vonnoh, 1901.
Owned by The Art Institute of Chicago.

HEINZ WARNEKE, American, 1895–

1218. Three Hissing Geese (1929)
Bronze, 7¼ in. high; base, 5½ x 5½ in.
Signed: h. warneke, 1929.
Owned by The Art Institute of Chicago.

HEINZ WARNEKE, American, 1895–

1219. Wild Boars (1929)
Black granite, 12¾ in. high; base, 13 x 9 in.
Signed: h. warneke, 1929.
Owned by The Art Institute of Chicago.

GERTRUDE VANDERBILT WHITNEY, American, 1876–

1220. Head for the Titanic Memorial (1922)
Belgian marble, 20 in. high; base, 7 x 7 in.
Signed: gertrude v. whitney.
Lent by The Whitney Museum of American Art, New York.

GERTRUDE VANDERBILT WHITNEY, American, 1876–

1221. Wherefore (1915)
Bronze, 16 in. high; base, 9¾ x 7 in.
Signed: gertrude v. whitney, 1915.
Owned by The Art Institute of Chicago.

WHEELER WILLIAMS, American, 1897–

†1223. Dawn (1927)
Bronze, 14¼ in. high; base, 5⅞ x 3¾ in.
Signed: wheeler williams, 27.
Lent by Ferargil, Inc., New York.

WALTER REID WILLIAMS, American, 1885–

†1224. Tragedy (1929)
Plaster, 12 in. high; base, 3½ x 3¼ in.
Lent by the Artist.

MAHONRI YOUNG, American, 1877–

†1225. Right to the Jaw (1927)
Bronze, 14 in. high; base, 19 x 7½ in.
Signed: mahonri.
Lent by The C. W. Kraushaar Art Galleries, New York.

EMIL ZETTLER, American, 1878–

†1226. David (1910)
Cerevezza marble, 16 in. high; base (oval), 16 x 10 in.
Signed: e. r. z., 1910.
Lent by the Artist.

WILLIAM ZORACH, American, 1887–

†*1227. Mother and Child (1928–1930) (Pl. XCIV)
Florida Rosa Spanish marble, 5 ft. 5 in. high; base, 32½ x 28½ in.
Lent by The Downtown Gallery, New York

Index

References are to catalogue numbers throughout.
Arabic numbers indicate oil paintings.
Italicized numbers indicate water colors, pastels and drawings.
SC *preceding numbers indicates sculpture.*

ARTISTS

Abrahamsen, Christian, 491.
Adams, Jean Crawford, 492.
Adams, Katherine L., 493.
Adams, Wayman, 494.
Albright, Malvin M., sc1095.
Albright, Ivan L., 495.
Allworthy, Joseph, 496.
Altdorfer, Albrecht, 1.
Amberger, Christoph, 2.
Amiens School, 3 a-g.
André, Albert, 321, 670–672.
André, Master, see Master André.
Andreotti, Libero, sc1096.
Angarola, Anthony, 497.
Anglada Camarasa, Hermengildo, 720, 721.
Angel, Rifka, *952*.
Angeli (Agnolo del Moro), *796*.
Angelico, Fra, 81.
Anisfeld, Boris, 498.
Archer, Edmund, 499.
Armin, Emil, 500.
Auer, Lili, sc1097.
Avignon School, 4.

Baldung, Hans (Grien), 5.
Bardin, Maurice, sc1098.
Bargue, Charles, *828*.
Barlach, Ernst, sc1099.
Barnard, George G., sc1100.
Bartlett, Frederic C., 501.
Bartolomeo Veneto, 102.
Barton, Macena, 502.
Barye, Antoine L., *829, 830*.
Bassano, Jacopo, 126.
Beal, Gifford, 503, *953, 954*.
Beardsley, Aubrey, *831–833*.
Beaux, Cecilia, 430.
Beckmann, Max, 744, 745.
Beerbohm, Max, *957, 958*.
Belling, Rudolf, sc1103, sc1104.
Bellini, Gentile, 103.
Bellini, Giovanni, 105.
Bellows, George, 431–434, *834–840*.
Benson, Frank W., 504.
Benson, Tressa E., 505.
Benton, Thomas H., 506.
Bernard, Joseph, *841, 842*.
Bernstein, Theresa, 507.
Besnard, Albert, *959*.
Betts, Louis, 508.
Biddle, George, 509.
Biesel, Fred, 510.
Bishop, Isabel, 511.
Blackburn, Joseph, 410.
Blakelock, Ralph A., 435.
Blanch, Arnold, 512.
Blume, Peter, 767.
Bloch, Albert, 766.
Blumenschein, Ernest L., 513.
Bohrod, Aaron, 514.
Boltraffio, Giovanni A., 106.
Bone, Muirhead, *960–962*.
Bonington, R. P., 187, 188.
Bonnard, Pierre, 673–677.
Bonvicino, A., *see* Moretto.
Borie, Adolphe, 516.
Botkin, Henry A., 517.
Botticelli, Sandro, 107–110.
Botticelli School, 111.
Botticini, Francesco, 112.
Bouchard, Henry, sc1105–1107.
Bouché, Louis, 518.
Boucher, François, 209.
Bourdelle, E. Antoine, *843*, sc1108–1111.
Brabazon, Hercules B., *844*.
Brancusi, Constantin, sc1112.
Braque, Georges, 768.
Breughel, Pieter, the Elder, 34.
Brcin, John D., sc1113.
Bronzino, Angelo, 127.
Brook, Alexander, 519.
Brouwer, Adriaen, 57.
Browne, George E., *963*.
Bruce, Edward, 520.
Brush, George de F., 520A.
Bruyn, Bartel, the Elder, 6.
Bruyn, Bartel, the Younger, 7.
Buck, Claude, 521.
Buehr, Karl A., 522.
Burchfield, Charles, *523*.
Burroughs, Bryson, 524.
Butinone (Bernardino Jacobi), 82, 83.

Calder, A. Stirling, sc1114.
Caliari, Carlo, *798*.
Cambiaso, Luca, *799, 800*.
Cameron, Edgar S., 525.
Campendonk, Heinrich, 746, 747, *964*.
Campigli, Massimo, 769.
Capon, Georges, 678.
Carena, Felice, 722.
Carles, Arthur, 526.
Carlsen, Emil, 436.
Carpaccio, Vittore, 113.
Cash, Harold, sc1116.
Carracci, Annibale, *801*.
Carrière, Eugène, 261.
Carroll, John, 527.
Carte, Anto, 723.
Casorati, Felice, 724.
Cassatt, Mary, 437, 438, 439.
Cézanne, Paul, 304–320, *845*.
Chagall, Marc, 725.
Chapin, Francis, 528, *965*.
Chapin, James, 529.
Chapiro, Jacques, 726.
Chardin, J. B. S., 210–212.
Chase, William M., 440.
Chassaing, Olga, sc1117, sc1118.
Chassériau, Théodore, 229.
Cheney, Russell, 530.
Chirico, Giorgio de, 771.
Christus, Petrus, 35.
Cikovsky, Nicolay, 531.
Clarkson, Ralph E., 532.
Cleve, Joos van, the Elder, 36.
Clouet, François, 9, 10, *802*.
Clouet, Jean, 8.
Coleman, Glenn, 533.
Conder, Charles, *846, 847*.
Constable, John, 189, 190.
Copley, John S., 412–414, *803*.
Corneille de Lyon, 11, 12.
Cornelisz van Amsterdam, J., 38, 39.
Corot, Camille, 230–235, *848*.
Costigan, John E., 534, *966*.
Coter, Colijn de, 37.
Courbet, Gustave, 236, 237, 238.
Cox, David, *849*.
Cranach, Lucas, the Elder, 13, 14, 16.
Credi, Lorenzo di, 114.
Credi, Lorenzo di, School, *804*.
Crisler, Richard M., 535.
Crivelli, Carlo, 115.

Curry, John S., 536.
Cuyp, Aelbert, 58.

Daddi, Bernardo, 84.
Dali, Salvador, 772.
Dalstrom, Gustaf, 537.
Daumier, Honoré, 239, 240, 242, *850–853*.
Davey, Randall, 538.
David, Geraerd, 40.
David, Hermine, *967, 968*.
David, J. L., 213.
Davidson, Jo, sc1119.
Davies, Arthur B., 441–451, *854–859*.
De Fiori, Ernesto, sc1120.
Degas, Edgar, 279–290, *860–863*, sc1121.
Dehn, Adolf, *969*.
Delacroix, Eugène, 243–248, *864, 865*.
Demuth, Charles, *970*.
Denis, Maurice, 679.
Derain, André, 680–687, *971, 972*.
Despiau, Charles, *973*, sc1122–1124.
Diederich, Hunt, sc1125.
Dix, Otto, 748, *974*.
Donoghue, John, sc1126.
Dougherty, Paul, *975*.
Du Bois, Guy Pène, 515.
Duchamp, Marcel, 773.
Dufresne, Charles, 688–690, *976, 977*.
Dufy, Raoul, 691, *978*.
Duveneck, Frank, 452, 453.
Dyck, Anthony van, 59.

Eakins, Thomas, 454–456.
Earl, Ralph, 415.
Edzard, Dietz, 749.
Eggers, George W., *979, 980*.
English(?) School, XIV C., 17.
Ennis, George P., *981*.
Epstein, Jacob, sc1127–1131.
Erickson, Christian, sc1132.
Etnier, Stephen, 539.
Ewald, Reinhard, 751.

Faggi, Alfeo, *981A*, sc1133.
Fantin-Latour, Henri, 322, *866*.
Farnsworth, Jerry, 540.
Fechin, Nicolai, 541.
Feke, Robert, 416.
Férat, Serge, *982*.
Ferrazzi, Ferruccio, 727.
Flint, W. Russell, *983, 984*.
Forain, Jean Louis, 262–264, *867–870*.
Ford, Lauren, 542.
Ford, Ruth van S., 543.
Forsberg, Elmer A., *985*.
Foy, Frances, 544.
Fragonard, J. H., 214, 215.
Free, Karl, *986*.
French Primitive (North), 30.
French School, c. 1540, 18.
Frieseke, Frederick C., 545, *987*.
Friesz, E. Othon, 692, 693.
Fromkes, Maurice, 546.
Fuller, George, 457.

Gainsborough, Thomas, 191–194.
Garber, Daniel, 547.
Gargallo, Pablo, sc1135.
Gaudier-Brzeska, H., *871*.
Gauguin, Paul, 352–366, *872–877*.
Gavarni, *878–879*.
Gay, Walter, 548.
Geissbuhler, Arnold, sc1136.
Gelder, Arent de, 60, *805*.
Gellée, Claude (Lorrain), 216.
Genin, Robert, 728.
Ghirlandajo, Ridolfo, 116.
Giesbert, Edmund, *988*.
Giles, Howard, 549, *989*.
Gill, Eric, *990*.
Giovanni di Paolo, 85a-f.
Glackens, William J., 550.
Gleizes, Albert, 774.
Goerg, Edouard, 694, 695.
Gogh, Vincent van, 375–387, *880, 881*.
Goldthwaite, Anne, 551.
Goltzius, Hendrik, (?), *806*.
Gossaert, Jan, *see* Mabuse.
Gottlieb, Harry, 552.
Goya, 161–166a-f.
Grabach, John R., 553.
Grafly, Charles, sc1137, sc1138.
Graham, Ralph W., *991*.
Grant, Frederic M., 554.
Grant, J. Jeffrey, 555.
Greaves, Walter, 265.
Greco, El, 167–177.
Greenbaum, Dorothea S., sc1139.
Greenman, Frances C., 556.
Grien, *see* Baldung, Hans.
Griffen, Davenport, 557.
Gris, Juan, 775.
Grosz, George, *992*.
Grover, Oliver Dennett, 558.
Guardi, Francesco, 144–146.
Guercino, *807, 808*.
Guys, Constantin, *882–887*.

Hallsthammar, Carl, sc1140, sc1141.
Halpert, Samuel, 559.
Hals, Frans, 61a-b, 62, 63, 64, 65.
Harding, Chester, 417, 418.
Hartley, Marsden, 560.
Hassam, Childe, 561.
Haseltine, Elisabeth, sc1142.
Hawthorne, Charles W., 458.
Heckel, Erich, 752.
Heitland, W. Emerton, *993–995*.
Heldner, Knute, 562.
Henderson, William P., *996–998*.
Henri, Robert, 459.
Hering, Harry, 999.
Hesselius, John, 419.
Hibbard, Frederick C., sc1143.
Higgins, W. Victor, 563.
Hirsch, Stefan, 776.
Hobbema, Meindert, 66.
Hodler, Ferdinand, 729, *888, 889*.
Hofer, Karl, 753.
Hoffman, Harry L., 564.
Hogarth, William, 195, 196.
Holbein, Hans, the Younger, 19, 20.
Holzhauer, Emil, 565, *1000*.
Homer, Winslow, 460–464, *890–908*.
Hooch, Pieter de, 67.
Hoogstraten, Samuel van, *809*.
Hopkins, James R., 566.
Hopkinson, Charles, 567, *1001*.
Hopper, Edward, 568, *1002–1005*.
Horter, Earl, 569, *1006*.
Howard, Cecil, sc1144.
Howell, Felicie W., *1007*.

Iannelli, Alfonso, sc1145.
Ingerle, Rudolph F., 570.
Ingres, J. A. D., 217, *909, 910*.
Innes, James D., *911*.
Inness, George, 465–467.
Isenbrant, Adriaen, 41–2.
Italian School, XV C., *797*.
Italian School, XVI C., *810*.

Jackson, John, 197.
Jacobello di Bonomo, 86.
Jacobsen, Norman, *1008*.
Jawlensky, Alexei, 754.
Jicha, Joseph W., *1009*.
Johansen, John C., 571.
John, Augustus E., 266, 730, *1010–1013*.
Johnson, J. Theodore, 572.
Johnsson, Ivar, sc1146, sc1147.
Jones, Lloyd R., *1014*.
Jongkind, Johan B., *912*.
Judson, Sylvia Shaw, sc1148.
Junyer, Joan, 731.

Kandinsky, Wassilj, 777–779.
Kantor, Morris, 573.
Karfiol, Bernard, 574.
Kars, Georges, 732.
Kauffmann, Camille Andrene, 575.
Keller, Henry G., 576, *1015*.
Kelly, Leon, 577.
Kent, Rockwell, 578, *1016, 1017*.
Kindler, Alice R., 579.
Klee, Paul, 780.
Kleinschmidt, Paul, 755.
Klitgaard, Georgina, 580.
Knaths, Karl, 581.
Knight, Laura, *1018*.
Koerbecke, Johann, 21.
Kokoschka, Oskar, 756.
Kolbe, Georg, *1019, 1020*, sc1149–1151.
Koningh, Philips de, *811*.
Korbel, J. Mario, sc1152.
Krawiec, Walter, 582.
Krogh, Per, 733.
Kroll, Leon, 583, *1021*.
Kronberg, Louis, 584.
Kuehne, Max, 585.
Kuhn, Walt, 586.
Kulmbach, Hans von, 22, 23.
Kuniyoshi, Yasuo, 587.

Lachaise, Gaston, sc1153.
La Farge, John, *913*.
Lachman, Harry B., 588.
Lamont, Frances K., sc1154.
Lancret, Nicolas, 218–220.
Laufman, Sidney, 589.
Laurencin, Marie, *1022, 1023*.
Laurent, Robert, sc1155.
Lavery, John, 267.

Lawrence, Alfred K., 734.
Lawrence, Thomas, 198, 199.
Lawson, Ernest, 590.
Lees, Derwent, *914*.
Léger, Fernand, 781.
Legros, Alphonse, *915*.
Lehmbruck, Wilhelm, sc1156–1159.
Le Nain, Louis, 221.
Le Nain, Mathieu, 222.
Leonardo da Vinci, 118.
Leonardo da Vinci (attributed to), 117.
Lepère, Auguste, *916*, *917*.
Lever, Hayley, 591.
Levy, Beatrice S., 592.
Lhôte, André, 696, 697.
Lie, Jonas, 593.
Liljefors, Bruno, 268.
Lintott, Barnard, 735.
Longhi, Pietro, 147–149.
Lorenzo Veneziano School, 87, 88.
Lorrain, *see* Gellée, Claude.
Lotto, Lorenzo, 128.
Lucas van Leyden, 43.
Lucioni, Luigi, 594.
Luks, George, 595, *1024*.
Lurçat, Jean, 782.

Mabuse (Jan Gossaert), 44.
MacMonnies, Frederick, sc1160.
MacLane, Jean, *1027*.
Magnasco, Alessandro, 150.
Maillol, Aristide, *1028*, sc1161, sc1162.
Maler, Hans, 24, 25.
Mancini, Antonio, 269.
Manet, Edouard, 323–333, *918*, *919*.
Mangravite, Peppino, 596.
Manoir, Irving, 597.
Manship, Paul, sc1163–1165.
Mantegna, Andrea, 120.
Marc, Franz, 757.
Marchand, Jean, 698, 699.
Marcoussis, Louis C., 784.
Marin, John, *1029*.
Marquet, Albert, 700, 701, *1030–1031*.
Marsh, Reginald, 598.
Masolino da Panicale, 89.
Massys, Quentin, 45.
Master André, 26.
Master of Alkmaar, 46.
Master of the Bambino Vispo, 90.
Master of Frankfort, 47a-b.
Master of the Krainburg Altar, 27.
Master of the Legend of St. Ursula, 48a-b.
Master of Moulins, 28.
Master of St. George, 178.
Master of St. Veronica, 29.
Master of Virgo inter Virgines, 49.
Matisse, Henri, 388–398, *1032–1035*, sc1166–1169.
Maufra, Maxime, *920*.
Maurer, Christoph, *812*.
McBey, James, *1025*.
McCall, Virginia A., 599.
McCosh, David J., *1026*.
McEvoy, Ambrose, *921*.
McFee, Henry L., 600.
Melchers, J. Gari, 468, 469.
Melzer, Moriz, 758.
Memling, Hans, 50, 51.
Menzel, Herman, 601.
Meštrovic, Ivan, *1036*, sc1170–1172.
Metcalf, Willard L., 602.
Meyer, Herbert, 603.
Meyerowitz, William, 604.
Meunier, Constantin, sc1173.
Miller, Edgar, sc1174.
Miller, Kenneth H., 605.
Milles, Carl, sc1175, sc1176.
Millet, J. F., 249–257, *922*, *923*.
Miró, Joan, 785.
Modigliani, Amedeo, 702, 703, *1037*.
Moffett, Ross, 606.
Mola, Pierfrancesco, 151.
Monet, Claude, 290a–300.
Monticelli, Adolphe, 258.
Morales, Luis de, 180.
More, Hermon, 607.
Moretto (Alessandro Bonvicino), 130.
Morisot, Berthe, 334, *924*.
Moro, Antonio, 52, 53.
Moroni, Giovanni Battista, 129.
Morse, Samuel F. B., 420.
Motley, Archibald J., Jr., 608.
Mueller, Otto, 759.
Muenter, Gabriele, 761.
Murphy, H. Dudley, 609.
Myers, Jerome, 610, *1038*, *1039*.

Nakian, Reuben, sc1177.
Nash, John, 736, *1041*, *1042*.
Nash, Paul, 1040.
Navarre(?), School of, 182.
Neroccio di Bartolommeo, 121.
Nielsen, Kai, sc1178.
Norman, Viola, sc1179.
Norton, John W., 611, *1043*.
Netscher, Caspar, 68.
Nuzi, Allegretto, 91, 92.

Ochtervelt, Jacobus, 69, 70.
Orloff, Chana, sc1180–1182.
Orpen, William, 270, 271, 272, *925–927*.
Ostade, Adriaen van, 71.
Ostrowsky, Sam, 612.

Palmer, Pauline, 613.
Paris (?), School of, 33.
Pascin, Jules, 704.
Pater, J. B. J., 223–225.
Patinir, Joachim, 54.
Pechstein, Max, 762, 763.
Peirce, Waldo, 616.
Perry, Maeble, sc1183.
Perugino, Pietro, 123a-d.
Phillip, Robert, 614.
Phillips, Marjorie, 615.
Philpot, Glyn, sc1184.
Piazzetta, Giovanni Battista, 152.
Picabia, Francis, 786.
Picasso, Pablo, 399–409, 787, *1044–1049*, sc1185, sc1186.
Piero di Cosimo, 122.
Pissarro, Camille, 301, *928*.
Pluym, Karel van der, 72.
Polášek, Albin, sc1187–1189.
Pollaiuolo, A., 124.
Pollet, Joseph, 617.
Ponsen, Tunis, 618.
Pontormo, 131, 132.
Poole, Abram, 619.
Poole, Frederick V., *1050*.
Poor, Henry V., 620.
Pougialis, Constantine, 621.
Poupelet, Jane, *1051–1053*, sc1190–1193.
Poussin, Nicolas, 226.
Prendergast, Maurice, 470, *1054*.
Proctor, Dod, 737.
Pruna, Pedro (Pablo), 1055.
Pryde, James, *1056–1058*.
Puvis de Chavannes, P. C., 273, *929*, *930*.

Raeburn, Henry, 200–202.
Raffaelli, J. F., *1059*.
Raffet, Auguste, *931*.
Raphael, 125.
Ravlin, Grace, 622.
Redfield, Edward W., 623.
Redon, Odilon, 707, *932*.
Regnault, Henri, 259.
Rembrandt, 73–75, *813*, *814*.
Renoir, Auguste, 335–351.
Reynolds, Joshua, 203.
Ribera, Jusepe (attributed to), 181.
Ricketts, Charles, *1060*, *1061*.
Ripley, Aiden L., *1062*.
Ritman, Louis, 624.
Rivera, Diego, 738.
Robert, Hubert, 227, 228, *815*.
Robinson, Increase, 625.
Robinson, Theodore, 471.
Robusti, J., *see* Tintoretto.
Rodin, Auguste, *933–935*, sc1194–1201.
Roecker, Leon, 626.
Romagnoli, Giovanni, 739.
Romney, George, 204.
Rops, Félicien, *936*, *937*.
Rosenthal, Doris, 627.
Rossetti, Dante G., 274.
Roszak, Theodore J., 788.
Rothenstein, William, *1063*, *1064*.
Rouault, Georges, 789, *1065*.
Rousseau, Henri, 367–369.
Rousseff, W. Vladimir, 628.
Rowlandson, Thomas, *816–820*.
Roy, Pierre, 790.
Rubens, Petrus Paulus, 76, 77.
Rumsey, Charles C., sc1202.
Rutherston, Albert D., *1066–1067*
Ryder, Albert P., 472–475.

Sabbagh, Georges H., *1068*.
St. Gaudens, Augustus, sc1203, sc1204.
Sano di Pietro, 93.
Sargent, John S., 476–480, *938–944*.
Sargent, Margarett, sc1205.
Sassetta, 94.
Savage, Edward, 421.
Savage, Eugene F., 629.
Sawyer, Helen, *1069*.
Schel, Sebastian, 32.
Schary, Saul, 791.

Scheibe, Richard, sc1206.
Schiavone (Andrea Meldolla), 133.
Schmidt-Rottluff, Karl, 764.
Schmitt, Carl, 630.
Schnakenberg, Henry E., 631, *1070*.
Schofield, Flora I., 632.
Schwabe, Randolph, *1071*.
Schwalbach, Carl, *1072*.
Schwartz, William S., 633.
Scudder, Janet, sc1207.
Seidel, Emory P., sc1208.
Segna di Bonaventura, 95.
Segonzac, André D. de, 710–712, *1073*.
Seurat, Georges, 370, *946*.
Seyffert, Leopold, 634.
Sheets, Millard, 636.
Sheeler, Charles, 635, *1074, 1075*.
Sherwood, Ruth, sc1209.
Shinn, Everett, 637.
Shonnard, Eugenie T., sc1209A.
Signac, Paul, *1076, 1076A*.
Sinclair, Gerrit V., 638.
Sintenis, Renée, sc1210, sc1211.
Sisley, Alfred, 302, 303.
Sloan, John, 639.
Smith, George Melville, 640.
Smith, Jacob G., 641.
Smith, Judson, 642.
Snapp, Frank, *1077*.
Solana, José G., 740.
Solimena, Francesco, 153.
Sommer, William, *1078*.
Sorolla, Joaquin, 275.
Soutine, Haim, 741.
Souverbie, Jean, 792.
Souza-Cardoso, Amadeo de, 793.
Soyer, Raphael, 643.
Spagna, Lo, 119.
Sparhawk-Jones, Elizabeth, 644.
Speicher, Eugene, 645.
Speight, Francis, 646.
Spencer, Robert, 647.
Spinello Aretino, 96.
Starnina, Gherardo, 97.
Steinlen, Théophile A., *947*.
Stephan, John, 648.
Sterne, Maurice, 649, *1079*.
Sterrer, Karl, 765.
Stevens, Alfred, 260.
Stoller, Alexander, sc1212.
Storrs, John, 1080, sc1213, sc1214.
Strigel, Bernhard, 32A.
Stuart, Gilbert, 422–425.
Sully, Thomas, 426.
Survage, Leopold, 794.

Taddeo di Bartolo, 98.
Taft, Lorado, sc1215.
Tanner, Henry O., 650.
Taylor, Helen J., 651.
Tchelitchew, Paul, 795.
Ter Borch, Geraerd, 79.
Tellander, Frederic, 652.
Terechkovitch, Costia, 742.
Thayer, Abbott H., 481, 482.
Theotocopuli, *see* Greco, El.
Thornycroft, William H., sc1216.
Tiepolo, Gianbattista, 154–160, *821*.
Tiepolo, Giandomenico, *822, 823*.
Tintoretto, 134–137.
Titian, 138–140.
Toulouse-Lautrec, H. de, 371–374, *948*.
Trebilcock, Paul, 653.
Turner, J. M. W., 205, 206.
Tuscan School, XIII C., 99, 100.
Tyson, Carroll, 654.
Twachtman, John H., 483–486.

Ufer, Walter, 655.
Utrillo, Maurice, 713, 714, *1081*.

Valadon, Suzanne, *1082*.
Van Gogh, *see* Gogh, Vincent van.
Van Pappelendam, Laura, 656.
Van Veen, Stuyvesant, 657.
Varian, Dorothy, 658.
Velasquez, 183–185.
Verdilhan, Mathieu, *1083*.
Vergé-Sarrat, Henri, 715, *1084*.
Vermeer, 80.
Veronese, Paolo, 141–143.
Veronese (?), Paolo, *824*.
Vlaminck, Maurice de, 716, 717, *1085–1086*.
Vonnoh, Bessie P., sc1217.
Vuillard, Edouard, 718, 719.

Waldo, Samuel L., 427, 428.
Walter, Martha, *1087*.
Watkins, Franklin C., 659.
Warneke, Heinz, sc1218, sc1219.
Weber, Max, 660, *1088*.
Webster, Herman A., *1089*.
Weir, J. Alden, 487.
Weisgerber, Albert, *949*.
West, Benjamin, 429.
Weston, Harold, 661.
Weyden, Rogier van der, 55, 56.
Wheelock, Warren, 662.
Wheatley, Francis, *825*.
Whistler, James M., 488–490, *950, 951*.
Whitney, Gertrude V., sc1220, sc1221.
Whorf, John, *1090, 1091*.
Wiggins, Guy C., 663.
Wiles, Irving, 665.
Wilimovsky, Charles A., 664.
Wilkie, David, *826*.
Williams, John S., *1092*.
Williams, Walter R., sc1224.
Williams, Wheeler, sc1223.
Wilson, Richard, 207.
Winholtz, Caleb, *1093*.
Wood, Grant, 666.
Woodward, Robert S., 667.
Wouwerman, Philips, *827*.

Young, Mahonri, sc1225.

Zak, Eugene, 743.
Zettler, Emil, sc1226.
Zoffany, Johann, 208.
Zoppo, Marco, 101.
Zorach, Marguerite, 668.
Zorach, William, *1094*, sc1227.
Zorn, Anders L., 276, 277.
Zsissly, 669.
Zuloaga, Ignacio, 278.
Zurbarán, Francisco de, 186.

LENDERS

Allerton, Mr. Robert, *855*, sc1160, sc1184.
Angell-Norris Collection, 61a-b, 245.
Anonymous, 12, 20, 38, 58, 64, 76, 88, 125, 128, 139, 142, 210, 211, 215, 381, 413, 559, 635, 658, 660, 738, 745, 767, 790.
Arensberg, Mr. and Mrs. Walter Conrad, 773.
Art Institute of Chicago 2, 3a-g, 6, 11, 17, 21, 28, 32, 33, 36, 37, 40–43, 45, 47a-b, 48a-b, 49, 50, 53, 55, 56, 60, 63, 65, 66, 68–70, 71, 74, 75, 77, 79, 82, 83, 85a-f, 90, 91, 93, 96–101, 105, 115, 116, 123, 129, 137, 141, 144, 145, 147, 150–152, 154–160, 166a-f, 169, 178, 182, 190, 191, 194, 195, 197, 198, 204, 205, 207, 209, 212, 221, 226, 227, 230, 231, 233, 235–237, 239, 243, 244, 246, 247, 250–257, 259, 260, 261, 263, 265–267, 270, 272–276, 278, 281, 286, 287, 289, 291a–299, 301–303, 304, 305, 309, 310, 321–323, 327, 328, 330–332, 334, 335, 339, 340, 342–344, 347–351, 355, 356, 358, 359, 362, 365, 369, 370, 371–373, 376, 377, 380, 389, 398, 402, 403, 411, 415, 417, 418, 421, 423, 424, 426, 428, 429, 431, 432, 436, 439–445, 447–449, 451, 455, 457–459, 464, 466–469, 474, 476, 480, 481, 483–485, 487–489, 494, 497, 503, 504, 508, 519, 520A, 524–526, 528, 531, 532, 534, 547–550, 553, 558, 561, 563, 564, 566, 570–573, 578, 583, 588, 590, 602, 609–611, 619, 622, 629, 637, 644, 647, 650, 655, 663, 666, 670–672, 679, 682–685, 690, 691, 693, 694, 697–702, 707, 712–714, 717, 718, 728, 729, 741, 743, 757, 761, 766, 768, 777–779, 782, 793.

796–817, 819–844, 846–854, 856, 909, 911–915, 918–944, 946–951, 953, 954, 957–960, 962–968, 970–

973, 975–977, 979–985, 987, 989, 990, 992–998, 1000–1024, 1027–1047, 1051–1068, 1070–1092, 1094.

sc1098, sc1100, sc1105–sc1108, sc1111, sc1118, sc1121, sc1126, sc1128, sc1132, sc1133, sc1137, sc1138, sc1140, sc1141, sc1150, sc1152, sc1159, sc1163–sc1165, sc1170–sc1173, sc1176, sc1182, sc1183, sc1187–sc1201, sc1203–sc1205, sc1207, sc1210, sc1214–sc1219, 1221.

Babcock Gallery, 456.
Bache, Mr. Jules S., 193.
Badger, Mr. Shreve, *1048*.
Bakwin, Dr. and Mrs. Harry, 314.
Barnhart, A. M., Estate of, 249.
Bartlett, Mr. Frederic Clay, 689.
Bartlett, Mr. and Mrs. Frederic Clay, Jr., 716.
Beal, Mr. Gifford, sc1161.
Becker, John, Gallery, 791.
Berwind, Mr. Edward J., 213, 225.
Bliss, Lizzie P., Estate of, 288, 308, 319, 407, 446.
Bontoux, Mr. August, 153.
Booth, Mrs. Ralph Harman, 16, 32A, 106, 223.
Boston, Museum of Fine Arts, 134, 282, 437, 461, 724, 736.
Bottenwieser Galleries, 132.
Brewster, Mr. and Mrs. Walter S., 363, 374, 674.
Brooklyn Museum, 285, 740, sc1131, sc1178, sc1222.
Brown, Mr. John Nicholas, 317.
Brummer Galleries, Inc., sc1122.
Buckingham, Miss Kate S., *818*.
Buffalo Fine Arts Academy, 404, 730, sc1129, sc1157.

Carnegie Institute, Pittsburgh, 271, 645, 723, 765.
Casey, Mr. Daniel V., *916, 917, 961, 1025*.
Chadbourne, Mrs. Emily Crane, 264.
Chicago, Art Institute of
see Art Institute of Chicago
Chicago Galleries Association, 618.
Cincinnati Art Museum, 120, 453.
Cincinnati Institute of Fine Arts, Taft Museum, 217.
Clark, Mr. Stephen C., 307, 397.
Cleveland Museum of Art, 102, 136, 434, 475.
Coburn, Mrs. L. L., Estate of, 493, *1050*.
Coe, Mr. and Mrs. Ralph M., 168, 390.
Cohn, Mr. and Mrs. Erich, 755.
College Art Association, 751, 754, 758, 762, 763.
Collins, Mr. M. H., 529.
Columbus Gallery of Fine Arts, 470, 560, 587.
Cone, Miss Etta, 394, sc1166–1169.

Crowninshield, Mr. Frank, 527, 673, 711, sc1123, sc1124.
Cudney, Mr. Ralph, 463, 472, 473.

Dale, Chester, Collection, 234, 341, 382, 438, 703.
Danielson, Mr. and Mrs. R. E., 165, 174, 185, 329, 486, 721.
Deering, Charles, Collection, 186, 277, 477.
Demotte, Inc., 795.
Detroit Institute of Arts, 34, 35, 692.
Downtown Gallery, 517, 533, 551, 581, 589, 617, 776, sc1155, sc1156, sc1177, sc1213, sc1227.
Dreier, Miss Katherine S., 747.
Drey, A. S., 1, 14.
Durand-Ruel, Inc., 338.
Duveen Brothers, Inc., 73, 140, 192.

Eddy, Mr. and Mrs. Jerome O., 774, 786.
Edwards, Mr. and Mrs. E. W., 117.
Ellis, Mr. Theodore T., 118.
Epstein, Mr. Max, 8, 30, 107, 108, 171, 183.
Everett, Mrs. H. A., 636.

Ferargil, Inc., sc1116, sc1125, sc1136, sc1212, sc1223, sc1224.
Findlay Galleries, Inc., sc1130.
Fisher, Mr. and Mrs. William A., 427.
Foote, Rev. Henry Wilder, 416.
Fuller, Mr. and Mrs. Gilbert E., 353.

Gallatin, Mr. Albert, 248.
Gallatin, Mr. Albert Eugene, 785.
Glasner, Mr. R. W., 498.
Goldman, Mr. William, 18, 46.
Goodman, Mr. and Mrs. William Owen, 130.
Goodyear, Mr. A. Conger, 313, 354, 379, 523.
Grand Central Art Galleries, 513, 538, 634, 665.
Griggs, Mr. Maitland F., 89, 94.

Hanna, Mr. Leonard C., Jr., 400.
Harding, Mrs. George F., 180.
Harriman, Marie, Gallery, 315, 352, 386, 406, 408, 681, 686.
Harrison, Mr. Carter H., 695, 704, 732, 733.
Harrison, Mr. and Mrs. William Preston, 605.
Hartford, Wadsworth Atheneum, 414.
Harvard University, Fogg Art Museum, 126, 262, 279, 296A, 336, 412.
Haskell, Mr. Frederick T., 199.
Havemeyer, Mr. Horace, 333.
Hawkes, Mrs. Forbes, 420.
Heun, Mr. Arthur, *952*.
Hill, Mrs. Patrick C., 368.
Hirschland, Dr. F. H., 173.
Hole, Mr. Willitts J., 181.

Jenkins, Mrs. John E., 613.
Johnson, Mr. Chester H., sc1112, sc1175.
Johnson, Chester H., Gallery, 196, 387, 771, 794.
Judson, Mr. Arthur, 630.

Kaufmann, Mr. Edgar J., 739.
Knoedler, M., and Co., 208, 311, 312, 375, 388.
Kraushaar, C. W., Art Galleries, 631, 639, 710; sc1225.
Kraushaar, Mr. John F., 515.
Kress, Mr. Samuel H., 59, 148, 149, 228.

La France Art Institute, 577, 784, 792, sc1135.
Lehman, Mr. Albert C., 659, 722, 731, 734.
Lehman, Governor Herbert H., 44.
Lewisohn, Adolph, Collection, 240, 318, 366, 433.
Libbey, Mrs. Edward Drummond, 19, 184.
Lilienfeld, Dr. Karl, 751, 754, 758, 762, 763.
Logan, Mr. Frank G., 664.
Los Angeles Museum, 605.

Macbeth Gallery, 603, 667.
Matisse Gallery, Pierre, 391, 392, 394, 789, sc1162.
Mayer, Mr. Oscar F., 678, 696, 715.
McCormick, Mr. and Mrs. Chauncey, 161, 163, 164, 176, 268, 269, 280, 478.
McCormick, Mr. and Mrs. Cyrus H., 189, 202.
McCormick, Mrs. Robert Rutherford, 306, 361, 367.
Mellon, Hon. Andrew W., 175.
Milch, E. and A., Inc., 110, 520, 539, 546, 591, 646.
Milwaukee, Layton Art Gallery, 482.
Minneapolis Institute of Arts, 54, sc1096.
Mogmar Art Foundation, Inc., 113.
Montross Gallery, 620.

Nef, Mr. and Mrs. John U., *978, 1049*.
Neilson, Mr. Francis, 187, 200.
Netcher, Mrs. Charles, *910*.
Neumann, Mr. J. B., 744, *974*.
New York, Metropolitan Museum of Art, 57, 170, 177.
New York, Museum of Modern Art, 288, 308, 319, 407, 446, 748, sc1158.
New York, Whitney Museum of American Art, 511, 516, 518, 536, 569, 574, 593, sc1144, sc1220.

Oppenheimer, Mr. Julius, 378, 385.
Osborn, Mr. William Church, 364.

Paine, Mr. Robert Treat 2nd, 384.
Palm, Mr. Tage, sc1146, sc1147.
Palmer, Mr. and Mrs. Potter, 283, 300, 405.
Paris, France, Louvre Museum, 490.

Parmelee, Mrs. James, 102.
Philadelphia, Pennsylvania Museum of Art, 409, 454.
Pittsburgh, Carnegie Institute, Department of Fine Arts, 271, 645, 723, 765.
Pratt, Mr. Herbert Lee, 410.
Providence, Rhode Island School of Design, Museum of Art, 229, 462, 567.

Rehn, Mr. Frank K. M., 509, 512, 552, 598, 600, sc1154.
Riggs, General Lawrason, 419.
Ringling Mus. of Art, John and Mable, 143.
Rockefeller, Mr. John D., sc1119.
Rosenbach Company, sc1109, sc1110.
Rumsey, Mrs. Charles Cary, sc1202.
Ryerson, Mrs. Martin A., 39, 92, 95, 111, 112, 119, 324, 337, 450, 460, *845*.

Sachs, Mr. Arthur, 135, 138, 162, 167.
Sachs, Mr. and Mrs. Howard J., 284.
Saint-Gaudens, Mr. Homer, 720.
St. Louis, City Art Museum, 67, 545
Sarasota, John and Mable Ringling Museum of Art, 143.
Scheyer, Mrs. Galka, 780.
Schofield, Mrs. Flora I., 769, 775, sc1180, sc1181.
Schuette, Mr. Robert W., 201.
Scott and Fowles, sc1127.
Secor, Mr. Arthur J., 203.
Seligmann, Rey and Co., Arnold, 10.
Seligmann and Co., Inc., Jacques, 214.
Shaskan, Mr. E. Felix, 657.
Sheafer, Mr. and Mrs. Lesley G., 568.
Smart, Mr. David A., 612, 726, 742.
Smith College Museum of Art, 216, 232, 238, 316.
Soby, Mr. and Mrs. James T., 680, 787.
Société Anonyme, New York, 746.
Steffen, Mr. LeRoy J., 628.
Stehli, Mr. E. J., 218.
Sternberg, Mr. Josef von, sc1104.
Sterner, Marie, sc1114.
Stillman, Mr. Chauncey Devereux, 131.
Stimmel, Mr. William S., 471, 541, 623, 727, 737.
Stransky, Mr. Josef, 401, 318A, 749.
Straus, Mr. and Mrs. Percy S., 81.
Sullivan, Mrs. Cornelius J., 687.
Sweeney, Mr. P. M., 725.

Tannahill, Mr. Robert H., 395.
Thompson, Mrs. John R., 62.
Thompson, Mr. John R., Jr., 62.
Timken, Mrs. William R., 9, 206, 224.
Toledo Museum of Art, 19, 184, 203, 430.
Tripp, Mr. Chester D., 72.
Tyson, Mr. Carroll, 325.

Valentiner, Dr. W. R., 752, 756, 759, 764.

Warburg, Mr. Edward M. M., sc1099.
Washington, D. C., Corcoran Gallery of Art, 596.
Washington, D. C., Phillips Memorial Gallery, 242, 345, 383, 399, 452, 586, 595, 649, 675, 676.
Washington, D. C., Smithsonian Institution, National Gallery of Art, 146.
Webb, Mr. and Mrs. J. Watson, 326.
Weis, Mr. Samuel W., 422.
Weyhe Gallery, sc1103, sc1120, sc1139, sc1151, sc1153, sc1185, sc1186, sc1211.
White, Mr. Samuel S., 3rd, 52, 396.
Whitney, Mr. John Hay, 346.
Whitney, Mrs. Payne, 479.
Widener, Mr. Joseph, 80, 114, 121.
Wildenstein and Co., Inc., 5, 109, 219, 220, 320.
Willys, Mr. John N., 51.
Winterbotham, Mr. Joseph, 172, 290, 772.
Worcester Art Museum, 4, 188, 222, 360, 425, 688, 753.
Worcester, Mr. and Mrs. Charles H., 7, 13, 22-27, 29, 86, 87, 103, 127, 133, 258, 357, 435, 465, 584, 677, 719, 781, sc1149, sc1206.

Yale University, Gallery of Fine Arts, 84, 122, 124.

ILLUSTRATIONS

PLATE I

13. LUCAS CRANACH, THE ELDER CRUCIFIXION
Mr. and Mrs. Charles H. Worcester

26. MASTER ANDRE CHRIST CARRYING THE CROSS
Mr. and Mrs. Charles H. Worcester

20. HANS HOLBEIN, THE YOUNGER HERMANN WEDIGH
Anonymous Loan

19. HANS HOLBEIN, THE YOUNGER CATHERINE HOWARD
The Toledo Museum of Arts

178. MASTER OF ST. GEORGE ST. GEORGE
The Art Institute of Chicago

4. AVIGNON SCHOOL, C. 1400 PRESENTATION OF A DONOR
The Worcester Art Museum

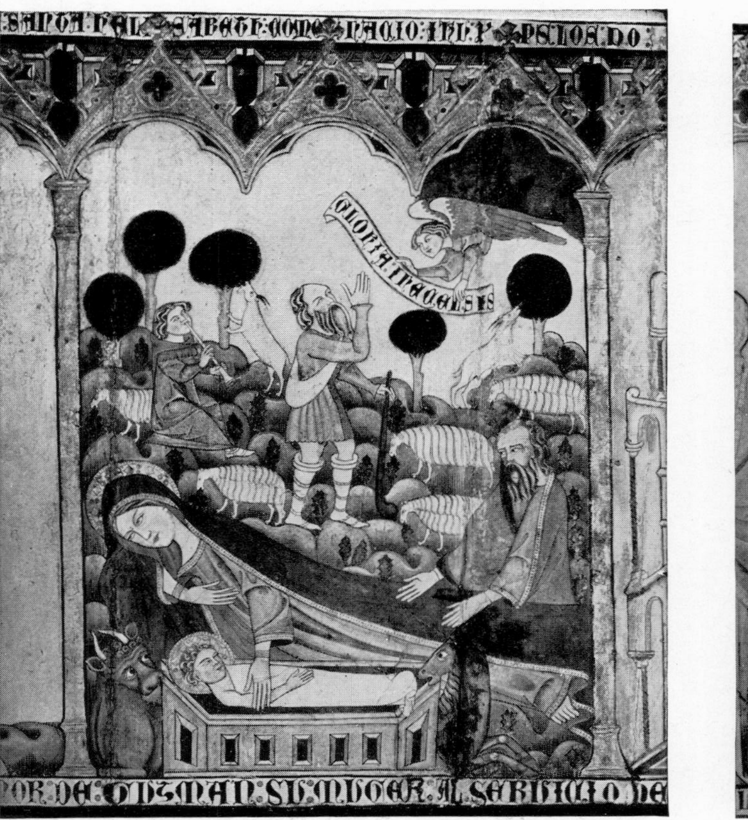

182. SCHOOL OF NAVARRE (?), 1396

ANNUNCIATION TO THE SHEPHERDS AND FLIGHT INTO EGYPT FROM AYALA ALTARPIECE

The Art Institute of Chicago

PLATE V

3. AMIENS SCHOOL, C. 1480 THE LAST SUPPER AND THE ASCENSION
The Art Institute of Chicago

28. MASTER OF MOULINS ANNUNCIATION
The Art Institute of Chicago

8. JEAN CLOUET — CHARLOTTE OF FRANCE

Mr. Max Epstein

55. ROGIER VAN DER WEYDEN — JAN DE GROS

The Art Institute of Chicago

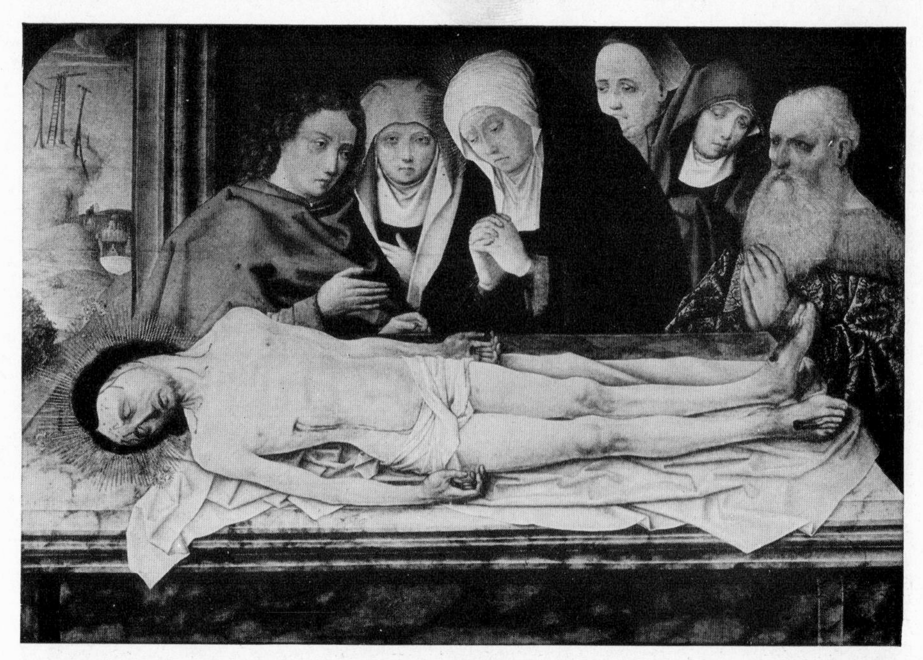

33. SCHOOL OF PARIS, C. 1500 ENTOMBMENT

The Art Institute of Chicago

43. LUCAS VAN LEYDEN ADORATION OF THE MAGI

The Art Institute of Chicago

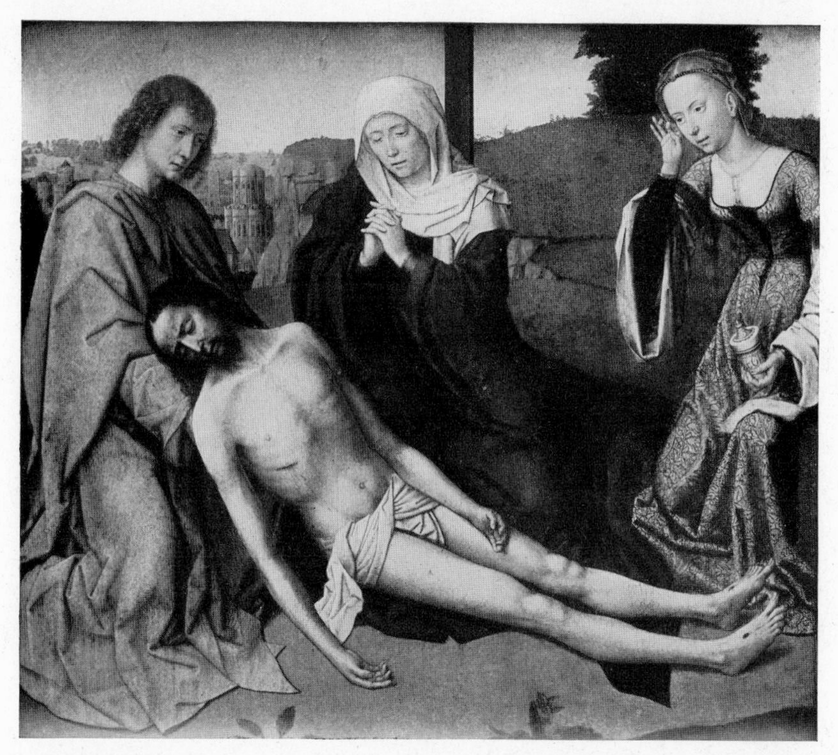

40. GERAERD DAVID LAMENTATION AT THE CROSS
The Art Institute of Chicago

34. PIETER BREUGHEL, THE ELDER THE WEDDING DANCE
The Detroit Institute of Arts

Plate IX

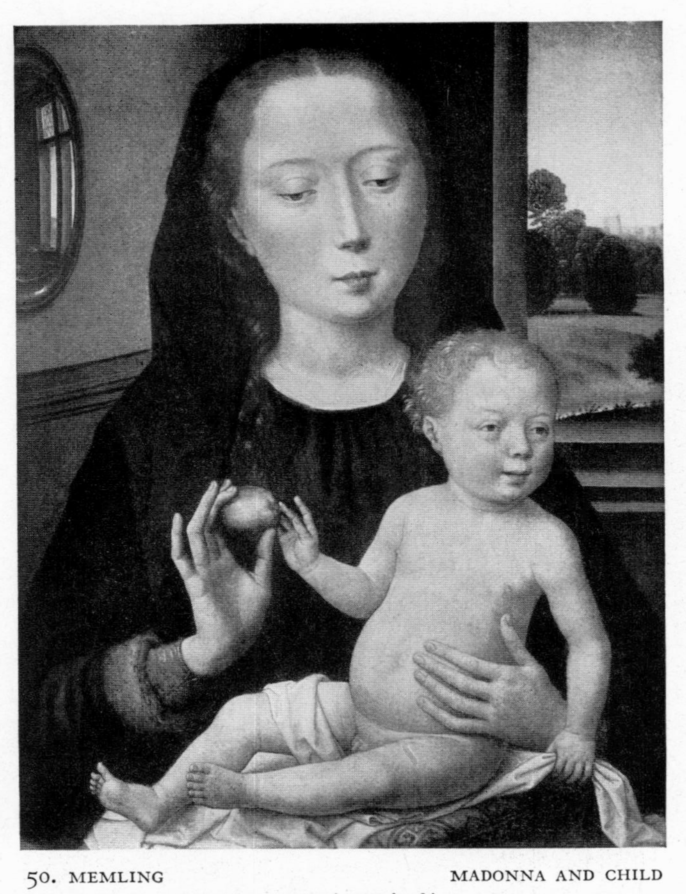

50. MEMLING MADONNA AND CHILD
The Art Institute of Chicago

45. QUENTIN MASSYS MAN WITH A PINK
The Art Institute of Chicago

38. JACOB CORNELISZ VAN AMSTERDAM HOLY FAMILY WITH ST. ANNE
Anonymous Loan

35. PETRUS CHRISTUS ST. JEROME
The Detroit Institute of Arts

89. MASOLINO — CRUCIFIXION

Mr. Maitland F. Griggs

99. TUSCAN SCHOOL, XIII C. — MADONNA

The Art Institute of Chicago

Plate XII

95. SEGNA DI BONAVENTURA MADONNA
Mrs. Martin A. Ryerson

85. GIOVANNI DI PAOLO ST. JOHN THE BAPTIST IN THE DESERT
The Art Institute of Chicago

124. ANTONIO POLLAIUOLO — RAPE OF DEIANIRA

Yale Gallery of Fine Arts

94. SASSETTA — JOURNEY OF THE MAGI

Mr. Maitland F. Griggs

120. MANTEGNA TARQUIN AND THE SIBYL

The Cincinnati Art Museum

121. NEROCCIO DI BARTOLO PORTRAIT OF A WOMAN

Mr. Joseph Widener

122. PIERO DI COSIMO LADY WITH A RABBIT

Yale Gallery of Fine Arts

116. RIDOLFO GHIRLANDAJO GENTLEMAN OF FLORENCE

The Art Institute of Chicago

108. BOTTICELLI MADONNA AND CHILD
Mr. Max Epstein

105. GIOVANNI BELLINI MADONNA AND CHILD
The Art Institute of Chicago

113. CARPACCIO ST. EUSTACE

Mogmar Art Foundation, New York

143. VERONESE REST ON THE FLIGHT

The John and Mable Ringling Museum

PLATE XIX

140. TITIAN — VENUS AND THE LUTE PLAYER

Duveen Brothers

139. TITIAN DANAE

Anonymous Loan

138. TITIAN ADORATION OF THE MAGI

Mr. Arthur Sachs

126. JACOPO BASSANO ADORATION OF THE MAGI

The Fogg Art Museum, Harvard

135. TINTORETTO CHRIST ON THE LAKE OF GALILEE

Mr. Arthur Sachs

131. PONTORMO HALBERDIER
Mr. C. D. Stillman

129. MORONI LUDOVICO MADRUZZO
The Art Institute of Chicago

151. PIERFRANCESCO MOLA HOMER DICTATING

The Art Institute of Chicago

153. SOLIMENA ERMINIA AND THE SHEPHERDS

Mr. August Bontoux

158. TIEPOLO ARMIDA ABANDONED BY RINALDO

The Art Institute of Chicago

146. GUARDI RUINS WITH FIGURES

The National Gallery of Art, Washington

169. EL GRECO ASSUMPTION OF THE VIRGIN

The Art Institute of Chicago

170. EL GRECO — CARDINAL GUEVARA

The Metropolitan Museum of Art

167. EL GRECO — AGONY IN THE GARDEN

Mr. Arthur Sachs

171. EL GRECO — CORONATION OF THE VIRGIN

Mr. Max Epstein

172. EL GRECO FEAST IN THE HOUSE OF SIMON

Mr. Joseph Winterbotham

177. EL GRECO VIEW OF TOLEDO

The Metropolitan Museum of Art

PLATE XXIX

180. MORALES — PIETA

Mr. George Harding

173. EL GRECO — HEAD OF A MAN

Dr. F. H. Hirschland

184. VELASQUEZ MAN WITH WINE GLASS
The Toledo Museum of Art

183. VELASQUEZ ISABELLA OF BOURBON
Mr. Max Epstein

166e. GOYA MARGATO SHOT

The Art Institute of Chicago

162. GOYA BULL FIGHT

Mr. Arthur Sachs

185. VELASQUEZ — ST. JOHN

Mr. and Mrs. R. E. Danielson

161. GOYA — BOY ON A RAM

Mr. and Mrs. Chauncey McCormick

PLATE XXXIII

73. REMBRANDT — ARISTOTLE

Duveen Brothers

PLATE XXXIV

53. MORO A NOBLEMAN

The Art Institute of Chicago

75. REMBRANDT GIRL AT OPEN HALF-DOOR

The Art Institute of Chicago

Plate XXXV

64. HALS — JUDITH LEYSTER

Anonymous Loan

62. HALS — MERRY LUTE PLAYER

Mrs. John R. Thompson and Mr. John R. Thompson, Jr.

PLATE XXXVI

57. BROUWER THE SMOKERS
The Metropolitan Museum of Art

79. TER BORCH THE MUSIC LESSON
The Art Institute of Chicago

69. OCHTERVELT ELEGANT COMPANY

The Art Institute of Chicago

58. CUYP LANDSCAPE WITH RIDERS

Anonymous Loan

77. RUBENS SAMSON AND DELILAH

The Art Institute of Chicago

66. HOBBEMA WATER MILL WITH GREAT RED ROOF

The Art Institute of Chicago

80. VERMEER WOMAN WEIGHING GOLD

Mr. Joseph Widener

60. DE GELDER PORTRAIT OF A GIRL

The Art Institute of Chicago

203. REYNOLDS — THE HONORABLE MRS. WATSON

Mr. Arthur J. Secor and The Toledo Museum of Art

198. LAWRENCE — MRS. WOLFF

The Art Institute of Chicago

201. RAEBURN THE JOHNSTONE GROUP

Mr. and Mrs. Robert W. Schuette

190. CONSTABLE STOKE-BY-NAYLAND

The Art Institute of Chicago

188. BONINGTON SANTA MARIA DELLA SALUTE

The Worcester Art Museum

192. GAINSBOROUGH LANDSCAPE WITH A BRIDGE

Duveen Brothers

Plate XLIII

193. GAINSBOROUGH QUEEN CHARLOTTE

Mr. Jules S. Bache

200. RAEBURN THE HONORABLE MRS. VEITCH

Mr. Francis Neilson

221. LOUIS LE NAIN PEASANT FAMILY

The Art Institute of Chicago

222. MATHIEU LE NAIN THE CARD PLAYERS

The Worcester Art Museum

225. PATER LOVE AND JEST

Mr. Edward J. Berwind

226. POUSSIN ST. JOHN ON PATMOS

The Art Institute of Chicago

210. CHARDIN THE INDUSTRIOUS MOTHER

A Private Collection

227. HUBERT ROBERT THE FOUNTAINS

The Art Institute of Chicago

213. DAVID MME. DE RICHEMONT AND HER SON

Mr. Edward J. Berwind

217. INGRES MLLE. GONIN

The Taft Collection

245. DELACROIX THE LION HUNT

The Angell-Norris Collection

234. COROT VIEW OF VOLTERRA

The Chester Dale Collection

242. DAUMIER THE UPRISING

The Phillips Memorial Gallery

238. COURBET TOILET OF A BRIDE

The Smith College Museum of Art

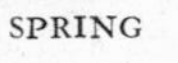

273. PUVIS DE CHAVANNES — FISHERMAN'S FAMILY

The Art Institute of Chicago

248. DELACROIX — SPRING

Mr. Albert Gallatin

PLATE LI

237. COURBET MERE GREGOIRE

The Art Institute of Chicago

240. DAUMIER THE DRINKERS

Adolph Lewisohn Collection

249. MILLET — THE BATHER

The A. M. Barnhart Estate

231. COROT — INTERRUPTED READING

The Art Institute of Chicago

282. DEGAS CARRIAGE AT THE RACES

The Museum of Fine Arts, Boston

286. DEGAS THE MILLINERY SHOP

The Art Institute of Chicago

291. MONET ARGENTEUIL

The Art Institute of Chicago

289. DEGAS UNCLE AND NIECE

The Art Institute of Chicago

PLATE LV

333. MANET — THE RAILROAD

Mr. Horace Havemeyer

325. MANET — FOLKESTONE BOAT

Mr. Carroll Tyson

337. RENOIR — AT THE PIANO

Mrs. Martin A. Ryerson

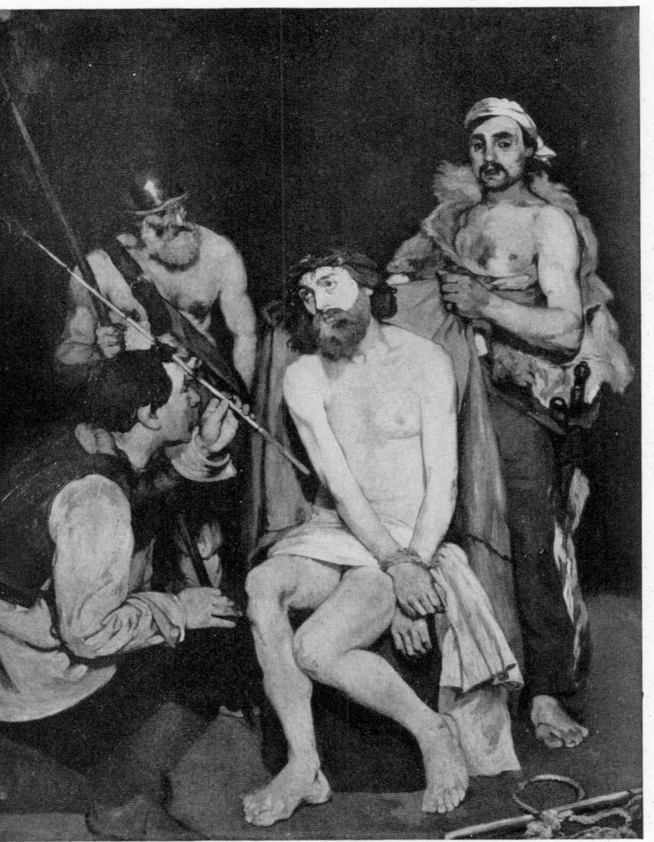

327. MANET — JESUS MOCKED

The Art Institute of Chicago

PLATE LVII

345. RENOIR LUNCHEON OF THE BOATING PARTY

The Phillips Memorial Gallery

351. RENOIR TWO LITTLE CIRCUS GIRLS
The Art Institute of Chicago

338. RENOIR BATHER
Durand-Ruel

334. BERTHE MORISOT — WOMAN AT HER TOILET

The Art Institute of Chicago

346. RENOIR — MOULIN DE LA GALETTE

Mr. John Hay Whitney

319. CEZANNE STILL LIFE WITH APPLES

Trustees of the Lizzie P. Bliss Estate

307. CEZANNE THE CARD PLAYERS

Mr. Stephen C. Clark

316. CEZANNE THE ROAD THAT TURNS

The Smith College Museum of Art

309. CEZANNE L'ESTAQUE

The Art Institute of Chicago

PLATE LXII

310. CEZANNE FLOWERS AND FRUIT

The Art Institute of Chicago

314. CEZANNE PORTRAIT OF A GIRL

Dr. and Mrs. Harry Bakwin

370. SEURAT SUNDAY ON LA GRANDE JATTE

The Art Institute of Chicago

371. TOULOUSE-LAUTREC AT THE MOULIN-ROUGE

The Art Institute of Chicago

366. GAUGUIN "WE GREET THEE, MARY"

The Adolph Lewisohn Collection

364. GAUGUIN TWO TAHITIAN WOMEN

Mr. Wm. Church Osborn

381. VAN GOGH THE PAVERS

Anonymous Loan

367. ROUSSEAU EXOTIC LANDSCAPE

Mrs. R. R. McCormick

382. VAN GOGH MLLE. GACHET

The Chester Dale Collection

384. VAN GOGH ROULIN, THE POSTMAN

Mr. Robert Treat Paine, 2nd

Plate LXVII

399. PICASSO — THE BLUE ROOM

The Phillips Memorial Gallery

396. MATISSE — STILL LIFE: "HISTOIRES JUIVES"

Mr. Samuel S. White, III

397. MATISSE — WHITE PLUMES

Mr. Stephen C. Clark

408. PICASSO — WOMAN WITH FAN

Marie Harriman Gallery

674. BONNARD THE DINING ROOM

Mr. and Mrs. Walter S. Brewster

673. BONNARD THE BREAKFAST ROOM

Mr. Frank Crowninshield

680. DERAIN THE BAGPIPE PLAYER

Mr. and Mrs. James T. Soby

703. MODIGLIANI GYPSY WOMAN AND CHILD

The Chester Dale Collection

718. VUILLARD — CHILD IN ROOM

The Art Institute of Chicago

692. FRIESZ — FIGURE COMPOSITION

The Detroit Institute of Arts

688. DUFRESNE SCENE IN MOROCCO

The Worcester Art Museum

710. SEGONZAC THE BRIDGE, JOINVILLE

C. W. Kraushaar Art Galleries

738. RIVERA — THE RIVALS

A Private Collection

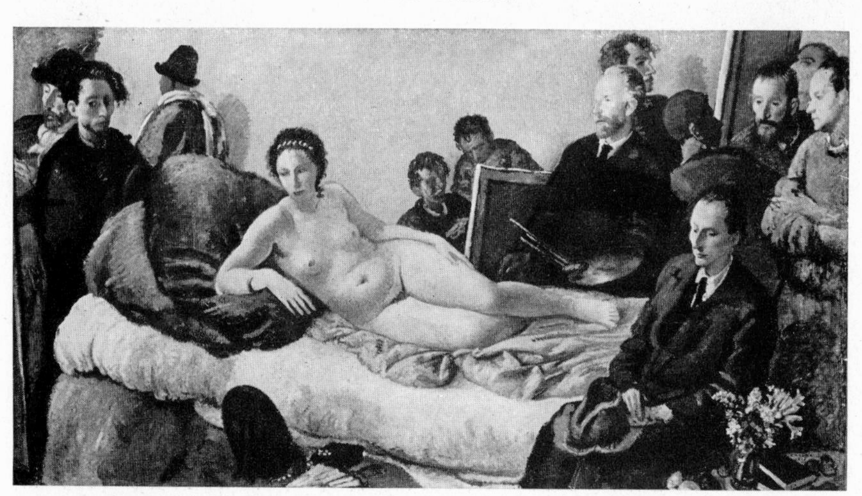

722. CARENA — THE CLASS

Mr. Albert C. Lehman

725. CHAGALL — RABBI

Mr. P. N. Sweeney

730. JOHN — DR. STRESEMANN

The Albright Art Gallery

PLATE LXXV

747. CAMPENDONK THE WHITE TREE

Miss Katherine S. Dreier

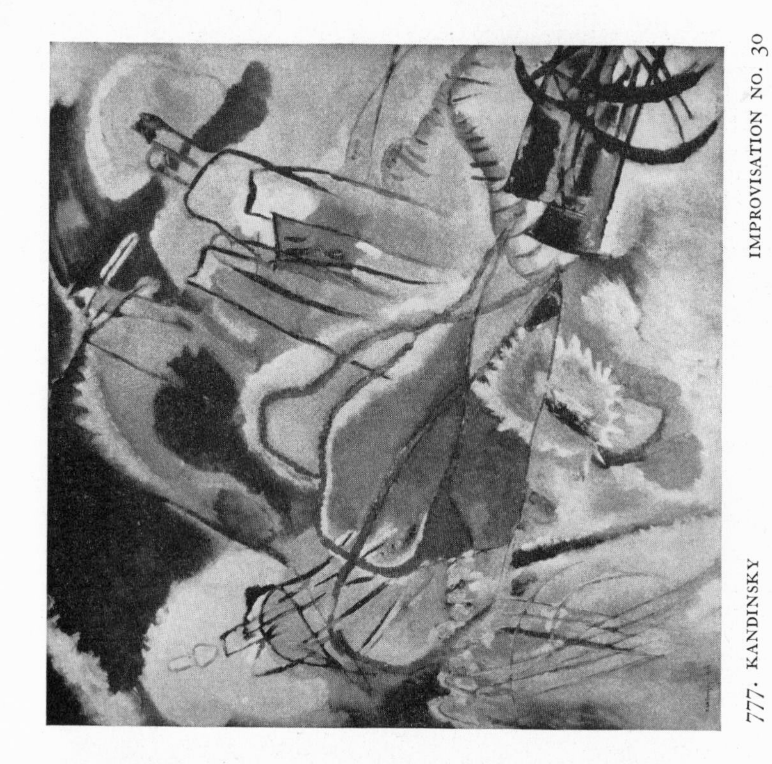

777. KANDINSKY IMPROVISATION NO. 30

The Art Institute of Chicago

753. KARL HOFER GIRL WITH MELONS
The Worcester Art Museum

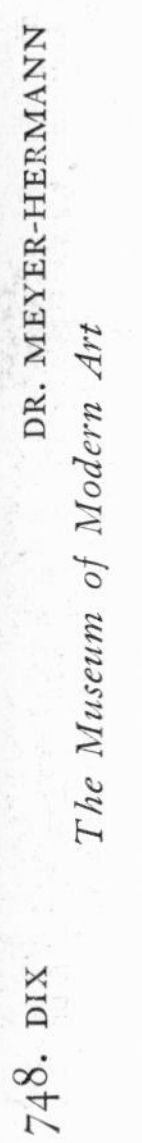

748. DIX DR. MEYER-HERMANN
The Museum of Modern Art

789. ROUAULT CLOWNS

Pierre Matisse Gallery

785. MIRO DOG BARKING AT THE MOON

Mr. A. E. Gallatin

787. PICASSO SEATED WOMAN

Mr. and Mrs. James T. Soby

773. DUCHAMP NUDE DESCENDING THE STAIRS

Mr. and Mrs. W. C. Arensberg

416. FEKE SELF-PORTRAIT

The Rev. H. W. Foote

415. EARL MOTHER AND CHILD

The Art Institute of Chicago

412. COPLEY DOROTHY MURRAY

The Fogg Art Museum, Harvard

413. COPLEY MASTER BRINE

A Private Collection

PLATE LXXXI

425. STUART — MRS. PEREZ MORTON

The Worcester Art Museum

424. STUART — MAJOR-GENERAL DEARBORN

The Art Institute of Chicago

490. WHISTLER THE ARTIST'S MOTHER

The Louvre Museum (through The Museum of Modern Art)

485. TWACHTMAN SNOW-BOUND

The Art Institute of Chicago

460. HOMER THE HERRING NET

Mrs. Martin A. Ryerson

479. SARGENT ROBERT LOUIS STEVENSON

Mrs. Payne Whitney

455. EAKINS MUSIC

The Art Institute of Chicago

PLATE LXXXV

438. CASSATT GIRL COMBING HER HAIR

The Chester Dale Collection

472. RYDER DIANA'S HUNT

Mr. Ralph Cudney

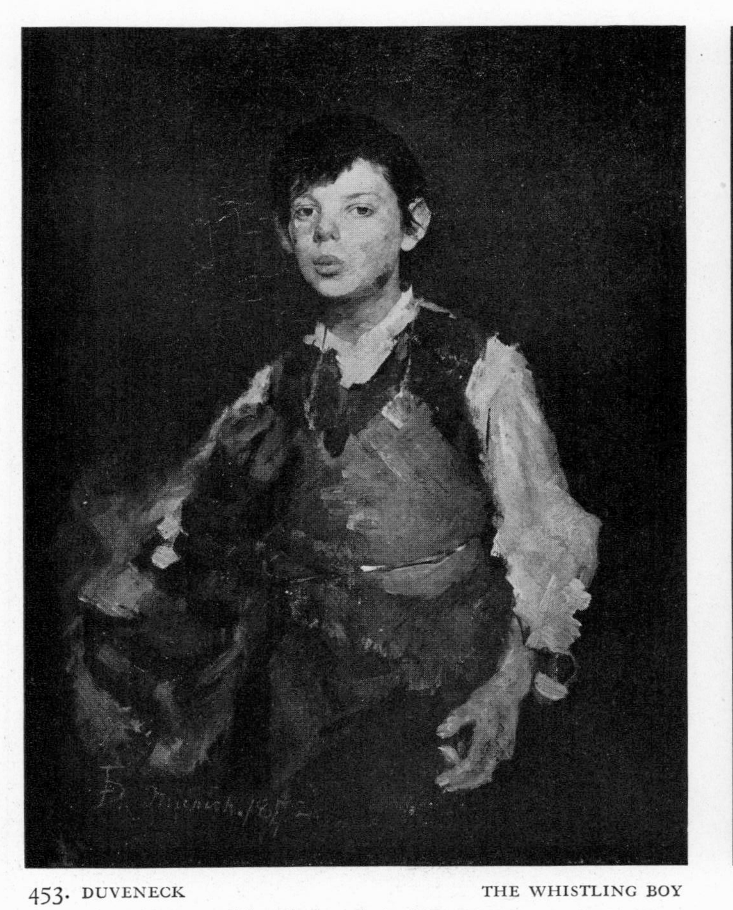

453. DUVENECK THE WHISTLING BOY

The Cincinnati Art Museum

459. HENRI HERSELF

The Art Institute of Chicago

446. ARTHUR B. DAVIES — ITALIAN LANDSCAPE

Trustees of the Lizzie P. Bliss Estate

523. BURCHFIELD — PROMENADE

Mr. A. Conger Goodyear

574. KARFIOL 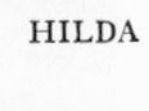 HILDA

The Whitney Museum of American Art

434. BELLOWS A STAG AT SHARKEY'S

The Cleveland Museum of Art

583. KROLL LEO ORNSTEIN AT THE PIANO

The Art Institute of Chicago

568. HOPPER AUTOMAT

Mr. and Mrs. Lesley G. Sheafer

519. BROOK THE CHILDREN'S LUNCH

The Art Institute of Chicago

536. CURRY BAPTISM IN KANSAS

The Whitney Museum of American Art

645. SPEICHER BABETTE

Department of Fine Arts, Carnegie Institute

550. GLACKENS CHEZ MOUQUIN

The Art Institute of Chicago

Plate XCII

649. STERNE AFTERNOON, ANTICOLI

The Phillips Memorial Gallery

666. WOOD AMERICAN GOTHIC

The Art Institute of Chicago

PLATE XCIII

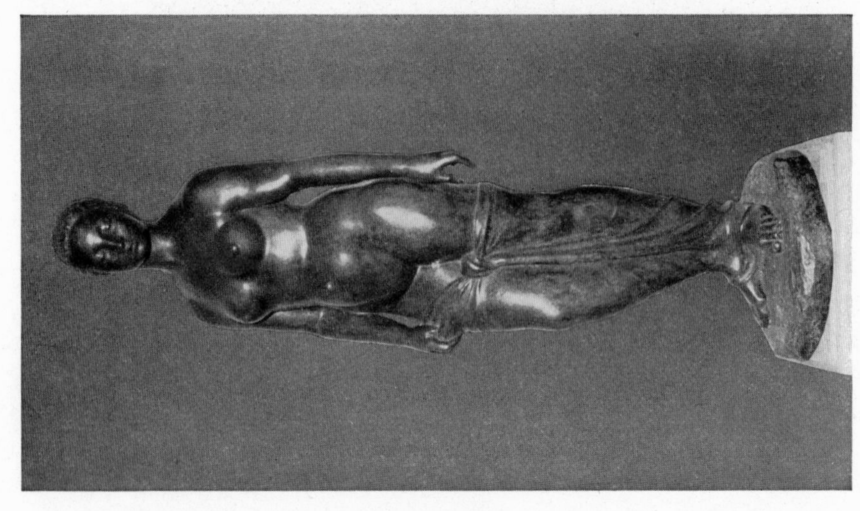

1158. LEHMBRUCK STANDING FIGURE

The Museum of Modern Art

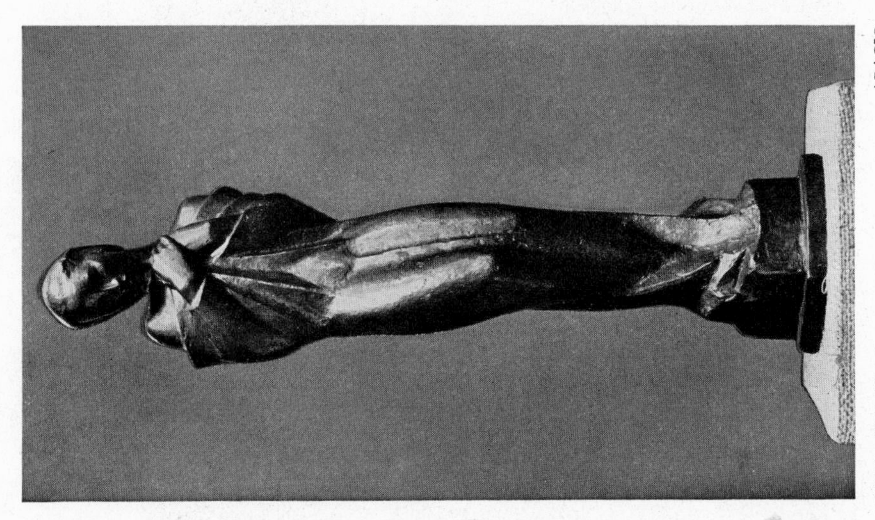

1149. KOLBE ADAGIO

Mr. and Mrs. C. H. Worcester

1129. EPSTEIN MEUM I
The Buffalo Fine Arts Academy

1227. ZORACH MOTHER AND CHILD
The Downtown Gallery

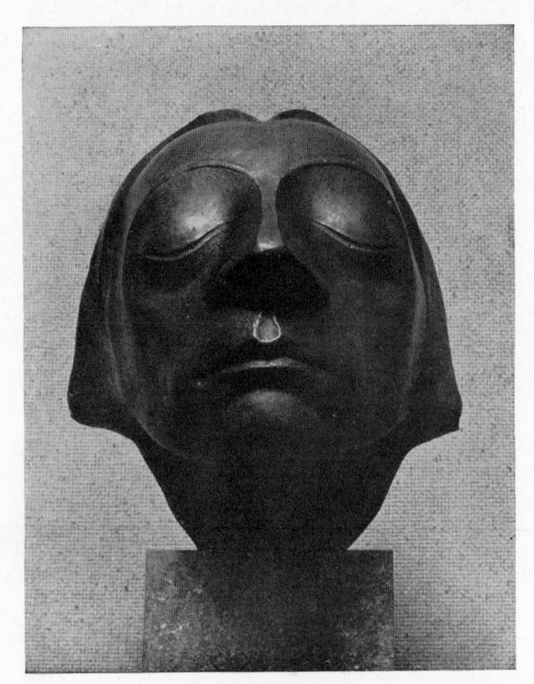

1099. BARLACH HEAD FROM A WAR MEMORIAL
Mr. E. M. M. Warburg

1202. RUMSEY PAGAN KIN
Mrs. Charles C. Rumsey